RSMeans
Residential
Repair &
Remodeling Costs

2012 CONTRACTOR'S PRICING GUIDE

Senior Editor
Bob Mewis, CCC

Contributing Editors
Christopher Babbitt
Ted Baker
Barbara Balboni
Adrian C. Charest, PE
Gary W. Christensen
David G. Drain, PE
Cheryl Elsmore
Robert J. Kuchta
Robert C. McNichols
Melville J. Mossman, PE
Jeannene D. Murphy
Marilyn Phelan, AIA
Stephen C. Plotner
Eugene R. Spencer
Phillip R. Waier, PE

Cover Design
Wendy McBay
Paul Robertson
Wayne Engebretson

President & CEO
Iain Melville

**Vice President,
Product & Development**
Richard Remington

**Vice President of
Finance & Operations**
David C. Walsh

**Vice President, Data
Aquisition & Fulfillment**
Marco Piovesan

Chief Customer Officer
Lisa Fiondella

**Senior Director,
Product Management**
Daimon Bridge

**Vice President, Marketing
& Business**
Steven Ritchie

Engineering Manager
Bob Mewis, CCC

Product Manager
Andrea Sillah

Product Marketing Manager
Ryan Cummings

Manager, Product Management
Jennifer Johnson

Production Manager
Michael Kokernak

Production Coordinator
Jill Goodman

Production Supervisor
Paula Reale-Camelio

Production
Jonathan Forgit
Mary Lou Geary
Debbie Panarelli
Sheryl A. Rose
Caroline Sullivan

Technical Support
Christopher Anderson
Tom Dion
Gary L. Hoitt
Genevieve Mede
Sharon Proulx
Kathryn S. Rodr

PRINTED WITH SOY INK

The 2012 *Contractor's Pricing Guide: Residential Repair & Remodeling Costs*, and all of the annual cost data books are dedicated to the memory of our respected friend and colleague, Hsiao-Cheng (John) Chiang, PE.

RSMeans

Contractor's Pricing Guide
Residential Repair &
Remodeling Costs

2012

Quick costs to help you estimate

Easy-to-use format . . . organized the way you build

Hundreds of work items with material, labor, and equipment

Built for the small residential contractor/insurance repair specialist

$39.95 per copy (in United States)
Price subject to change without prior notice.

RSMeans

Copyright 2011
A division of Reed Construction Data
Construction Publishers & Consultants
700 Longwater Drive
Norwell, MA 02061
www.rsmeans.com

Printed in the United States of America

ISSN 1074-0481

ISBN 978-1-936335-48-0

This book is printed on recycled paper, using soy-based printing ink. This book is recyclable.

Foreword

Our Mission

Since 1942, RSMeans has been actively engaged in construction cost publishing and consulting throughout North America.

Today, more than 65 years after RSMeans began, our primary objective remains the same: to provide you, the construction and facilities professional, with the most current and comprehensive construction cost data possible.

Whether you are a contractor, owner, architect, engineer, facilities manager, or anyone else who needs a reliable construction cost estimate, you'll find this publication to be a highly useful and necessary tool.

With the constant flow of new construction methods and materials today, it's difficult to find the time to look at and evaluate all the different construction cost possibilities. In addition, because labor and material costs keep changing, last year's cost information is not a reliable basis for today's estimate or budget.

That's why so many construction professionals turn to RSMeans. We keep track of the costs for you, along with a wide range of other key information, from city cost indexes . . . to productivity rates . . . to crew composition . . . to contractors' overhead and profit rates.

RSMeans performs these functions by collecting data from all facets of the industry and organizing it in a format that is instantly accessible to you. From the preliminary budget to the detailed unit price estimate, you'll find the data in this book useful for all phases of construction cost determination.

The Staff, the Organization, and Our Services

When you purchase one of RSMeans' publications, you are, in effect, hiring the services of a full-time staff of construction and engineering professionals.

Our thoroughly experienced and highly qualified staff works daily at collecting, analyzing, and disseminating comprehensive cost information for your needs. These staff members have years of practical construction experience and engineering training prior to joining the firm. As a result, you can count on them not only for accurate cost figures, but also for additional background reference information that will help you create a realistic estimate.

The RSMeans organization is always prepared to help you solve construction problems through its variety of data solutions, including online, CD, and print book formats, as well as cost estimating expertise available via our Business Solutions, training, and seminars.

Besides a full array of construction cost estimating books, RSMeans also publishes a number of other reference works for the construction industry. Subjects include construction estimating and project and business management, special topics such as green building and job order contracting, and a library of facility management references.

In addition, you can access all of our construction cost data electronically in convenient CD format or on the web. Visit **MeansCostworks.com** for more information on our 24/7 online cost data.

What's more, you can increase your knowledge and improve your construction estimating and management performance with an RSMeans construction seminar or in-house training program. These two-day seminar programs offer unparalleled opportunities for everyone in your organization to become updated on a wide variety of construction-related issues.

RSMeans is also a worldwide provider of construction cost management and analysis services for commercial and government owners.

In short, RSMeans can provide you with the tools and expertise for constructing accurate and dependable construction estimates and budgets in a variety of ways.

Robert Snow Means Established a Tradition of Quality That Continues Today

Robert Snow Means spent years building RSMeans, making certain he always delivered a quality product.

Today, at RSMeans, we do more than talk about the quality of our data and the usefulness of our books. We stand behind all of our data, from historical cost indexes to construction materials and techniques to current costs.

If you have any questions about our products or services, please call us toll-free at 1-800-334-3509. Our customer service representatives will be happy to assist you. You can also visit our Web site at **www.rsmeans.com**.

Table of Contents

How the Book Is Built: An Overview

A Powerful Construction Tool

You have in your hands one of the most powerful construction tools available today. A successful project is built on the foundation of an accurate and dependable estimate. This book will enable you to construct just such an estimate.

For the casual user the book is designed to be:

- quickly and easily understood so you can get right to your estimate.
- filled with valuable information so you can understand the necessary factors that go into the cost estimate.

For the regular user, the book is designed to be:

- a handy desk reference that can be quickly referred to for key costs.
- a comprehensive, fully reliable source of current construction costs, so you'll be prepared to estimate any project.
- a source book for project cost, product selections, and alternate materials and methods.

To meet all of these requirements we have organized the book into the following clearly defined sections.

Unit Price Section

The cost data has been divided into 23 sections representing the order of construction. Within each section is a listing of components and variations to those components applicable to that section. Costs are shown for the various actions that must be done to that component.

Reference Section

This section includes information on Location Factors and a listing of Abbreviations.

Location Factors: You can adjust total project costs to over 900 locations throughout the U.S. and Canada by using the data in this section.

Abbreviations: A listing of the abbreviations used throughout this book, along with the terms they represent, is included.

Index

A comprehensive listing of all terms and subjects in this book will help you quickly find what you need when you are not sure where it falls in the order of construction.

The Scope of This Book

This book is designed to be as comprehensive and as easy to use as possible. To that end we have made certain assumptions and limited its scope in two key ways:

1. We have established material prices based on a national average.
2. We have computed labor costs based on a seven major-region average of open shop wage rates.

Project Size

This book is intended for use by those involved primarily in residential repair and remodeling construction costing between $10,000–$100,000.

With reasonable exercise of judgment, the figures can be used for any building work. For other types of projects, such as new home construction or commercial buildings, consult the appropriate RSMeans publication for more information.

How to Use the Book: The Details

What's Behind the Numbers? The Development of Cost Data

The staff at RSMeans continually monitors developments in the construction industry in order to ensure reliable, thorough, and up-to-date cost information.

While *overall* construction costs may vary relative to general economic conditions, price fluctuations within the industry are dependent upon many factors. Individual price variations may, in fact, be opposite to overall economic trends. Therefore, costs are constantly tracked and complete updates are published yearly. Also, new items are frequently added in response to changes in materials and methods.

Costs–$ (U.S.)

All costs represent U.S. national averages and are given in U.S. dollars. The RSMeans Location Factors can be used to adjust costs to a particular location. The Location Factors for Canada can be used to adjust U.S. national averages to local costs in Canadian dollars. No exchange rate conversion is necessary.

Material Costs

The RSMeans staff contacts manufacturers, dealers, distributors, and contractors all across the U.S. and Canada to determine national average material costs. If you have access to current material costs for your specific location, you may wish to make adjustments to reflect differences from the national average.

Included within material costs are fasteners for a normal installation. RSMeans engineers use manufacturers' recommendations, written specifications, and/or standard construction practice for size and spacing of fasteners. Adjustments to material costs may be required for your specific application or location. Material costs do not include sales tax.

Labor Costs

Labor costs are based on the average of residential wages from across the U.S. for the current year. Rates, along with overhead and profit markups, are listed on the inside back cover of this book.

- If wage rates in your area vary from those used in this book, or if rate increases are expected within a given year, labor costs should be adjusted accordingly.

Labor costs reflect productivity based on actual working conditions. These figures include time spent during a normal workday on tasks other than actual installation, such as material receiving and handling, mobilization at site, site movement, breaks, and cleanup.

Productivity data is developed over an extended period so as not to be influenced by abnormal variations and reflects a typical average.

Equipment Costs

Equipment costs include not only rental costs, but also operating costs for equipment under normal use. Equipment and rental rates are obtained from industry sources throughout North America—contractors, suppliers, dealers, manufacturers, and distributors.

Factors Affecting Costs

Costs can vary depending upon a number of variables. Here's how we have handled the main factors affecting costs.

Quality—The prices for materials and the workmanship upon which productivity is based represent sound construction work. They are also in line with U.S. government specifications.

Overtime—We have made no allowance for overtime. If you anticipate premium time or work beyond normal working hours, be sure to make an appropriate adjustment to your labor costs.

Productivity—The labor costs for each line item are based on working an eight-hour day in daylight hours in moderate temperatures. For work that extends beyond normal work hours or is performed under adverse conditions, productivity may decrease.

Size of Project—The size, scope of work, and type of construction project will have a significant impact on cost. Economies of scale can reduce costs for large projects. Unit costs can often run higher for small projects. Costs in this book are intended for the size and type of project as previously described in "How the Book Is Built: An Overview." Costs for projects of a significantly different size or type should be adjusted accordingly.

Location—Material prices in this book are for metropolitan areas. However, in dense urban areas, traffic and site storage limitations may increase costs. Beyond a 20-mile radius of large cities, extra trucking or transportation charges may also increase the material costs slightly. On the other hand, lower wage rates may be in effect. Be sure to consider both of these factors when preparing an estimate, particularly if the job site is located in a central city or remote rural location.

In addition, highly specialized subcontract items may require travel and per diem expenses for mechanics.

Other Factors—

- season of year
- contractor management
- weather conditions
- building code requirements
- availability of:
  - adequate energy
  - skilled labor
  - building materials
- owner's special requirements/restrictions
- safety requirements
- environmental considerations

Overhead & Profit—The extreme right-hand column of each chart gives the "Totals." These figures contain the installing contractor's O&P. Therefore, it is necessary for a general contractor to add a percentage of all subcontracted items. For a detailed breakdown of O&P see the inside back cover of this book.

Unpredictable Factors—General business conditions influence "in-place" costs of all items. Substitute materials and construction methods may have to be employed. These may affect the installed cost and/or life cycle costs. Such factors may be difficult to evaluate and cannot necessarily be predicted on the basis of the job's location in a particular section of the country. Thus, where these factors apply, you may find significant but unavoidable cost variations for which you will have to apply a measure of judgment to your estimate.

Final Checklist

Estimating can be a straightforward process provided you remember the basics. Here's a checklist of some of the steps you should remember to complete before finalizing your estimate.

Did you remember to . . .

- factor in the Location Factor for your locale?
- take into consideration which items have been marked up and by how much?
- mark up the entire estimate sufficiently for your purposes?
- include all components of your project in the final estimate?
- double check your figures to be sure of your accuracy?
- call RSMeans if you have any questions about your estimate or the data you've found in our publications?

Remember, RSMeans stands behind its publications. If you have any questions about your estimate . . . about the costs you've used from our books . . . or even about the technical aspects of the job that may affect your estimate, feel free to call the RSMeans editors at 1-800-334-3509.

Unit Price Section

Table of Contents

Table of Contents (cont.)

How to Use the Unit Price Pages

The prices in this publication include all overhead and profit mark-ups for the installing contractor. If a general contractor is involved, an additional 10% should be added to the cost shown in the "Total" column.

The costs for material, labor and any equipment are shown here. Material costs include delivery and a 10% mark-up. No sales taxes are included. Labor costs include all mark-ups as shown on the inside back cover of this book. Equipment costs also include a 10% mark-up.

The cost in the total column should be multiplied by the quantity of each item to determine the total cost for that item. The sum of all item's total costs becomes the project's total cost.

The book is arranged into 23 categories that follow the order of construction for residential projects. The category is shown as white letters on a black background at the top of each page.

A brief specification of the cost item is shown here.

Graphics representing some of the cost items are found at the beginning of each category.

The cost data is arranged in a tree structure format. Major cost sections are left justified and are shown as bold headings within a grey background. Cost items and sub-cost items are found under the bold headings. The complete description should read as "bold heading, cost item, sub-cost item." For example, the identified item's description is "Beam/Girder, Solid Wood Beam, 2″ x 8″."

Each action performed to the cost item is conveniently listed to the right of the description. See the explanation below for the scope of work included as part of the action.

The unit of measure upon which all the costs are based is shown here. An abbreviations list is included within the reference section found at the back of this book.

Rough Frame / Structure

Rough Framing

Beam / Girder		Unit	Material	Labor	Equip.	Total	Specification
Solid Wood Beam							
2″ x 8″							
	Demolish	L.F.		.83		.83	Cost includes material and labor to install 2″ x 8″ beam.
	Install	L.F.	.83	1.28		2.11	
	Demolish and Install	L.F.	.83	2.11		2.94	
	Clean	L.F.	.15	.27		.42	
	Paint	L.F.	.13	1.92		2.05	
	Minimum Charge	Job		207		207	
2″ x 10″							
	Demolish	L.F.		1.02		1.02	Cost includes material and labor to install 2″ x 10″ beam.
	Install	L.F.	1.11	1.38		2.49	
	Demolish and Install	L.F.	1.11	2.40		3.51	
	Clean	L.F.	.19	.33		.52	
	Paint	L.F.	.19	1.18		1.37	
	Minimum Charge	Job		207		207	
2″ x 12″							
	Demolish	L.F.		1.24		1.24	Cost includes material and labor to install 2″ x 12″ beam.
	Install	L.F.	1.41	1.51		2.92	
	Demolish and Install	L.F.	1.41	2.75		4.16	
	Clean	L.F.	.22	.38		.60	
	Paint	L.F.	.20	2.84		3.04	
	Minimum Charge	Job		207		207	
4″ x 8″							
	Demolish	L.F.		2.55		2.55	Cost includes material and labor to install 4″ x 8″ beam.
	Install	L.F.	3.74	1.88	.67	6.29	
	Demolish and Install	L.F.	3.74	4.43	.67	8.84	
	Clean	L.F.	.19	.33		.52	
	Paint	L.F.	.19	1.18		1.37	
	Minimum Charge	Job		207		207	
4″ x 10″							
	Demolish	L.F.		3.19		3.19	Cost includes material and labor to install 4″ x 10″ beam.
	Install	L.F.	4.68	1.98	.71	7.37	
	Demolish and Install	L.F.	4.68	5.17	.71	10.56	
	Clean	L.F.	.22	.38		.60	
	Paint	L.F.	.21	1.38		1.59	
	Minimum Charge	Job		207		207	
4″ x 12″							
	Demolish	L.F.		3.82		3.82	Cost includes material and labor to install 4″ x 12″ beam.
	Install	L.F.	6.05	2.09	.75	8.89	
	Demolish and Install	L.F.	6.05	5.91	.75	12.71	
	Clean	L.F.	.25	.44		.69	
	Paint	L.F.	.20	2.84		3.04	
	Minimum Charge	Job		207		207	

Action	Scope
Demolish	Includes removal of the item and hauling the debris to a truck, dumpster, or storage area.
Install	Includes the installation of the item with normal placement and spacing of fasteners.
Demolish and Install	Includes the demolish action and the install action.
Reinstall	Includes the reinstallation of a removed item.
Clean	Includes cleaning of the item.
Paint	Includes up to two coats of finish on the item (unless otherwise indicated).
Minimum Charge	Includes the minimum labor or the minimum labor and equipment cost. Use this charge for small quantities of material.

Job Costs

Scaffolding   Temporary Electrical Service   Air Compressor

Construction Fees		Unit	Material	Labor	Equip.	Total	Specification
Asbestos Test							
	Minimum Charge	Job		243		243	Minimum charge for testing.
Architectural							
	Minimum Charge	Day	1975			1975	Minimum labor charge for architect.
Engineering							
	Minimum Charge	Day	1850			1850	Minimum labor charge for field engineer.

Construction Permits		Unit	Material	Labor	Equip.	Total	Specification
Job (less than 5K)							
	Minimum Charge	Job	110			110	Permit fees, job less than 5K.
Job (5K to 10K)							
	Minimum Charge	Job	220			220	Permit fees, job more than 5K, but less than 10K.
Job (10K to 25K)							
	Minimum Charge	Job	550			550	Permit fees, job more than 10K, but less than 25K.
Job (25K to 50K)							
	Minimum Charge	Job	1100			1100	Permit fees, job more than 25K, but less than 50K.
Job (50K to 100K)							
	Minimum Charge	Job	2200			2200	Permit fees, job more than 50K, but less than 100K.
Job (100K to 250K)							
	Minimum Charge	Job	5500			5500	Permit fees, job more than 100K, but less than 250K.
Job (250K to 500K)							
	Minimum Charge	Job	11000			11000	Permit fees, job more than 250K, but less than 500K.
Job (500K to 1M)							
	Minimum Charge	Job	22000			22000	Permit fees, job more than 500K, but less than 1 million.

Job Costs

Trade Labor		Unit	Material	Labor	Equip.	Total	Specification
Carpenter							
Daily (8 hours)							
	Install	Day		415		415	Daily labor rate for one carpenter.
	Minimum Charge	Job		207		207	
Weekly (40 hours)							
	Install	Week		2075		2075	Weekly labor rate for one carpenter.
	Minimum Charge	Job		207		207	
Drywaller							
Daily (8 hours)							
	Install	Day		415		415	Daily labor rate for one carpenter.
	Minimum Charge	Job		207		207	
Weekly (40 hours)							
	Install	Week		2075		2075	Weekly labor rate for one carpenter.
	Minimum Charge	Job		207		207	
Roofer							
Daily (8 hours)							
	Install	Day		375		375	Daily labor rate for one skilled roofer.
	Minimum Charge	Job		188		188	
Weekly (40 hours)							
	Install	Week		1875		1875	Weekly labor rate for one skilled
	Minimum Charge	Job		188		188	roofer.
Painter							
Daily (8 hours)							
	Install	Day		355		355	Daily labor rate for one painter.
	Minimum Charge	Job		178		178	
Weekly (40 hours)							
	Install	Week		1775		1775	Weekly labor rate for one painter.
	Minimum Charge	Job		178		178	
Mason							
Daily (8 hours)							
	Install	Day		405		405	Daily labor rate for one skilled mason.
	Minimum Charge	Job		204		204	
Weekly (40 hours)							
	Install	Week		2025		2025	Weekly labor rate for one skilled
	Minimum Charge	Job		204		204	mason.
Electrician							
Daily (8 hours)							
	Install	Day		450		450	Daily labor rate for an electrician.
	Minimum Charge	Job		226		226	
Weekly (40 hours)							
	Install	Week		2250		2250	Weekly labor rate for an electrician.
	Minimum Charge	Job		226		226	
Plumber							
Daily (8 hours)							
	Install	Day		475		475	Daily labor rate for a plumber.
	Minimum Charge	Job		238		238	
Weekly (40 hours)							
	Install	Week		2375		2375	Weekly labor rate for a plumber.
	Minimum Charge	Job		238		238	
Common Laborer							
Daily (8 hours)							
	Install	Day		305		305	Daily labor rate for a common
	Minimum Charge	Job		153		153	laborer.

Job Costs

Trade Labor

		Unit	Material	Labor	Equip.	Total	Specification
Weekly (40 hours)	Install	Week		1525		1525	Weekly labor rate for a common
	Minimum Charge	Job		153		153	laborer.

Temporary Utilities

		Unit	Material	Labor	Equip.	Total	Specification
Power Pole							
Job Site Electricity	Install	Month	55			55	Includes average cost of electricity per
	Minimum Charge	Job		226		226	month.
Water Service							
Job Site Water	Install	Month	69.50			69.50	Includes average costs for water for
	Minimum Charge	Month	69.50			69.50	one month.
Telephone	Install	Month	89			89	Includes average cost for local and
	Minimum Charge	Month	89			89	long distance telephone service for one month.
Chemical Toilet	Install	Month			285	285	Monthly rental of portable toilet.
	Minimum Charge	Day			14.25	14.25	
Office Trailer							
Place and Remove	Install	Job	370			370	Includes cost to a contractor to deliver,
	Minimum Charge	Job		166		166	place and level an office trailer and remove at end of job.
Storage Container	Install	Job	209			209	Includes cost to a contractor to deliver
	Minimum Charge	Job		166		166	and place a storage container and remove at end of job.
Fencing	Install	L.F.	3.62			3.62	Includes material costs for temporary
	Minimum Charge	L.F.	275			275	fencing.
Railing	Install	L.F.	15.95	11.75	.76	28.46	Includes material and labor to install
	Minimum Charge	L.F.	275			275	primed steel pipe.

Equipment Rental

		Unit	Material	Labor	Equip.	Total	Specification
Flatbed Truck							
Daily Rental	Install	Day			232	232	Daily rental of flatbed truck.
	Minimum Charge	Job			232	232	
Weekly Rental	Install	Week			1150	1150	Weekly rental of flatbed truck.
	Minimum Charge	Job			232	232	
Monthly Rental	Install	Month			4650	4650	Monthly rental of flatbed truck.
	Minimum Charge	Job			232	232	

Equipment Rental		Unit	Material	Labor	Equip.	Total	Specification
Dump Truck							
Daily Rental							
	Install	Day			395	395	Daily rental of dump truck.
	Minimum Charge	Day			395	395	
Weekly Rental							
	Install	Week			1975	1975	Weekly rental of dump truck.
	Minimum Charge	Day			395	395	
Monthly Rental							
	Install	Month			7850	7850	Monthly rental of dump truck.
	Minimum Charge	Day			395	395	
Forklift							
Daily Rental							
	Install	Day			325	325	Daily rental of forklift.
	Minimum Charge	Day			325	325	
Weekly Rental							
	Install	Week			1625	1625	Weekly rental of forklift.
	Minimum Charge	Day			325	325	
Monthly Rental							
	Install	Month			6500	6500	Monthly rental of forklift.
	Minimum Charge	Day			325	325	
Bobcat							
Daily Rental							
	Install	Day			176	176	Daily rental of wheeled, skid steer
	Minimum Charge	Day			176	176	loader.
Weekly Rental							
	Install	Week			880	880	Weekly rental of wheeled, skid steer
	Minimum Charge	Day			176	176	loader.
Monthly Rental							
	Install	Month			3500	3500	Monthly rental of wheeled, skid steer
	Minimum Charge	Day			176	176	loader.
Air Compressor							
Daily Rental							
	Install	Day			132	132	Daily rental of air compressor.
	Minimum Charge	Day			132	132	
Weekly Rental							
	Install	Week			660	660	Weekly rental of air compressor.
	Minimum Charge	Day			132	132	
Monthly Rental							
	Install	Month			2650	2650	Monthly rental of air compressor.
	Minimum Charge	Day			132	132	
Jackhammer							
Daily Rental							
	Install	Day			10.80	10.80	Daily rental of air tool, jackhammer.
	Minimum Charge	Day			10.80	10.80	
Weekly Rental							
	Install	Week			54	54	Weekly rental of air tool, jackhammer.
	Minimum Charge	Day			10.80	10.80	
Monthly Rental							
	Install	Month			216	216	Monthly rental of air tool,
	Minimum Charge	Day			10.80	10.80	jackhammer.
Concrete Mixer							
Daily Rental							
	Install	Day			144	144	Daily rental of concrete mixer.
	Minimum Charge	Day			144	144	

Job Costs

Equipment Rental		Unit	Material	Labor	Equip.	Total	Specification
Weekly Rental							
	Install	Week			720	720	Weekly rental of concrete mixer.
	Minimum Charge	Day			144	144	
Monthly Rental							
	Install	Month			2875	2875	Monthly rental of concrete mixer.
	Minimum Charge	Day			144	144	
Concrete Bucket							
Daily Rental							
	Install	Day			21	21	Daily rental of concrete bucket.
	Minimum Charge	Day			21	21	
Weekly Rental							
	Install	Week			106	106	Weekly rental of concrete bucket.
	Minimum Charge	Day			21	21	
Monthly Rental							
	Install	Month			420	420	Monthly rental of concrete bucket.
	Minimum Charge	Day			21	21	
Concrete Pump							
Daily Rental							
	Install	Day			785	785	Daily rental of concrete pump.
	Minimum Charge	Day			785	785	
Weekly Rental							
	Install	Week			3925	3925	Weekly rental of concrete pump.
	Minimum Charge	Day			785	785	
Monthly Rental							
	Install	Month			15700	15700	Monthly rental of concrete pump.
	Minimum Charge	Day			785	785	
Generator							
Daily Rental							
	Install	Day			35	35	Daily rental of generator.
	Minimum Charge	Day			35	35	
Weekly Rental							
	Install	Week			174	174	Weekly rental of generator.
	Minimum Charge	Day			35	35	
Monthly Rental							
	Install	Month			695	695	Monthly rental of generator.
	Minimum Charge	Day			35	35	
Welder							
Daily Rental							
	Install	Day			29.50	29.50	Daily rental of welder.
	Minimum Charge	Day			29.50	29.50	
Weekly Rental							
	Install	Week			148	148	Weekly rental of welder.
	Minimum Charge	Day			29.50	29.50	
Monthly Rental							
	Install	Month			590	590	Monthly rental of welder.
	Minimum Charge	Day			29.50	29.50	
Sandblaster							
Daily Rental							
	Install	Day			22.50	22.50	Daily rental of sandblaster.
	Minimum Charge	Day			22.50	22.50	
Weekly Rental							
	Install	Week			112	112	Weekly rental of sandblaster.
	Minimum Charge	Day			22.50	22.50	

Job Costs

Equipment Rental		Unit	Material	Labor	Equip.	Total	Specification
Monthly Rental							
	Install	Month			450	450	Monthly rental of sandblaster.
	Minimum Charge	Day			22.50	22.50	
Space Heater							
Daily Rental							
	Install	Day			21.50	21.50	Daily rental of space heater.
	Minimum Charge	Day			11.30	11.30	
Weekly Rental							
	Install	Day			107	107	Weekly rental of space heater.
	Minimum Charge	Day			11.30	11.30	
Monthly Rental							
	Install	Day			430	430	Monthly rental of space heater.
	Minimum Charge	Day			11.30	11.30	

Move / Reset Contents		Unit	Material	Labor	Equip.	Total	Specification
Small Room							
	Install	Room		37		37	Includes cost to remove and reset the
	Minimum Charge	Job		153		153	contents of a small room.
Average Room							
	Install	Room		45		45	Includes cost to remove and reset the
	Minimum Charge	Job		153		153	contents of an average room.
Large Room							
	Install	Room		62		62	Includes cost to remove and reset the
	Minimum Charge	Job		153		153	contents of a large room.
Extra Large Room							
	Install	Room		98		98	Includes cost to remove and reset the
	Minimum Charge	Job		153		153	contents of a extra large room.
Store Contents							
Weekly							
	Install	Week	275			275	Storage fee, per week.
Monthly							
	Install	Month	825			825	Storage fee, per month.

Cover and Protect		Unit	Material	Labor	Equip.	Total	Specification
Cover / Protect Walls							
	Install	SF Wall		.12		.12	Includes labor costs to cover and
	Minimum Charge	Job		153		153	protect walls.
Cover / Protect Floors							
	Install	SF Flr.		.12		.12	Includes labor costs to cover and
	Minimum Charge	Job		153		153	protect floors.

Temporary Bracing		Unit	Material	Labor	Equip.	Total	Specification
Shim Support Piers							
	Install	Ea.	4.36	120		124.36	Includes labor and material to install
	Minimum Charge	Job		360		360	shims support for piers.

Job Costs

Jack and Relevel

		Unit	Material	Labor	Equip.	Total	Specification
Single Story							
	Install	S.F.	1.85	1.44		3.29	Includes labor and equipment to jack
	Minimum Charge	Job		360		360	and relevel single-story building.
Two-story							
	Install	S.F.	1.85	2.41		4.26	Includes labor and equipment to jack
	Minimum Charge	Job		360		360	and relevel two-story building.

Dumpster Rental

		Unit	Material	Labor	Equip.	Total	Specification
Small Load							
	Install	Week			450	450	Dumpster, weekly rental, 2 dumps, 5
	Minimum Charge	Week			450	450	yard container.
Medium Load							
	Install	Week			700	700	Dumpster, weekly rental, 2 dumps, 10
	Minimum Charge	Week			700	700	yard container.
Large Load							
	Install	Week			1125	1125	Dumpster, weekly rental, 2 dumps, 30
	Minimum Charge	Week			1125	1125	yard container.

Debris Hauling

		Unit	Material	Labor	Equip.	Total	Specification
Per Ton							
	Install	Ton		94.50	47.50	142	Includes hauling of debris by trailer or
	Minimum Charge	Ton		710	355	1065	dump truck.
Per Cubic Yard							
	Install	C.Y.		31.50	15.90	47.40	Includes hauling of debris by trailer or
	Minimum Charge	Job		710	355	1065	dump truck.
Per Pick-up Truck Load							
	Install	Ea.		170		170	Includes hauling of debris by pick-up
	Minimum Charge	Ea.		170		170	truck.

Dump Fees

		Unit	Material	Labor	Equip.	Total	Specification
Per Cubic Yard							
	Install	C.Y.	35			35	Dump charges, building materials.
	Minimum Charge	C.Y.	35			35	
Per Ton							
	Install	Ton	95.50			95.50	Dump charges, building materials.
	Minimum Charge	Ton	95.50			95.50	

Scaffolding

		Unit	Material	Labor	Equip.	Total	Specification
4' to 6' High							
	Install	Month	67			67	Includes monthly rental of scaffolding,
	Minimum Charge	Month	67			67	steel tubular, 30" wide, 7' long, 5' high.
7' to 11' High							
	Install	Month	80.50			80.50	Includes monthly rental of scaffolding,
	Minimum Charge	Month	80.50			80.50	steel tubular, 30" wide, 7' long, 10' high.

Job Costs

Scaffolding

Scaffolding		Unit	Material	Labor	Equip.	Total	Specification
12' to 16' High							
	Install	Month	93.50			93.50	Includes monthly rental of scaffolding, steel tubular, 30" wide, 7' long, 15' high.
	Minimum Charge	Month	93.50			93.50	
17' to 21' High							
	Install	Month	122			122	Includes monthly rental of scaffolding, steel tubular, 30" wide, 7' long, 20' high.
	Minimum Charge	Month	122			122	
22' to 26' High							
	Install	Month	135			135	Includes monthly rental of scaffolding, steel tubular, 30" wide, 7' long, 25' high.
	Minimum Charge	Month	135			135	
27' to 30' High							
	Install	Month	149			149	Includes monthly rental of scaffolding, steel tubular, 30" wide, 7' long, 30' high.
	Minimum Charge	Month	149			149	

Construction Clean-up

Construction Clean-up		Unit	Material	Labor	Equip.	Total	Specification
Initial							
	Clean	S.F.		.38		.38	Includes labor for general clean-up.
	Minimum Charge	Job		153		153	
Progressive							
	Clean	S.F.		.19		.19	Includes labor for progressive site/job clean-up on a weekly basis.
	Minimum Charge	Job		153		153	

Building Demolition		Unit	Material	Labor	Equip.	Total	Specification
Wood-framed Building							
1 Story Demolition							
	Demolish	S.F.		1.43	1.76	3.19	Includes demolition of 1 floor only light wood-framed building, including hauling of debris. Dump fees not included.
	Minimum Charge	Job		2250	2775	5025	
2nd Story Demolition							
	Demolish	S.F.		1.45	1.79	3.24	Includes demolition of 2nd floor only light wood-framed building, including hauling of debris. Dump fees not included.
	Minimum Charge	Job		2250	2775	5025	
3rd Story Demolition							
	Demolish	S.F.		1.89	2.33	4.22	Includes demolition of 3rd floor only light wood-framed building, including hauling of debris. Dump fees not included.
	Minimum Charge	Job		2250	2775	5025	
Masonry Building							
	Demolish	S.F.		2.03	2.50	4.53	Includes demolition of one story masonry building, including hauling of debris. Dump fees not included.
	Minimum Charge	Job		2250	2775	5025	
Concrete Building							
Unreinforced							
	Demolish	S.F.		4.20	1.12	5.32	Includes demolition of a one story non-reinforced concrete building, including hauling of debris. Dump fees not included.
	Minimum Charge	Job		2250	2775	5025	
Reinforced							
	Demolish	S.F.		4.81	1.29	6.10	Includes demolition of a one story reinforced concrete building, including hauling of debris. Dump fees not included.
	Minimum Charge	Job		2250	2775	5025	
Steel Building							
	Demolish	S.F.		2.71	3.34	6.05	Includes demolition of a metal building, including hauling of debris. Dump fees not included. No salvage value assumed for scrap metal.
	Minimum Charge	Job		2250	2775	5025	

Job Preparation

General Clean-up

General Clean-up	Unit	Material	Labor	Equip.	Total	Specification
Remove Debris						Includes removal of debris caused by the loss including contents items and loose debris.
Clean	S.F.		.94	.23	1.17	
Minimum Charge	Job		470	116	586	
Muck-out						Includes labor to remove 2″ of muck and mud after a flood loss.
Clean	S.F.		.59		.59	
Minimum Charge	Job		153		153	
Deodorize / Disinfect						Includes deodorizing building with application of mildicide and disinfectant to floors and walls - will vary depending on the extent of deodorization required.
Clean	SF Flr.		.20		.20	
Minimum Charge	Job		153		153	
Clean Walls						
Heavy						Includes labor and material for heavy cleaning (multiple applications) with detergent and solvent.
Clean	S.F.		.14		.14	
Minimum Charge	Job		153		153	
Clean Ceiling						
Light						Includes labor and material to clean light to moderate smoke and soot.
Clean	S.F.		.24		.24	
Minimum Charge	Job		153		153	
Heavy						Includes labor and material to clean heavy smoke and soot.
Clean	S.F.		.36		.36	
Minimum Charge	Job		153		153	

Flood Clean-up

Flood Clean-up	Unit	Material	Labor	Equip.	Total	Specification
Emergency Service Call						
After Hours / Weekend						Includes minimum charges for deflooding clean-up after hours or on weekends.
Minimum Charge	Job		204		204	
Grey Water / Sewage						Includes minimum charges for deflooding clean-up.
Minimum Charge	Job		153		153	
Water Extraction						
Clean (non-grey)						Includes labor to remove clean uncontaminated water from the loss.
Clean	SF Flr.	.06	.61		.67	
Minimum Charge	Job		153		153	
Grey (non-solids)						Includes labor to remove non-solid grey water from the loss.
Clean	SF Flr.	.06	1.23		1.29	
Minimum Charge	Job		153		153	
Sewage / Solids						Includes labor to remove water from the loss that may contain sewage or solids.
Clean	SF Flr.	.10	1.53		1.63	
Minimum Charge	Job		153		153	

Job Preparation

Flood Clean-up		Unit	Material	Labor	Equip.	Total	Specification
Mildicide Walls							
Topographical							
	Clean	SF Wall		.28		.28	Clean-up of deflooding including
	Minimum Charge	Job		153		153	topographical mildicide application.
Injection Treatments							
	Clean	SF Flr.	31	4.71		35.71	Clean-up of deflooding including
	Minimum Charge	Job		153		153	mildicide injection.
Carpet Cleaning							
Uncontaminated							
	Clean	SF Flr.		.19		.19	Includes labor to clean carpet.
	Minimum Charge	Job		153		153	
Contaminated							
	Clean	SF Flr.		.31		.31	Includes labor to clean contaminated
	Minimum Charge	Job		153		153	carpet.
Stairway							
	Clean	Ea.	.11	3.60		3.71	Includes labor to clean contaminated
	Minimum Charge	Job		153		153	carpet on a stairway.
Carpet Treatment							
Disinfect / Deodorize							
	Clean	SF Flr.		.19		.19	Includes disinfecting and deodorizing
	Minimum Charge	Job		153		153	of carpet.
Disinfect For Sewage							
	Clean	SF Flr.		.49		.49	Includes labor to disinfect and
	Minimum Charge	Job		153		153	deodorize carpet exposed to sewage.
Mildicide							
	Clean	SF Flr.	.01	.19		.20	Includes labor and materials to apply
	Minimum Charge	Job		153		153	mildicide to carpet.
Thermal Fog Area							
	Clean	SF Flr.	.03	.47		.50	Includes labor and materials to
	Minimum Charge	Job		153		153	perform thermal fogging during
							deflooding clean-up.
Wet Fog / ULV Area							
	Clean	SF Flr.	.02	.27		.29	Includes labor and materials to
	Minimum Charge	Job		153		153	perform wet fogging / ULV during
							deflooding clean-up.
Steam Clean Fixtures							
	Clean	Ea.	.01	30.50		30.51	Includes labor and materials to steam
	Minimum Charge	Job		153		153	clean fixtures during deflooding
							clean-up.
Pressure Wash Sewage							
	Clean	SF Flr.		2.79		2.79	Includes labor to pressure wash
	Minimum Charge	Job		153		153	sewage contamination.
Air Mover							
	Minimum Charge	Day			22.50	22.50	Daily rental of air mover.

Job Preparation

Flood Clean-up

		Unit	Material	Labor	Equip.	Total	Specification
Dehumidifier							
Medium Size							
	Minimum Charge	Day			48	48	Daily rental of dehumidifier, medium.
Large Size							
	Minimum Charge	Day			97	97	Daily rental of dehumidifier, large.
Air Purifier							
HEPA Filter-Bacteria							
	Minimum Charge	Ea.	345			345	HEPA filter for air purifier.

Asbestos Removal

		Unit	Material	Labor	Equip.	Total	Specification
Asbestos Analysis							
	Minimum Charge	Job		243		243	Minimum charge for testing.
Asbestos Pipe Insulation							
1/2" to 3/4" Diameter							
	Demolish	L.F.	.35	6.30		6.65	Minimum charge to remove asbestos. Includes full Tyvek suits for workers changed four times per eight-hour shift with respirators, air monitoring and supervision by qualified professionals.
	Minimum Charge	Job		3900		3900	
1" to 3" Diameter							
	Demolish	L.F.	1.09	19.50		20.59	Minimum charge to remove asbestos. Includes full Tyvek suits for workers changed four times per eight-hour shift with respirators, air monitoring and supervision by qualified professionals.
	Minimum Charge	Job		3900		3900	
Asbestos-based Siding							
	Demolish	S.F.	2.42	43.50		45.92	Minimum charge to remove asbestos. Includes full Tyvek suits for workers changed four times per eight-hour shift with respirators, air monitoring and supervision by qualified professionals.
	Minimum Charge	Job		3900		3900	
Asbestos-based Plaster							
	Demolish	S.F.	1.87	33.50		35.37	Minimum charge to remove asbestos. Includes full Tyvek suits for workers changed four times per eight-hour shift with respirators, air monitoring and supervision by qualified professionals.
	Minimum Charge	Job		3900		3900	
Encapsulate Asbestos Ceiling							
	Install	S.F.	.30	.19		.49	Includes encapsulation with penetrating sealant sprayed onto ceiling and walls with airless sprayer.
	Minimum Charge	Job		3900		3900	
Scrape Acoustical Ceiling							
	Demolish	S.F.	.07	1.10		1.17	Minimum charge to remove asbestos. Includes full Tyvek suits for workers changed four times per eight-hour shift with respirators, air monitoring and supervision by qualified professionals.
	Minimum Charge	Job		3900		3900	

Job Preparation

Asbestos Removal

		Unit	Material	Labor	Equip.	Total	Specification
Seal Ceiling Asbestos							
	Install	S.F.	2.26	3.67		5.93	Includes attaching plastic cover to ceiling area and sealing where asbestos exists, taping all seams, caulk or foam insulation in cracks and negative air system.
	Minimum Charge	Job		3900		3900	
Seal Wall Asbestos							
	Install	S.F.	2.26	3.26		5.52	Includes attaching plastic cover to wall area and sealing where asbestos exists, taping all seams, caulk or foam insulation in cracks and negative air system.
	Minimum Charge	Job		3900		3900	
Seal Floor Asbestos							
	Install	S.F.	3.61	6.50		10.11	Includes attaching plastic cover to floor area and sealing where asbestos exists, taping all seams, caulk or foam insulation in cracks and negative air system.
	Minimum Charge	Job		3900		3900	
Negative Air Vent System							
	Install	Day			44.50	44.50	Daily rental of negative air vent system.
	Minimum Charge	Week			223	223	
HEPA Vacuum Cleaner							
	Install	Day			18.40	18.40	Daily rental of HEPA vacuum, 16 gallon.
	Minimum Charge	Week			92	92	
Airless Sprayer							
	Install	Day			59	59	Daily rental of airless sprayer.
	Minimum Charge	Week			296	296	
Decontamination Unit							
	Install	Day			140	140	Daily rental of decontamination unit.
	Minimum Charge	Week			700	700	
Light Stand							
	Install	Day			13.20	13.20	Daily rental of floodlight w/tripod.
	Minimum Charge	Week			66	66	

Room Demolition

		Unit	Material	Labor	Equip.	Total	Specification
Strip Typical Room							
	Demolish	S.F.		3.06		3.06	Includes 4 labor hours for general demolition.
	Minimum Charge	Job		170		170	
Strip Typical Bathroom							
	Demolish	S.F.		4.09		4.09	Includes 4 labor hours for general demolition.
	Minimum Charge	Job		170		170	
Strip Typical Kitchen							
	Demolish	S.F.		3.93		3.93	Includes 4 labor hours for general demolition.
	Minimum Charge	Job		170		170	
Strip Typical Laundry							
	Demolish	S.F.		3.50		3.50	Includes 4 labor hours for general demolition.
	Minimum Charge	Job		170		170	

Selective Demolition		Unit	Material	Labor	Equip.	Total	Specification
Concrete Slab							
4" Unreinforced							
	Demolish	S.F.		2.04	.30	2.34	Includes labor and equipment to remove unreinforced concrete slab and haul debris to truck or dumpster.
	Minimum Charge	Job		865	128	993	
6" Unreinforced							
	Demolish	S.F.		2.89	.43	3.32	Includes labor and equipment to remove unreinforced concrete slab and haul debris to truck or dumpster.
	Minimum Charge	Job		865	128	993	
8" Unreinforced							
	Demolish	S.F.		4.75	.70	5.45	Includes labor and equipment to remove unreinforced concrete slab and haul debris to truck or dumpster.
	Minimum Charge	Job		865	128	993	
4" Reinforced							
	Demolish	S.F.		2.57	.38	2.95	Includes labor and equipment to remove reinforced concrete slab and haul debris to truck or dumpster.
	Minimum Charge	Job		865	128	993	
6" Reinforced							
	Demolish	S.F.		3.85	.57	4.42	Includes labor and equipment to remove reinforced concrete slab and haul debris to truck or dumpster.
	Minimum Charge	Job		865	128	993	
8" Reinforced							
	Demolish	S.F.		6.30	.93	7.23	Includes labor and equipment to remove reinforced concrete slab and haul debris to truck or dumpster.
	Minimum Charge	Job		865	128	993	
Brick Wall							
4" Thick							
	Demolish	S.F.		2.83	.42	3.25	Includes labor and equipment to remove brick wall and haul debris to a central location for disposal.
	Minimum Charge	Job		865	128	993	
8" Thick							
	Demolish	S.F.		3.90	.58	4.48	Includes labor and equipment to remove brick wall and haul debris to a central location for disposal.
	Minimum Charge	Job		865	128	993	
12" Thick							
	Demolish	S.F.		5.20	.77	5.97	Includes labor and equipment to remove brick wall and haul debris to a central location for disposal.
	Minimum Charge	Job		865	128	993	
Concrete Masonry Wall							
4" Thick							
	Demolish	S.F.		3.15	.46	3.61	Includes minimum labor and equipment to remove 4" block wall and haul debris to a central location for disposal.
	Minimum Charge	Job		865	128	993	
6" Thick							
	Demolish	S.F.		3.90	.58	4.48	Includes minimum labor and equipment to remove 6" block wall and haul debris to a central location for disposal.
	Minimum Charge	Job		865	128	993	

Job Preparation

Selective Demolition		Unit	Material	Labor	Equip.	Total	Specification
8" Thick							
	Demolish	S.F.		4.80	.71	5.51	Includes minimum labor and equipment to remove 8" block wall and haul debris to a central location for disposal.
	Minimum Charge	Job		865	128	993	
12" Thick							
	Demolish	S.F.		6.95	1.02	7.97	Includes minimum labor and equipment to remove 12" block wall and haul debris to a central location for disposal.
	Minimum Charge	Job		865	128	993	
Tree Removal							
Small, 4" - 8"							
	Demolish	Ea.		110	90.50	200.50	Minimum charge, tree removal.
	Minimum Charge	Job		153		153	
Medium, 9" - 12"							
	Demolish	Ea.		165	135	300	Minimum charge, tree removal.
	Minimum Charge	Job		153		153	
Large, 13" - 18"							
	Demolish	Ea.		198	162	360	Minimum charge, tree removal.
	Minimum Charge	Job		510	209	719	
Very Large, 19" - 24"							
	Demolish	Ea.		248	203	451	Minimum charge, tree removal.
	Minimum Charge	Job		510	209	719	
Stump Removal							
	Demolish	Ea.		68	146	214	Includes minimum charges for a site demolition crew and backhoe / loader.
	Minimum Charge	Job		283	102	385	

Excavation

Backhoe/Loader - Wheel Type   Tractor Loader - Wheel Type   Backhoe - Crawler Type

Excavation		Unit	Material	Labor	Equip.	Total	Specification
Footings							
Hand Trenching							
	Install	L.F.		1.92		1.92	Includes hand excavation for footing or trench up to 10" deep and 12" wide.
	Minimum Charge	Job		76.50		76.50	
Machine Trenching							
	Install	L.F.		.73	.37	1.10	Includes machine excavation for footing or trench up to 10" deep and 12" wide.
	Minimum Charge	Job		365	184	549	
Trenching w / Backfill							
Hand							
	Install	L.F.		3.06		3.06	Includes hand excavation, backfill and compaction.
	Minimum Charge	Job		76.50		76.50	
Machine							
	Install	L.F.		3.65	15.65	19.30	Includes machine excavation, backfill and compaction.
	Minimum Charge	Job		153	34.50	187.50	

Backfill		Unit	Material	Labor	Equip.	Total	Specification
Hand (no compaction)							
	Install	L.C.Y.		25.50		25.50	Includes backfill by hand in average soil without compaction.
	Minimum Charge	Job		153		153	
Hand (w / compaction)							
	Install	E.C.Y.		36		36	Includes backfill by hand in average soil with compaction.
	Minimum Charge	Job		153		153	
Machine (no compaction)							
	Install	L.C.Y.		3.65	1.84	5.49	Includes backfill, by 55 HP wheel loader, of trenches from loose material piled adjacent without compaction.
	Minimum Charge	Job		365	184	549	
Machine (w / compaction)							
	Install	L.C.Y.		9.75	4.90	14.65	Includes backfill, by 55 HP wheel loader, of trenches from loose material piled adjacent with compaction by vibrating tampers.
	Minimum Charge	Job		365	184	549	

Concrete Footing and Formwork   **Wood Pile**

Piles	Unit	Material	Labor	Equip.	Total	Specification
Treated Wood, 12″ Butt						
To 30′						
Demolish	L.F.		4.93	1.78	6.71	Includes material, labor and
Install	V.L.F.	20.50	4.58	3.22	28.30	equipment to install up to 30′ long
Demolish and Install	V.L.F.	20.50	9.51	5	35.01	treated wood piling.
Paint	L.F.	.41	2.03		2.44	
Minimum Charge	Job		2850	2025	4875	
30′ to 40′						
Demolish	L.F.		4.93	1.78	6.71	Includes material, labor and
Install	V.L.F.	22	4.09	2.88	28.97	equipment to install 30′ to 40′ long
Demolish and Install	V.L.F.	22	9.02	4.66	35.68	treated wood piling.
Paint	L.F.	.41	2.03		2.44	
Minimum Charge	Job		2850	2025	4875	
40′ to 50′						
Demolish	L.F.		4.93	1.78	6.71	Includes material, labor and
Install	V.L.F.	22	3.97	2.80	28.77	equipment to install 40′ to 50′ long
Demolish and Install	V.L.F.	22	8.90	4.58	35.48	treated wood piling.
Paint	L.F.	.41	2.03		2.44	
Minimum Charge	Job		2850	2025	4875	
50′ to 60′						
Demolish	L.F.		4.93	1.78	6.71	Includes material, labor and
Install	V.L.F.	23	3.58	2.52	29.10	equipment to install 50′ to 60′ long
Demolish and Install	V.L.F.	23	8.51	4.30	35.81	treated wood piling.
Paint	L.F.	.41	2.03		2.44	
Minimum Charge	Job		2850	2025	4875	
60′ to 80′						
Demolish	L.F.		4.93	1.78	6.71	Includes material, labor and
Install	V.L.F.	35	3.41	2.93	41.34	equipment to install 60′ to 80′ long
Demolish and Install	V.L.F.	35	8.34	4.71	48.05	treated wood piling.
Paint	L.F.	.41	2.03		2.44	
Minimum Charge	Job		2850	2025	4875	
Untreated Wood, 12″ Butt						
To 30′						
Demolish	L.F.		4.93	1.78	6.71	Includes material, labor and
Install	V.L.F.	22	4.58	3.22	29.80	equipment to install up to 30′ long
Demolish and Install	V.L.F.	22	9.51	5	36.51	untreated wood piling.
Paint	L.F.	.41	2.03		2.44	
Minimum Charge	Job		2850	2025	4875	

Foundation

Piles

	Unit	Material	Labor	Equip.	Total	Specification
30' to 40'						
Demolish	L.F.		4.93	1.78	6.71	Includes material, labor and
Install	V.L.F.	22	4.09	2.88	28.97	equipment to install 30' to 40' long
Demolish and Install	V.L.F.	22	9.02	4.66	35.68	untreated wood piling.
Paint	L.F.	.41	2.03		2.44	
Minimum Charge	Job		2850	2025	4875	
40' to 50'						
Demolish	L.F.		4.93	1.78	6.71	Includes material, labor and
Install	V.L.F.	22	3.97	2.80	28.77	equipment to install 40' to 50' long
Demolish and Install	V.L.F.	22	8.90	4.58	35.48	untreated wood piling.
Paint	L.F.	.41	2.03		2.44	
Minimum Charge	Job		2850	2025	4875	
50' to 60'						
Demolish	L.F.		4.93	1.78	6.71	Includes material, labor and
Install	V.L.F.	22	3.58	2.52	28.10	equipment to install 50' to 60' long
Demolish and Install	V.L.F.	22	8.51	4.30	34.81	untreated wood piling.
Paint	L.F.	.41	2.03		2.44	
Minimum Charge	Job		2850	2025	4875	
60' to 80'						
Demolish	L.F.		4.93	1.78	6.71	Includes material, labor and
Install	V.L.F.	27.50	3.41	2.40	33.31	equipment to install 60' to 80' long
Demolish and Install	V.L.F.	27.50	8.34	4.18	40.02	untreated wood piling.
Paint	L.F.	.41	2.03		2.44	
Minimum Charge	Job		2850	2025	4875	

Precast Concrete

	Unit	Material	Labor	Equip.	Total	Specification
10" Square						
Demolish	L.F.		5.05	1.81	6.86	Includes material, labor and
Install	V.L.F.	17.45	4.09	2.88	24.42	equipment to install a precast,
Demolish and Install	V.L.F.	17.45	9.14	4.69	31.28	prestressed, 40' long, 10" square
Paint	L.F.	.41	2.03		2.44	concrete pile.
Minimum Charge	Job		2850	2025	4875	
12" Square						
Demolish	L.F.		5.40	1.94	7.34	Includes material, labor and
Install	V.L.F.	22	4.21	2.96	29.17	equipment to install a precast,
Demolish and Install	V.L.F.	22	9.61	4.90	36.51	prestressed, 40' long, 12" square
Paint	L.F.	.41	2.03		2.44	concrete pile.
Minimum Charge	Job		2850	2025	4875	
14" Square						
Demolish	L.F.		5.55	1.99	7.54	Includes material, labor and
Install	V.L.F.	26	4.77	3.36	34.13	equipment to install a precast,
Demolish and Install	V.L.F.	26	10.32	5.35	41.67	prestressed, 40' long, 14" square
Paint	L.F.	.41	2.03		2.44	concrete pile.
Minimum Charge	Job		2850	2025	4875	
16" Square						
Demolish	L.F.		5.80	2.09	7.89	Includes material, labor and
Install	V.L.F.	40.50	5.10	3.60	49.20	equipment to install a precast,
Demolish and Install	V.L.F.	40.50	10.90	5.69	57.09	prestressed, 40' long, 16" square
Paint	L.F.	.41	2.03		2.44	concrete pile.
Minimum Charge	Job		2850	2025	4875	
18" Square						
Demolish	L.F.		6.30	2.27	8.57	Includes material, labor and
Install	V.L.F.	49	5.50	4.73	59.23	equipment to install a precast,
Demolish and Install	V.L.F.	49	11.80	7	67.80	prestressed, 40' long, 18" square
Paint	L.F.	.41	2.03		2.44	concrete pile.
Minimum Charge	Job		2850	2025	4875	

Foundation

Piles

	Unit	Material	Labor	Equip.	Total	Specification
Cross Bracing						
Treated 2" x 6"						
Demolish	L.F.		1		1	Cost includes material and labor to
Install	L.F.	.69	5.80		6.49	install 2" x 6" lumber for cross-bracing
Demolish and Install	L.F.	.69	6.80		7.49	of foundation piling or posts.
Reinstall	L.F.		4.66		4.66	
Clean	S.F.		.38		.38	
Paint	L.F.	.37	1.37		1.74	
Minimum Charge	Job		720		720	
Treated 2" x 8"						
Demolish	L.F.		1		1	Cost includes material and labor to
Install	L.F.	.97	6		6.97	install 2" x 8" lumber for cross-bracing
Demolish and Install	L.F.	.97	7		7.97	of foundation piling or posts.
Reinstall	L.F.		4.81		4.81	
Clean	S.F.		.38		.38	
Paint	L.F.	.50	1.42		1.92	
Minimum Charge	Job		720		720	
Treated 2" x 10"						
Demolish	L.F.		1.03		1.03	Cost includes material and labor to
Install	L.F.	1.29	6.20		7.49	install 2" x 10" lumber for
Demolish and Install	L.F.	1.29	7.23		8.52	cross-bracing of foundation piling or
Reinstall	L.F.		4.98		4.98	posts.
Clean	S.F.		.38		.38	
Paint	L.F.	.61	1.45		2.06	
Minimum Charge	Job		720		720	
Treated 2" x 12"						
Demolish	L.F.		1.24		1.24	Cost includes material and labor to
Install	L.F.	1.72	6.45		8.17	install 2" x 12" lumber for
Demolish and Install	L.F.	1.72	7.69		9.41	cross-bracing of foundation piling or
Reinstall	L.F.		5.16		5.16	posts.
Clean	S.F.		.38		.38	
Paint	L.F.	.72	1.48		2.20	
Minimum Charge	Job		720		720	
Metal Pipe						
6" Concrete Filled						
Demolish	L.F.		7	2.52	9.52	Includes material, labor and
Install	V.L.F.	26	5.95	4.20	36.15	equipment to install concrete filled
Demolish and Install	V.L.F.	26	12.95	6.72	45.67	steel pipe pile.
Paint	L.F.	.32	2.03		2.35	
Minimum Charge	Job		2850	2025	4875	
6" Unfilled						
Demolish	L.F.		7	2.52	9.52	Includes material, labor and
Install	V.L.F.	22	5.45	3.84	31.29	equipment to install unfilled steel pipe
Demolish and Install	V.L.F.	22	12.45	6.36	40.81	pile.
Paint	L.F.	.32	2.03		2.35	
Minimum Charge	Job		2850	2025	4875	
8" Concrete Filled						
Demolish	L.F.		7	2.52	9.52	Includes material, labor and
Install	V.L.F.	23.50	6.20	4.38	34.08	equipment to install concrete filled
Demolish and Install	V.L.F.	23.50	13.20	6.90	43.60	steel pipe pile.
Paint	L.F.	.32	2.03		2.35	
Minimum Charge	Job		2850	2025	4875	
8" Unfilled						
Demolish	L.F.		7	2.52	9.52	Includes material, labor and
Install	V.L.F.	22.50	5.70	4.03	32.23	equipment to install unfilled steel pipe
Demolish and Install	V.L.F.	22.50	12.70	6.55	41.75	pile.
Paint	L.F.	.32	2.03		2.35	
Minimum Charge	Job		2850	2025	4875	

Foundation

Piles

Piles		Unit	Material	Labor	Equip.	Total	Specification
10" Concrete Filled							
	Demolish	L.F.		7.20	2.60	9.80	Includes material, labor and
	Install	V.L.F.	30.50	6.35	4.48	41.33	equipment to install concrete filled
	Demolish and Install	V.L.F.	30.50	13.55	7.08	51.13	steel pipe pile.
	Paint	L.F.	.32	2.03		2.35	
	Minimum Charge	Job		2850	2025	4875	
10" Unfilled							
	Demolish	L.F.		7.20	2.60	9.80	Includes material, labor and
	Install	V.L.F.	28	5.70	4.03	37.73	equipment to install unfilled steel pipe
	Demolish and Install	V.L.F.	28	12.90	6.63	47.53	pile.
	Paint	L.F.	.32	2.03		2.35	
	Minimum Charge	Job		2850	2025	4875	
12" Concrete Filled							
	Demolish	L.F.		7.20	2.60	9.80	Includes material, labor and
	Install	V.L.F.	35	6.90	4.86	46.76	equipment to install concrete filled
	Demolish and Install	V.L.F.	35	14.10	7.46	56.56	steel pipe pile.
	Paint	L.F.	.32	2.03		2.35	
	Minimum Charge	Job		2850	2025	4875	
12" Unfilled							
	Demolish	L.F.		7.20	2.60	9.80	Includes material, labor and
	Install	V.L.F.	34	6	4.24	44.24	equipment to install unfilled steel pipe
	Demolish and Install	V.L.F.	34	13.20	6.84	54.04	pile.
	Paint	L.F.	.32	2.03		2.35	
	Minimum Charge	Job		2850	2025	4875	
Steel H Section							
H Section 8 x 8 x 36#							
	Demolish	L.F.		4.89	1.76	6.65	Includes material, labor and
	Install	V.L.F.	21	4.47	3.15	28.62	equipment to install steel H section pile.
	Demolish and Install	V.L.F.	21	9.36	4.91	35.27	
	Paint	L.F.	.32	2.03		2.35	
	Minimum Charge	Job		2850	2025	4875	
H Section 10 x 10 x 57#							
	Demolish	L.F.		5.35	1.93	7.28	Includes material, labor and
	Install	V.L.F.	33.50	4.69	3.30	41.49	equipment to install steel H section pile.
	Demolish and Install	V.L.F.	33.50	10.04	5.23	48.77	
	Paint	L.F.	.32	2.03		2.35	
	Minimum Charge	Job		2850	2025	4875	
H Section 12 x 12 x 74#							
	Demolish	L.F.		5.55	1.99	7.54	Includes material, labor and
	Install	V.L.F.	44.50	4.85	4.17	53.52	equipment to install steel H section pile.
	Demolish and Install	V.L.F.	44.50	10.40	6.16	61.06	
	Paint	L.F.	.32	2.03		2.35	
	Minimum Charge	Job		2850	2025	4875	
H Section 14 x 14 x 89#							
	Demolish	L.F.		5.80	2.09	7.89	Includes material, labor and
	Install	V.L.F.	54	5.30	4.55	63.85	equipment to install steel H section pile.
	Demolish and Install	V.L.F.	54	11.10	6.64	71.74	
	Paint	L.F.	.32	2.03		2.35	
	Minimum Charge	Job		2850	2025	4875	

Foundation

Foundation Post

	Unit	Material	Labor	Equip.	Total	Specification
Wood Foundation Post						
4" x 4"						
Demolish	L.F.		.79	.29	1.08	Cost includes material and labor to
Install	L.F.	1.24	5.10		6.34	install 4" x 4" treated wood post by
Demolish and Install	L.F.	1.24	5.89	.29	7.42	hand in normal soil conditions.
Reinstall	L.F.		4.09		4.09	
Minimum Charge	Job		720		720	
4" x 6"						
Demolish	L.F.		.79	.29	1.08	Cost includes material and labor to
Install	L.F.	1.85	5.10		6.95	install 4" x 6" treated wood post by
Demolish and Install	L.F.	1.85	5.89	.29	8.03	hand in normal soil conditions.
Reinstall	L.F.		4.09		4.09	
Minimum Charge	Job		720		720	
6" x 6"						
Demolish	L.F.		.79	.29	1.08	Cost includes material and labor to
Install	L.F.	2.75	5.10		7.85	install 6" x 6" treated wood post by
Demolish and Install	L.F.	2.75	5.89	.29	8.93	hand in normal soil conditions.
Reinstall	L.F.		4.09		4.09	
Minimum Charge	Job		720		720	
Water Jet						
Demolish	Ea.		91		91	Includes material, labor and
Install	Ea.	72.50	700		772.50	equipment to water jet a 6" x 6" wood
Demolish and Install	Ea.	72.50	791		863.50	post under an existing building. Cost
Reinstall	Ea.		700.34		700.34	may vary depending upon location
Minimum Charge	Job		615		615	and access.
Shim						
Install	Ea.	4.04	72		76.04	Includes labor and material to trim or
Minimum Charge	Job		720		720	readjust existing foundation posts under an existing building. Access of 2 - 4 foot assumed.
Cross-bracing						
Treated 2" x 6"						
Demolish	L.F.		1		1	Cost includes material and labor to
Install	L.F.	.69	5.80		6.49	install 2" x 6" lumber for cross-bracing
Demolish and Install	L.F.	.69	6.80		7.49	of foundation piling or posts.
Reinstall	L.F.		4.66		4.66	
Clean	S.F.		.38		.38	
Paint	L.F.	.37	1.37		1.74	
Minimum Charge	Job		720		720	
Treated 2" x 8"						
Demolish	L.F.		1		1	Cost includes material and labor to
Install	L.F.	.97	6		6.97	install 2" x 8" lumber for cross-bracing
Demolish and Install	L.F.	.97	7		7.97	of foundation piling or posts.
Reinstall	L.F.		4.81		4.81	
Clean	S.F.		.38		.38	
Paint	L.F.	.50	1.42		1.92	
Minimum Charge	Job		720		720	
Treated 2" x 10"						
Demolish	L.F.		1.03		1.03	Cost includes material and labor to
Install	L.F.	1.29	6.20		7.49	install 2" x 10" lumber for
Demolish and Install	L.F.	1.29	7.23		8.52	cross-bracing of foundation piling or
Reinstall	L.F.		4.98		4.98	posts.
Clean	S.F.		.38		.38	
Paint	L.F.	.61	1.45		2.06	
Minimum Charge	Job		720		720	

Foundation

Foundation Post

	Unit	Material	Labor	Equip.	Total	Specification
Treated 2″ x 12″						Cost includes material and labor to install 2″ x 12″ lumber for cross-bracing of foundation piling or posts.
Demolish	L.F.		1.24		1.24	
Install	L.F.	1.72	6.45		8.17	
Demolish and Install	L.F.	1.72	7.69		9.41	
Reinstall	L.F.		5.16		5.16	
Clean	S.F.		.38		.38	
Paint	L.F.	.72	1.48		2.20	
Minimum Charge	Job		720		720	

Concrete Footing

	Unit	Material	Labor	Equip.	Total	Specification
Continuous						
12″ w x 6″ d						Includes material and labor to install continuous reinforced concrete footing poured by chute cast against earth including reinforcing, forming and finishing.
Demolish	L.F.		1.49	1.29	2.78	
Install	L.F.	4.14	3.41	.02	7.57	
Demolish and Install	L.F.	4.14	4.90	1.31	10.35	
Minimum Charge	Job		830		830	
12″ w x 12″ d						Includes material and labor to install continuous reinforced concrete footing poured by chute cast against earth including reinforcing, forming and finishing.
Demolish	L.F.		2.87	2.47	5.34	
Install	L.F.	8.55	6.80	.04	15.39	
Demolish and Install	L.F.	8.55	9.67	2.51	20.73	
Minimum Charge	Job		830		830	
18″ w x 10″ d						Includes material and labor to install continuous reinforced concrete footing poured by chute cast against earth including reinforcing, forming and finishing.
Demolish	L.F.		3.72	3.22	6.94	
Install	L.F.	8.05	8.40	.05	16.50	
Demolish and Install	L.F.	8.05	12.12	3.27	23.44	
Minimum Charge	Job		830		830	
24″ w x 24″ d						Includes material and labor to install continuous reinforced concrete footing poured by chute cast against earth including reinforcing, forming and finishing.
Demolish	L.F.		6.20	5.35	11.55	
Install	L.F.	24	27.50	.15	51.65	
Demolish and Install	L.F.	24	33.70	5.50	63.20	
Minimum Charge	Job		830		830	
Stem Wall						
Single Story						Includes material and labor to install stem wall 24″ above and 18″ below grade for a single story structure. Includes 12″ wide and 8″ deep footing.
Demolish	L.F.		13.80	11.90	25.70	
Install	L.F.	20.50	73	63	156.50	
Demolish and Install	L.F.	20.50	86.80	74.90	182.20	
Minimum Charge	Job		830		830	
Two Story						Includes material and labor to install stem wall 24″ above and 18″ below grade typical for a two story structure, includes 18″ wide and 10″ deep footing.
Demolish	L.F.		13.80	11.90	25.70	
Install	L.F.	25.50	105	90.50	221	
Demolish and Install	L.F.	25.50	118.80	102.40	246.70	
Minimum Charge	Job		830		830	

Foundation

Concrete Slab

	Unit	Material	Labor	Equip.	Total	Specification
Reinforced						
4″						
Demolish	S.F.		2.57	.38	2.95	Cost includes material and labor to
Install	S.F.	2.18	.39		2.57	install 4″ reinforced concrete
Demolish and Install	S.F.	2.18	2.96	.38	5.52	slab-on-grade poured by chute
Clean	S.F.	.08	.34		.42	including forms, vapor barrier, wire
Paint	S.F.	.15	.77		.92	mesh, 3000 PSI concrete, float finish,
Minimum Charge	Job		191		191	and curing.
6″						
Demolish	S.F.		3.85	.57	4.42	Cost includes material and labor to
Install	S.F.	2.98	.59	.01	3.58	install 6″ reinforced concrete
Demolish and Install	S.F.	2.98	4.44	.58	8	slab-on-grade poured by chute
Clean	S.F.	.08	.34		.42	including forms, vapor barrier, wire
Paint	S.F.	.15	.77		.92	mesh, 3000 PSI concrete, float finish,
Minimum Charge	Job		191		191	and curing.
8″						
Demolish	S.F.		6.30	.93	7.23	Cost includes material and labor to
Install	S.F.	3.81	.77	.01	4.59	install 8″ reinforced concrete
Demolish and Install	S.F.	3.81	7.07	.94	11.82	slab-on-grade poured by chute
Clean	S.F.	.08	.34		.42	including forms, vapor barrier, wire
Paint	S.F.	.15	.77		.92	mesh, 3000 PSI concrete, float finish,
Minimum Charge	Job		191		191	and curing.
Unreinforced						
4″						
Demolish	S.F.		2.04	.30	2.34	Cost includes material and labor to
Install	S.F.	1.42	.95	.01	2.38	install 4″ concrete slab-on-grade
Demolish and Install	S.F.	1.42	2.99	.31	4.72	poured by chute, including forms,
Clean	S.F.	.08	.34		.42	vapor barrier, 3000 PSI concrete, float
Paint	S.F.	.15	.77		.92	finish, and curing.
Minimum Charge	Job		191		191	
6″						
Demolish	S.F.		2.89	.43	3.32	Cost includes material and labor to
Install	S.F.	2.08	.97	.01	3.06	install 6″ concrete slab-on-grade
Demolish and Install	S.F.	2.08	3.86	.44	6.38	poured by chute, including forms,
Clean	S.F.	.08	.34		.42	vapor barrier, 3000 PSI concrete, float
Paint	S.F.	.15	.77		.92	finish, and curing.
Minimum Charge	Job		191		191	
8″						
Demolish	S.F.		4.75	.70	5.45	Cost includes material and labor to
Install	S.F.	2.85	1.02	.01	3.88	install 8″ concrete slab-on-grade
Demolish and Install	S.F.	2.85	5.77	.71	9.33	poured by chute, including forms,
Clean	S.F.	.08	.34		.42	vapor barrier, 3000 PSI concrete, float
Paint	S.F.	.15	.77		.92	finish, and curing.
Minimum Charge	Job		191		191	
Lightweight						
Demolish	S.F.		.91	.22	1.13	Includes material and labor to install
Install	S.F.	1.80	2.85		4.65	lightweight concrete, 3″ - 4″ thick.
Demolish and Install	S.F.	1.80	3.76	.22	5.78	
Clean	S.F.	.08	.34		.42	
Paint	S.F.	.15	.77		.92	
Minimum Charge	Job		191		191	

Foundation

Concrete Slab

	Unit	Material	Labor	Equip.	Total	Specification
Gunite						
Demolish	S.F.		1.13	.41	1.54	Includes material and labor to install
Install	S.F.	.36	1.22	.17	1.75	gunite on flat plane per inch of
Demolish and Install	S.F.	.36	2.35	.58	3.29	thickness using 1" as base price. No
Clean	S.F.	.08	.34		.42	forms or reinforcing are included.
Paint	S.F.	.15	.77		.92	
Minimum Charge	Job		1075		1075	
Epoxy Inject						
Install	L.F.	6.50	3.82		10.32	Includes labor and material to inject
Minimum Charge	Job		191		191	epoxy into cracks.
Pressure Grout						
Install	S.F.	2.95	2.83		5.78	Includes labor, material and
Minimum Charge	Job		191		191	equipment to install pressure grout under an existing building.
Scrape and Paint						
Paint	S.F.	.24	.89		1.13	Includes labor and materials to scrape
Minimum Charge	Job		178		178	and paint a concrete floor.
Vapor Barrier						
Install	S.F.	.03	.11		.14	Cost includes material and labor to
Minimum Charge	Job		207		207	install 4 mil polyethylene vapor barrier 10' wide sheets with 6" overlaps.

Rough Framing

Beam / Girder	Unit	Material	Labor	Equip.	Total	Specification
Solid Wood Beam						
2" x 8"						
Demolish	L.F.		.83		.83	Cost includes material and labor to
Install	L.F.	.83	1.28		2.11	install 2" x 8" beam.
Demolish and Install	L.F.	.83	2.11		2.94	
Clean	L.F.	.15	.27		.42	
Paint	L.F.	.13	1.92		2.05	
Minimum Charge	Job		207		207	
2" x 10"						
Demolish	L.F.		1.02		1.02	Cost includes material and labor to
Install	L.F.	1.11	1.38		2.49	install 2" x 10" beam.
Demolish and Install	L.F.	1.11	2.40		3.51	
Clean	L.F.	.19	.33		.52	
Paint	L.F.	.19	1.18		1.37	
Minimum Charge	Job		207		207	
2" x 12"						
Demolish	L.F.		1.24		1.24	Cost includes material and labor to
Install	L.F.	1.41	1.51		2.92	install 2" x 12" beam.
Demolish and Install	L.F.	1.41	2.75		4.16	
Clean	L.F.	.22	.38		.60	
Paint	L.F.	.20	2.84		3.04	
Minimum Charge	Job		207		207	
4" x 8"						
Demolish	L.F.		2.55		2.55	Cost includes material and labor to
Install	L.F.	3.74	1.88	.67	6.29	install 4" x 8" beam.
Demolish and Install	L.F.	3.74	4.43	.67	8.84	
Clean	L.F.	.19	.33		.52	
Paint	L.F.	.19	1.18		1.37	
Minimum Charge	Job		207		207	
4" x 10"						
Demolish	L.F.		3.19		3.19	Cost includes material and labor to
Install	L.F.	4.68	1.98	.71	7.37	install 4" x 10" beam.
Demolish and Install	L.F.	4.68	5.17	.71	10.56	
Clean	L.F.	.22	.38		.60	
Paint	L.F.	.21	1.38		1.59	
Minimum Charge	Job		207		207	
4" x 12"						
Demolish	L.F.		3.82		3.82	Cost includes material and labor to
Install	L.F.	6.05	2.09	.75	8.89	install 4" x 12" beam.
Demolish and Install	L.F.	6.05	5.91	.75	12.71	
Clean	L.F.	.25	.44		.69	
Paint	L.F.	.20	2.84		3.04	
Minimum Charge	Job		207		207	

Beam / Girder		Unit	Material	Labor	Equip.	Total	Specification
6" x 8"							
	Demolish	L.F.		3.82		3.82	Cost includes material and labor to
	Install	L.F.	5.30	3.58	1.28	10.16	install 6" x 8" beam.
	Demolish and Install	L.F.	5.30	7.40	1.28	13.98	
	Clean	L.F.	.22	.38		.60	
	Paint	L.F.	.21	1.38		1.59	
	Minimum Charge	Job		207		207	
6" x 10"							
	Demolish	L.F.		4.78		4.78	Cost includes material and labor to
	Install	L.F.	3.32	1.66		4.98	install 6" x 10" triple beam.
	Demolish and Install	L.F.	3.32	6.44		9.76	
	Clean	L.F.	.25	.44		.69	
	Paint	L.F.	.24	1.58		1.82	
	Minimum Charge	Job		207		207	
6" x 12"							
	Demolish	L.F.		5.70		5.70	Cost includes material and labor to
	Install	L.F.	4.21	1.74		5.95	install 6" x 12" triple beam.
	Demolish and Install	L.F.	4.21	7.44		11.65	
	Clean	L.F.	.29	.49		.78	
	Paint	L.F.	.26	1.78		2.04	
	Minimum Charge	Job		207		207	
Steel I-type							
W8 x 31							
	Demolish	L.F.		8.85	3.41	12.26	Includes material and labor to install
	Install	L.F.	47	2.79	1.52	51.31	W shaped steel beam / girder.
	Demolish and Install	L.F.	47	11.64	4.93	63.57	
	Minimum Charge	Job		510		510	
W8 x 48							
	Demolish	L.F.		8.85	3.41	12.26	Includes material and labor to install
	Install	L.F.	72.50	2.92	1.60	77.02	W shaped steel beam / girder.
	Demolish and Install	L.F.	72.50	11.77	5.01	89.28	
	Minimum Charge	Job		510		510	
W8 x 67							
	Demolish	L.F.		8.85	3.41	12.26	Includes material and labor to install
	Install	L.F.	101	3.06	1.67	105.73	W shaped steel beam / girder.
	Demolish and Install	L.F.	101	11.91	5.08	117.99	
	Minimum Charge	Job		510		510	
W10 x 45							
	Demolish	L.F.		8.85	3.41	12.26	Includes material and labor to install
	Install	L.F.	68	2.92	1.60	72.52	W shaped steel beam / girder.
	Demolish and Install	L.F.	68	11.77	5.01	84.78	
	Minimum Charge	Job		510		510	
W10 x 68							
	Demolish	L.F.		8.85	3.41	12.26	Includes material and labor to install
	Install	L.F.	103	3.06	1.67	107.73	W shaped steel beam / girder.
	Demolish and Install	L.F.	103	11.91	5.08	119.99	
	Minimum Charge	Job		510		510	
W12 x 50							
	Demolish	L.F.		8.85	3.41	12.26	Includes material and labor to install
	Install	L.F.	76	2.92	1.60	80.52	W shaped steel beam / girder.
	Demolish and Install	L.F.	76	11.77	5.01	92.78	
	Minimum Charge	Job		510		510	
W12 x 87							
	Demolish	L.F.		13.05	5	18.05	Includes material and labor to install
	Install	L.F.	132	3.06	1.67	136.73	W shaped steel beam / girder.
	Demolish and Install	L.F.	132	16.11	6.67	154.78	
	Minimum Charge	Job		510		510	

Rough Frame / Structure

Beam / Girder

Beam / Girder		Unit	Material	Labor	Equip.	Total	Specification
W12 x 120							
	Demolish	L.F.		13.05	5	18.05	Includes material and labor to install
	Install	L.F.	182	3.14	1.72	186.86	W shaped steel beam / girder.
	Demolish and Install	L.F.	182	16.19	6.72	204.91	
	Minimum Charge	Job		510		510	
W14 x 74							
	Demolish	L.F.		13.05	5	18.05	Includes material and labor to install
	Install	L.F.	112	3.06	1.67	116.73	W shaped steel beam / girder.
	Demolish and Install	L.F.	112	16.11	6.67	134.78	
	Minimum Charge	Job		510		510	
W14 x 120							
	Demolish	L.F.		13.05	5	18.05	Includes material and labor to install
	Install	L.F.	182	3.14	1.72	186.86	W shaped steel beam / girder.
	Demolish and Install	L.F.	182	16.19	6.72	204.91	
	Minimum Charge	Job		510		510	

Column

Column		Unit	Material	Labor	Equip.	Total	Specification
Concrete							
Small Diameter							
	Demolish	L.F.		14.45	2.13	16.58	Includes material and labor to install
	Install	L.F.	68	13.25	2.56	83.81	small diameter concrete column.
	Demolish and Install	L.F.	68	27.70	4.69	100.39	
	Minimum Charge	Job		665	128	793	
Large Diameter							
	Demolish	L.F.		43.50	6.40	49.90	Includes material and labor to install
	Install	L.F.	262	15.60	3.01	280.61	large diameter concrete column.
	Demolish and Install	L.F.	262	59.10	9.41	330.51	
	Minimum Charge	Job		665	128	793	

Floor Framing System

Floor Framing System		Unit	Material	Labor	Equip.	Total	Specification
12" O.C.							
2" x 6" Joists							
	Demolish	S.F.		.70		.70	Cost includes material and labor to
	Install	S.F.	.68	.66		1.34	install 2" x 6" joists, 12" O.C.
	Demolish and Install	S.F.	.68	1.36		2.04	including box or band joist. Blocking
	Reinstall	S.F.		.53		.53	or bridging not included.
	Minimum Charge	Job		207		207	
2" x 8" Joists							
	Demolish	S.F.		.73		.73	Cost includes material and labor to
	Install	S.F.	.97	.75		1.72	install 2" x 8" joists, 12" O.C.
	Demolish and Install	S.F.	.97	1.48		2.45	including box or band joist. Blocking
	Reinstall	S.F.		.60		.60	or bridging not included.
	Minimum Charge	Job		207		207	
2" x 10" Joists							
	Demolish	S.F.		.75		.75	Cost includes material and labor to
	Install	S.F.	1.30	.92		2.22	install 2" x 10" joists, 12" O.C.
	Demolish and Install	S.F.	1.30	1.67		2.97	including box or band joist. Blocking
	Reinstall	S.F.		.74		.74	or bridging not included.
	Minimum Charge	Job		207		207	

Rough Frame / Structure

Floor Framing System		Unit	Material	Labor	Equip.	Total	Specification
2″ x 12″ Joists							
	Demolish	S.F.		.77		.77	Cost includes material and labor to
	Install	S.F.	1.64	.95		2.59	install 2″ x 12″ joists, 12″ O.C.
	Demolish and Install	S.F.	1.64	1.72		3.36	including box or band joist. Blocking
	Reinstall	S.F.		.76		.76	or bridging not included.
	Minimum Charge	Job		207		207	
Block / Bridge							
	Demolish	Ea.		1.06		1.06	Includes material and labor to install
	Install	Ea.	1.49	2.33		3.82	set of cross bridging or per block of
	Demolish and Install	Ea.	1.49	3.39		4.88	solid bridging for 2″ x 10″ joists cut to
	Minimum Charge	Job		207		207	size on site.

16″ O.C.

		Unit	Material	Labor	Equip.	Total	Specification
2″ x 6″ Joists							
	Demolish	S.F.		.53		.53	Cost includes material and labor to
	Install	S.F.	.53	.50		1.03	install 2″ x 6″ joists including box or
	Demolish and Install	S.F.	.53	1.03		1.56	band joist installed 16″ O.C. Does not
	Reinstall	S.F.		.40		.40	include beams, blocking or bridging.
	Minimum Charge	Job		207		207	
2″ x 8″ Joists							
	Demolish	S.F.		.54		.54	Cost includes material and labor to
	Install	S.F.	.75	.57		1.32	install 2″ x 8″ joists including box or
	Demolish and Install	S.F.	.75	1.11		1.86	band joist installed 16″ O.C. Does not
	Reinstall	S.F.		.45		.45	include beams, blocking or bridging.
	Minimum Charge	Job		207		207	
2″ x 10″ Joists							
	Demolish	S.F.		.56		.56	Cost includes material and labor to
	Install	S.F.	.99	.69		1.68	install 2″ x 10″ joists including box or
	Demolish and Install	S.F.	.99	1.25		2.24	band joist 16″ O.C. Does not include
	Reinstall	S.F.		.55		.55	beams, blocking or bridging.
	Minimum Charge	Job		207		207	
2″ x 12″ Joists							
	Demolish	S.F.		.58		.58	Cost includes material and labor to
	Install	S.F.	1.27	.71		1.98	install 2″ x 12″ joists including box or
	Demolish and Install	S.F.	1.27	1.29		2.56	band joist installed 16″ O.C. Does not
	Reinstall	S.F.		.57		.57	include beams, blocking or bridging.
	Minimum Charge	Job		207		207	
Block / Bridge							
	Demolish	Ea.		1.06		1.06	Includes material and labor to install
	Install	Ea.	1.49	2.33		3.82	set of cross bridging or per block of
	Demolish and Install	Ea.	1.49	3.39		4.88	solid bridging for 2″ x 10″ joists cut to
	Minimum Charge	Job		207		207	size on site.

24″ O.C.

		Unit	Material	Labor	Equip.	Total	Specification
2″ x 6″ Joists							
	Demolish	S.F.		.35		.35	Cost includes material and labor to
	Install	S.F.	.37	.33		.70	install 2″ x 6″ joists including box or
	Demolish and Install	S.F.	.37	.68		1.05	band joist installed 24″ O.C. Does not
	Reinstall	S.F.		.26		.26	include beams, blocking or bridging.
	Minimum Charge	Job		207		207	
2″ x 8″ Joists							
	Demolish	S.F.		.36		.36	Cost includes material and labor to
	Install	S.F.	.53	.38		.91	install 2″ x 8″ joists including box or
	Demolish and Install	S.F.	.53	.74		1.27	band joist installed 24″ O.C. Does not
	Reinstall	S.F.		.30		.30	include beams, blocking or bridging.
	Minimum Charge	Job		207		207	

Rough Frame / Structure

Floor Framing System		Unit	Material	Labor	Equip.	Total	Specification
2" x 10" Joists							
	Demolish	S.F.		.37		.37	Cost includes material and labor to
	Install	S.F.	.70	.46		1.16	install 2" x 10" joists including box or
	Demolish and Install	S.F.	.70	.83		1.53	band joist installed 24" O.C. Does not
	Reinstall	S.F.		.37		.37	include beams, blocking or bridging.
	Minimum Charge	Job		207		207	
2" x 12" Joists							
	Demolish	S.F.		.39		.39	Cost includes material and labor to
	Install	S.F.	.90	.47		1.37	install 2" x 12" joists including box or
	Demolish and Install	S.F.	.90	.86		1.76	band joist installed 24" O.C. Does not
	Reinstall	S.F.		.38		.38	include beams, blocking or bridging.
	Minimum Charge	Job		207		207	
Block / Bridge							
	Demolish	Ea.		1.06		1.06	Includes material and labor to install
	Install	Ea.	1.49	2.33		3.82	set of cross bridging or per block of
	Demolish and Install	Ea.	1.49	3.39		4.88	solid bridging for 2" x 10" joists cut to
	Minimum Charge	Job		207		207	size on site.
Engineered Lumber, Joist							
9-1/2"							
	Demolish	S.F.		.56		.56	Includes material and labor to install
	Install	S.F.	1.60	.41		2.01	engineered lumber truss / joists per
	Demolish and Install	S.F.	1.60	.97		2.57	S.F. of floor area based on joists 16"
	Reinstall	S.F.		.33		.33	O.C. Beams, supports and bridging
	Minimum Charge	Job		207		207	are not included.
11-7/8"							
	Demolish	S.F.		.58		.58	Includes material and labor to install
	Install	S.F.	1.80	.42		2.22	engineered lumber truss / joists per
	Demolish and Install	S.F.	1.80	1		2.80	S.F. of floor area based on joists 16"
	Reinstall	S.F.		.34		.34	O.C. Beams, supports and bridging
	Minimum Charge	Job		207		207	are not included.
14"							
	Demolish	S.F.		.60		.60	Includes material and labor to install
	Install	S.F.	2.49	.45		2.94	engineered lumber truss / joists per
	Demolish and Install	S.F.	2.49	1.05		3.54	S.F. of floor area based on joists 16"
	Reinstall	S.F.		.36		.36	O.C. Beams, supports and bridging
	Minimum Charge	Job		207		207	are not included.
16"							
	Demolish	S.F.		.62		.62	Includes material and labor to install
	Install	S.F.	3.08	.48		3.56	engineered lumber truss / joists per
	Demolish and Install	S.F.	3.08	1.10		4.18	S.F. of floor area based on joists 16"
	Reinstall	S.F.		.38		.38	O.C. Beams, supports and bridging
	Minimum Charge	Job		207		207	are not included.
Block / Bridge							
	Demolish	Pr.		1.06		1.06	Includes material and labor to install
	Install	Pr.	2.04	3.07		5.11	set of steel, one-nail type cross
	Demolish and Install	Pr.	2.04	4.13		6.17	bridging for trusses placed 16" O.C.
	Minimum Charge	Job		207		207	
Block / Bridge							
2" x 6"							
	Demolish	Ea.		1.06		1.06	Includes material and labor to install
	Install	Ea.	.78	1.87		2.65	set of cross bridging or per block of
	Demolish and Install	Ea.	.78	2.93		3.71	solid bridging for 2" x 6" joists cut to
	Minimum Charge	Job		207		207	size on site.

Rough Frame / Structure

Floor Framing System		Unit	Material	Labor	Equip.	Total	Specification
2″ x 8″							
	Demolish	Ea.		1.06		1.06	Includes material and labor to install
	Install	Ea.	1.11	2.07		3.18	set of cross bridging or per block of
	Demolish and Install	Ea.	1.11	3.13		4.24	solid bridging for 2″ x 8″ joists cut to
	Minimum Charge	Job		207		207	size on site.
2″ x 10″							
	Demolish	Ea.		1.06		1.06	Includes material and labor to install
	Install	Ea.	1.49	2.33		3.82	set of cross bridging or per block of
	Demolish and Install	Ea.	1.49	3.39		4.88	solid bridging for 2″ x 10″ joists cut to
	Minimum Charge	Job		207		207	size on site.
2″ x 12″							
	Demolish	Ea.		1.06		1.06	Includes material and labor to install
	Install	Ea.	1.88	2.74		4.62	set of cross bridging or per block of
	Demolish and Install	Ea.	1.88	3.80		5.68	solid bridging for 2″ x 12″ joists cut to
	Minimum Charge	Job		207		207	size on site.
Ledger Strips							
1″ x 2″							
	Demolish	L.F.		.28		.28	Cost includes material and labor to
	Install	L.F.	.28	1.20		1.48	install 1″ x 2″ ledger strip nailed to the
	Demolish and Install	L.F.	.28	1.48		1.76	face of studs, beams or joist.
	Minimum Charge	Job		207		207	
1″ x 3″							
	Demolish	L.F.		.28		.28	Includes material and labor to install
	Install	L.F.	.45	1.38		1.83	up to 1″ x 4″ ledger strip nailed to the
	Demolish and Install	L.F.	.45	1.66		2.11	face of studs, beams or joist.
	Minimum Charge	Job		207		207	
1″ x 4″							
	Demolish	L.F.		.28		.28	Includes material and labor to install
	Install	L.F.	.45	1.38		1.83	up to 1″ x 4″ ledger strip nailed to the
	Demolish and Install	L.F.	.45	1.66		2.11	face of studs, beams or joist.
	Minimum Charge	Job		207		207	
2″ x 2″							
	Demolish	L.F.		.31		.31	Cost includes material and labor to
	Install	L.F.	.36	1.26		1.62	install 2″ x 2″ ledger strip nailed to the
	Demolish and Install	L.F.	.36	1.57		1.93	face of studs, beams or joist.
	Minimum Charge	Job		207		207	
2″ x 4″							
	Demolish	L.F.		.34		.34	Cost includes material and labor to
	Install	L.F.	.36	1.66		2.02	install 2″ x 4″ ledger strip nailed to the
	Demolish and Install	L.F.	.36	2		2.36	face of studs, beams or joist.
	Reinstall	L.F.		1.33		1.33	
	Minimum Charge	Job		207		207	
Ledger Boards							
2″ x 6″							
	Demolish	L.F.		.34		.34	Cost includes material and labor to
	Install	L.F.	4.63	2.59		7.22	install 2″ x 6″ ledger board fastened to
	Demolish and Install	L.F.	4.63	2.93		7.56	a wall, joists or studs.
	Reinstall	L.F.		2.07		2.07	
	Minimum Charge	Job		207		207	
4″ x 6″							
	Demolish	L.F.		.57		.57	Cost includes material and labor to
	Install	L.F.	8.10	2.59		10.69	install 4″ x 6″ ledger board fastened to
	Demolish and Install	L.F.	8.10	3.16		11.26	a wall, joists or studs.
	Reinstall	L.F.		2.07		2.07	
	Minimum Charge	Job		207		207	

Rough Frame / Structure

Floor Framing System

Floor Framing System		Unit	Material	Labor	Equip.	Total	Specification
4″ x 8″							
	Demolish	L.F.		.76		.76	Cost includes material and labor to
	Install	L.F.	9.10	2.59		11.69	install 4″ x 8″ ledger board fastened to
	Demolish and Install	L.F.	9.10	3.35		12.45	a wall, joists or studs.
	Reinstall	L.F.		2.07		2.07	
	Minimum Charge	Job		207		207	
Sill Plate Per L.F.							
2″ x 4″							
	Demolish	L.F.		.29		.29	Cost includes material and labor to
	Install	L.F.	.36	1.51		1.87	install 2″ x 4″ pressure treated lumber,
	Demolish and Install	L.F.	.36	1.80		2.16	drilled and installed on foundation
	Reinstall	L.F.		1.21		1.21	bolts 48″ O.C. Bolts, nuts and washers
	Minimum Charge	Job		207		207	are not included.
2″ x 6″							
	Demolish	L.F.		.44		.44	Cost includes material and labor to
	Install	L.F.	.69	1.66		2.35	install 2″ x 6″ pressure treated lumber,
	Demolish and Install	L.F.	.69	2.10		2.79	drilled and installed on foundation
	Reinstall	L.F.		1.33		1.33	bolts 48″ O.C. Bolts, nuts and washers
	Minimum Charge	Job		207		207	not included.
2″ x 8″							
	Demolish	L.F.		.58		.58	Cost includes material and labor to
	Install	L.F.	.97	1.84		2.81	install 2″ x 8″ pressure treated lumber,
	Demolish and Install	L.F.	.97	2.42		3.39	drilled and installed on foundation
	Reinstall	L.F.		1.47		1.47	bolts 48″ O.C. Bolts, nuts and washers
	Minimum Charge	Job		207		207	not included.
Earthquake Strapping							
	Install	Ea.	2.99	2.59		5.58	Includes labor and material to replace
	Minimum Charge	Job		207		207	an earthquake strap.

Subflooring

Subflooring		Unit	Material	Labor	Equip.	Total	Specification
Plywood							
1/2″							
	Demolish	S.F.		.89		.89	Cost includes material and labor to
	Install	SF Flr.	.39	.45		.84	install 1/2″ plywood subfloor, CD
	Demolish and Install	SF Flr.	.39	1.34		1.73	standard interior grade, plugged and
	Minimum Charge	Job		207		207	touch sanded.
5/8″							
	Demolish	S.F.		.90		.90	Cost includes material and labor to
	Install	SF Flr.	.52	.50		1.02	install 5/8″ plywood subfloor, CD
	Demolish and Install	SF Flr.	.52	1.40		1.92	standard interior grade, plugged and
	Reinstall	SF Flr.		.40		.40	touch sanded.
	Minimum Charge	Job		207		207	
3/4″							
	Demolish	S.F.		.91		.91	Cost includes material and labor to
	Install	SF Flr.	.59	.53		1.12	install 3/4″ plywood subfloor, CD
	Demolish and Install	SF Flr.	.59	1.44		2.03	standard interior grade, plugged and
	Reinstall	SF Flr.		.43		.43	touch sanded.
	Minimum Charge	Job		207		207	

Rough Frame / Structure

Subflooring

	Unit	Material	Labor	Equip.	Total	Specification
Particle Board						
1/2"						
Demolish	S.F.		.44		.44	Cost includes material and labor to
Install	SF Flr.	.40	.55		.95	install 1/2" particle board subfloor.
Demolish and Install	SF Flr.	.40	.99		1.39	
Minimum Charge	Job		207		207	
5/8"						
Demolish	S.F.		.45		.45	Cost includes material and labor to
Install	SF Flr.	.51	.60		1.11	install 5/8" particle board subfloor.
Demolish and Install	SF Flr.	.51	1.05		1.56	
Minimum Charge	Job		207		207	
3/4"						
Demolish	S.F.		.45		.45	Cost includes material and labor to
Install	SF Flr.	.72	.66		1.38	install 3/4" particle board subfloor.
Demolish and Install	SF Flr.	.72	1.11		1.83	
Minimum Charge	Job		207		207	
Plank Board						
Demolish	S.F.		1.42		1.42	Cost includes material and labor to
Install	SF Flr.	1.73	.92		2.65	install 1" x 6" standard grade plank
Demolish and Install	SF Flr.	1.73	2.34		4.07	flooring.
Reinstall	SF Flr.		.92		.92	
Minimum Charge	Job		207		207	
Felt Underlay						
Demolish	S.F.		.08		.08	Includes material and labor to install
Install	S.F.	.07	.11		.18	#15 felt building paper.
Demolish and Install	S.F.	.07	.19		.26	
Minimum Charge	Job		207		207	
Prep (for flooring)						
Install	S.F.		.35		.35	Preparation of subflooring for
Minimum Charge	Job		184		184	installation of new finished flooring. Cost reflects average time to prep area.

Wall Framing System

	Unit	Material	Labor	Equip.	Total	Specification
2" x 4"						
8' High						
Demolish	L.F.		4.54		4.54	Cost includes material and labor to
Install	L.F.	3.61	4.88		8.49	install 2" x 4" x 8' high wall system,
Demolish and Install	L.F.	3.61	9.42		13.03	including studs, treated bottom plate,
Reinstall	L.F.		3.90		3.90	double top plate and one row of fire
Minimum Charge	Job		207		207	blocking.
9' High						
Demolish	L.F.		5.10		5.10	Cost includes material and labor to
Install	L.F.	3.88	4.88		8.76	install 2" x 4" x 9' wall system
Demolish and Install	L.F.	3.88	9.98		13.86	including studs, treated bottom plate,
Reinstall	L.F.		3.90		3.90	double top plate and one row of fire
Minimum Charge	Job		207		207	blocking.
10' High						
Demolish	L.F.		5.65		5.65	Cost includes material and labor to
Install	L.F.	4.15	4.88		9.03	install 2" x 4" x 10' wall system
Demolish and Install	L.F.	4.15	10.53		14.68	including studs, treated bottom plate,
Reinstall	L.F.		3.90		3.90	double top plate and one row of fire
Minimum Charge	Job		207		207	blocking.

Rough Frame / Structure

Wall Framing System	Unit	Material	Labor	Equip.	Total	Specification
12' High						
Demolish	L.F.		6.80		6.80	Cost includes material and labor to
Install	L.F.	4.69	5.90		10.59	install 2" x 4" x 12' wall system
Demolish and Install	L.F.	4.69	12.70		17.39	including studs, treated bottom plate,
Reinstall	L.F.		4.74		4.74	double top plate and one row of fire
Minimum Charge	Job		207		207	blocking.
2" x 6"						
8' High						
Demolish	L.F.		4.26		4.26	Cost includes material and labor to
Install	L.F.	6	9.05		15.05	install 2" x 6" x 8' wall system
Demolish and Install	L.F.	6	13.31		19.31	including studs, treated bottom plate,
Reinstall	L.F.		7.22		7.22	double top plate and one row of fire
Minimum Charge	Job		207		207	blocking.
9' High						
Demolish	L.F.		4.80		4.80	Cost includes material and labor to
Install	L.F.	6.45	9.05		15.50	install 2" x 6" x 9' wall system
Demolish and Install	L.F.	6.45	13.85		20.30	including studs, treated bottom plate,
Reinstall	L.F.		7.22		7.22	double top plate and one row of fire
Minimum Charge	Job		207		207	blocking.
10' High						
Demolish	L.F.		5.25		5.25	Cost includes material and labor to
Install	L.F.	6.90	9.05		15.95	install 2" x 6" x 10' wall system
Demolish and Install	L.F.	6.90	14.30		21.20	including studs, treated bottom plate,
Reinstall	L.F.		7.22		7.22	double top plate and one row of fire
Minimum Charge	Job		207		207	blocking.
12' High						
Demolish	L.F.		6.20		6.20	Cost includes material and labor to
Install	L.F.	7.75	11.10		18.85	install 2" x 6" x 12' wall system
Demolish and Install	L.F.	7.75	17.30		25.05	including studs, treated bottom plate,
Reinstall	L.F.		8.89		8.89	double top plate and one row of fire
Minimum Charge	Job		207		207	blocking.
Fireblock						
2" x 4", 16" O.C. System						
Demolish	L.F.		.57		.57	Cost includes material and labor to
Install	L.F.	.36	1.38		1.74	install 2" x 4" fireblocks in wood frame
Demolish and Install	L.F.	.36	1.95		2.31	walls per L.F. of wall to be blocked.
Reinstall	L.F.		1.11		1.11	
Minimum Charge	Job		207		207	
2" x 4", 24" O.C. System						
Demolish	L.F.		.57		.57	Cost includes material and labor to
Install	L.F.	.36	1.38		1.74	install 2" x 4" fireblocks in wood frame
Demolish and Install	L.F.	.36	1.95		2.31	walls per L.F. of wall to be blocked.
Reinstall	L.F.		1.11		1.11	
Minimum Charge	Job		207		207	
2" x 6", 16" O.C. System						
Demolish	L.F.		.85		.85	Cost includes material and labor to
Install	L.F.	.58	1.38		1.96	install 2" x 6" fireblocks in wood frame
Demolish and Install	L.F.	.58	2.23		2.81	walls per L.F. of wall to be blocked.
Reinstall	L.F.		1.11		1.11	
Minimum Charge	Job		207		207	
2" x 6", 24" O.C. System						
Demolish	L.F.		.85		.85	Cost includes material and labor to
Install	L.F.	.58	1.38		1.96	install 2" x 6" fireblocks in wood frame
Demolish and Install	L.F.	.58	2.23		2.81	walls per L.F. of wall to be blocked.
Reinstall	L.F.		1.11		1.11	
Minimum Charge	Job		207		207	

Wall Framing System		Unit	Material	Labor	Equip.	Total	Specification
Bracing							
1" x 3"							
	Demolish	L.F.		.32		.32	Cost includes material and labor to
	Install	L.F.	.37	2.59		2.96	install 1" x 3" let-in bracing.
	Demolish and Install	L.F.	.37	2.91		3.28	
	Minimum Charge	Job		207		207	
1" x 4"							
	Demolish	L.F.		.32		.32	Cost includes material and labor to
	Install	L.F.	.45	2.59		3.04	install 1" x 4" let-in bracing.
	Demolish and Install	L.F.	.45	2.91		3.36	
	Minimum Charge	Job		207		207	
1" x 6"							
	Demolish	L.F.		.32		.32	Cost includes material and labor to
	Install	L.F.	.79	2.76		3.55	install 1" x 6" let-in bracing.
	Demolish and Install	L.F.	.79	3.08		3.87	
	Minimum Charge	Job		207		207	
2" x 3"							
	Demolish	L.F.		.43		.43	Cost includes material and labor to
	Install	L.F.	.36	2.76		3.12	install 2" x 3" let-in bracing.
	Demolish and Install	L.F.	.36	3.19		3.55	
	Reinstall	L.F.		2.21		2.21	
	Minimum Charge	Job		207		207	
2" x 4"							
	Demolish	L.F.		.43		.43	Cost includes material and labor to
	Install	L.F.	.36	2.76		3.12	install 2" x 4" let-in bracing.
	Demolish and Install	L.F.	.36	3.19		3.55	
	Reinstall	L.F.		2.21		2.21	
	Minimum Charge	Job		207		207	
2" x 6"							
	Demolish	L.F.		.43		.43	Cost includes material and labor to
	Install	L.F.	.58	2.96		3.54	install 2" x 6" let-in bracing.
	Demolish and Install	L.F.	.58	3.39		3.97	
	Reinstall	L.F.		2.37		2.37	
	Minimum Charge	Job		207		207	
2" x 8"							
	Demolish	L.F.		.43		.43	Cost includes material and labor to
	Install	L.F.	.83	2.96		3.79	install 2" x 8" let-in bracing.
	Demolish and Install	L.F.	.83	3.39		4.22	
	Reinstall	L.F.		2.37		2.37	
	Minimum Charge	Job		207		207	
Earthquake Strapping							
	Install	Ea.	2.99	2.59		5.58	Includes labor and material to replace
	Minimum Charge	Job		207		207	an earthquake strap.
Hurricane Clips							
	Install	Ea.	1.12	2.86		3.98	Includes labor and material to install a
	Minimum Charge	Job		207		207	hurricane clip.
Stud							
2" x 4"							
	Demolish	L.F.		.34		.34	Cost includes material and labor to
	Install	L.F.	.36	.75		1.11	install 2" x 4" wall stud per L.F. of stud.
	Demolish and Install	L.F.	.36	1.09		1.45	
	Reinstall	L.F.		.60		.60	
	Minimum Charge	Job		207		207	

Rough Frame / Structure

Wall Framing System		Unit	Material	Labor	Equip.	Total	Specification
2" x 6"							
	Demolish	L.F.		.43		.43	Cost includes material and labor to
	Install	L.F.	.58	.83		1.41	install 2" x 6" stud per L.F. of stud.
	Demolish and Install	L.F.	.58	1.26		1.84	
	Reinstall	L.F.		.66		.66	
	Minimum Charge	Job		207		207	
Plates							
2" x 4"							
	Demolish	L.F.		.31		.31	Cost includes material and labor to
	Install	L.F.	.36	1.04		1.40	install 2" x 4" plate per L.F. of plate.
	Demolish and Install	L.F.	.36	1.35		1.71	
	Reinstall	L.F.		.83		.83	
	Minimum Charge	Job		207		207	
2" x 6"							
	Demolish	L.F.		.32		.32	Cost includes material and labor to
	Install	L.F.	.58	1.10		1.68	install 2" x 6" plate per L.F. of plate.
	Demolish and Install	L.F.	.58	1.42		2	
	Reinstall	L.F.		.88		.88	
	Minimum Charge	Job		207		207	
Headers							
	Demolish	L.F.		.30		.30	Includes material and labor to install
	Install	L.F.	.58	2.30		2.88	header over wall openings and
	Demolish and Install	L.F.	.58	2.60		3.18	around floor, ceiling and roof
	Clean	L.F.	.02	.39		.41	openings or flush beam.
	Paint	L.F.	.10	1.42		1.52	
	Minimum Charge	Job		207		207	
2" x 8"							
	Demolish	L.F.		.32		.32	Includes material and labor to install
	Install	L.F.	.83	2.44		3.27	header over wall openings and
	Demolish and Install	L.F.	.83	2.76		3.59	around floor, ceiling and roof
	Clean	L.F.	.03	.39		.42	openings or flush beam.
	Paint	L.F.	.13	1.92		2.05	
	Minimum Charge	Job		207		207	
2" x 10"							
	Demolish	L.F.		.32		.32	Includes material and labor to install
	Install	L.F.	1.11	2.59		3.70	header over wall openings and
	Demolish and Install	L.F.	1.11	2.91		4.02	around floor, ceiling and roof
	Clean	L.F.	.04	.39		.43	openings or flush beam.
	Paint	L.F.	.17	2.37		2.54	
	Minimum Charge	Job		207		207	
2" x 12"							
	Demolish	L.F.		.34		.34	Includes material and labor to install
	Install	L.F.	1.41	2.76		4.17	header over wall openings and
	Demolish and Install	L.F.	1.41	3.10		4.51	around floor, ceiling and roof
	Clean	L.F.	.04	.39		.43	openings or flush beam.
	Paint	L.F.	.20	2.84		3.04	
	Minimum Charge	Job		207		207	
4" x 8"							
	Demolish	L.F.		.61		.61	Includes material and labor to install
	Install	L.F.	3.74	3.19		6.93	header over wall openings and
	Demolish and Install	L.F.	3.74	3.80		7.54	around floor, ceiling and roof
	Clean	L.F.	.03	.39		.42	openings or flush beam.
	Paint	L.F.	.13	1.92		2.05	
	Minimum Charge	Job		207		207	

Rough Frame / Structure

Wall Framing System

Wall Framing System	Unit	Material	Labor	Equip.	Total	Specification
4" x 10"						
Demolish	L.F.		.65		.65	Includes material and labor to install
Install	L.F.	4.68	3.45		8.13	header over wall openings and
Demolish and Install	L.F.	4.68	4.10		8.78	around floor, ceiling and roof
Clean	L.F.	.04	.39		.43	openings or flush beam.
Paint	L.F.	.17	2.37		2.54	
Minimum Charge	Job		207		207	
4" x 12"						
Demolish	L.F.		.68		.68	Includes material and labor to install
Install	L.F.	6.05	4.36		10.41	header over wall openings and
Demolish and Install	L.F.	6.05	5.04		11.09	around floor, ceiling and roof
Clean	L.F.	.04	.39		.43	openings or flush beam.
Paint	L.F.	.20	2.84		3.04	
Minimum Charge	Job		207		207	
6" x 8"						
Demolish	L.F.		.61		.61	Includes material and labor to install
Install	L.F.	5.30	2.30		7.60	header over wall openings and
Demolish and Install	L.F.	5.30	2.91		8.21	around floor, ceiling and roof
Clean	L.F.	.03	.39		.42	openings or flush beam.
Paint	L.F.	.13	1.92		2.05	
Minimum Charge	Job		207		207	
6" x 10"						
Demolish	L.F.		.65		.65	Includes material and labor to install
Install	L.F.	7.15	5		12.15	header over wall openings and
Demolish and Install	L.F.	7.15	5.65		12.80	around floor, ceiling and roof
Clean	L.F.	.04	.39		.43	openings or flush beam.
Paint	L.F.	.17	2.37		2.54	
Minimum Charge	Job		207		207	
6" x 12"						
Demolish	L.F.		.68		.68	Includes material and labor to install
Install	L.F.	11.15	5.90		17.05	header over wall openings and
Demolish and Install	L.F.	11.15	6.58		17.73	around floor, ceiling and roof
Clean	L.F.	.04	.39		.43	openings or flush beam.
Paint	L.F.	.20	.99		1.19	
Minimum Charge	Job		207		207	

Rough-in Opening

Rough-in Opening	Unit	Material	Labor	Equip.	Total	Specification
Door w / 2" x 4" Lumber						
3' Wide						
Demolish	Ea.		10.65		10.65	Includes material and labor to install
Install	Ea.	15.35	12.95		28.30	header, double studs each side,
Demolish and Install	Ea.	15.35	23.60		38.95	cripples, blocking and nails, up to 3'
Reinstall	Ea.		10.36		10.36	opening in 2" x 4" stud wall 8' high.
Minimum Charge	Job		207		207	
4' Wide						
Demolish	Ea.		10.65		10.65	Includes material and labor to install
Install	Ea.	16.50	12.95		29.45	header, double studs each side,
Demolish and Install	Ea.	16.50	23.60		40.10	cripples, blocking and nails, up to 4'
Reinstall	Ea.		10.36		10.36	opening in 2" x 4" stud wall 8' high.
Minimum Charge	Job		207		207	
5' Wide						
Demolish	Ea.		10.65		10.65	Includes material and labor to install
Install	Ea.	20	12.95		32.95	header, double studs each side,
Demolish and Install	Ea.	20	23.60		43.60	cripples, blocking and nails, up to 5'
Reinstall	Ea.		10.36		10.36	opening in 2" x 4" stud wall 8' high.
Minimum Charge	Job		207		207	

Rough Frame / Structure

Rough-in Opening		Unit	Material	Labor	Equip.	Total	Specification
6' Wide							
	Demolish	Ea.		10.65		10.65	Includes material and labor to install
	Install	Ea.	22	12.95		34.95	header, double studs each side,
	Demolish and Install	Ea.	22	23.60		45.60	cripples, blocking and nails, up to 6'
	Reinstall	Ea.		10.36		10.36	opening in 2" x 4" stud wall 8' high.
	Minimum Charge	Job		207		207	
8' Wide							
	Demolish	Ea.		11.35		11.35	Includes material and labor to install
	Install	Ea.	29.50	13.80		43.30	header, double studs each side,
	Demolish and Install	Ea.	29.50	25.15		54.65	cripples, blocking and nails, up to 8'
	Reinstall	Ea.		11.05		11.05	opening in 2" x 4" stud wall 8' high.
	Minimum Charge	Job		207		207	
10' Wide							
	Demolish	Ea.		11.35		11.35	Includes material and labor to install
	Install	Ea.	40	13.80		53.80	header, double studs each side,
	Demolish and Install	Ea.	40	25.15		65.15	cripples, blocking and nails, up to 10'
	Reinstall	Ea.		11.05		11.05	opening in 2" x 4" stud wall 8' high.
	Minimum Charge	Job		207		207	
12' Wide							
	Demolish	Ea.		11.35		11.35	Includes material and labor to install
	Install	Ea.	57	13.80		70.80	header, double studs each side,
	Demolish and Install	Ea.	57	25.15		82.15	cripples, blocking and nails, up to 12'
	Reinstall	Ea.		11.05		11.05	opening in 2" x 4" stud wall 8' high.
	Minimum Charge	Job		207		207	
Door w / 2" x 6" Lumber							
3' Wide							
	Demolish	Ea.		10.65		10.65	Includes material and labor to install
	Install	Ea.	22.50	12.95		35.45	header, double studs each side,
	Demolish and Install	Ea.	22.50	23.60		46.10	cripples, blocking and nails, up to 3'
	Reinstall	Ea.		10.36		10.36	opening in 2" x 6" stud wall 8' high.
	Minimum Charge	Job		207		207	
4' Wide							
	Demolish	Ea.		10.65		10.65	Includes material and labor to install
	Install	Ea.	23.50	12.95		36.45	header, double studs each side,
	Demolish and Install	Ea.	23.50	23.60		47.10	cripples, blocking and nails, up to 4'
	Reinstall	Ea.		10.36		10.36	opening in 2" x 6" stud wall 8' high.
	Minimum Charge	Job		207		207	
5' Wide							
	Demolish	Ea.		10.65		10.65	Includes material and labor to install
	Install	Ea.	27.50	12.95		40.45	header, double studs each side,
	Demolish and Install	Ea.	27.50	23.60		51.10	cripples, blocking and nails up to 5'
	Reinstall	Ea.		10.36		10.36	opening in 2" x 6" stud wall 8' high.
	Minimum Charge	Job		207		207	
6' Wide							
	Demolish	Ea.		10.65		10.65	Includes material and labor to install
	Install	Ea.	29	12.95		41.95	header, double studs each side,
	Demolish and Install	Ea.	29	23.60		52.60	cripples, blocking and nails up to 6'
	Reinstall	Ea.		10.36		10.36	opening in 2" x 6" stud wall 8' high.
	Minimum Charge	Job		207		207	
8' Wide							
	Demolish	Ea.		11.35		11.35	Includes material and labor to install
	Install	Ea.	37	13.80		50.80	header, double studs each side,
	Demolish and Install	Ea.	37	25.15		62.15	cripples, blocking and nails up to 8'
	Reinstall	Ea.		11.05		11.05	opening in 2" x 6" stud wall 8' high.
	Minimum Charge	Job		207		207	
10' Wide							
	Demolish	Ea.		11.35		11.35	Includes material and labor to install
	Install	Ea.	47.50	13.80		61.30	header, double studs each side,
	Demolish and Install	Ea.	47.50	25.15		72.65	cripples, blocking and nails up to 10'
	Reinstall	Ea.		11.05		11.05	opening in 2" x 6" stud wall 8' high.
	Minimum Charge	Job		207		207	

Rough Frame / Structure

Rough-in Opening

	Unit	Material	Labor	Equip.	Total	Specification
12' Wide						Includes material and labor to install header, double studs each side, cripples, blocking and nails, up to 12' opening in 2" x 6" stud wall 8' high.
Demolish	Ea.		11.35		11.35	
Install	Ea.	64.50	13.80		78.30	
Demolish and Install	Ea.	64.50	25.15		89.65	
Reinstall	Ea.		11.05		11.05	
Minimum Charge	Job		207		207	

Rough-in Opening

	Unit	Material	Labor	Equip.	Total	Specification
Window w / 2" x 4" Lumber						
2' Wide						Includes material and labor to install header, double studs each side of opening, cripples, blocking, nails and sub-sills for opening up to 2' in a 2" x 4" stud wall 8' high.
Demolish	Ea.		14.20		14.20	
Install	Ea.	16	17.25		33.25	
Demolish and Install	Ea.	16	31.45		47.45	
Reinstall	Ea.		13.81		13.81	
Minimum Charge	Job		207		207	
3' Wide						Includes material and labor to install header, double studs each side of opening, cripples, blocking, nails and sub-sills for opening up to 3' in a 2" x 4" stud wall 8' high.
Demolish	Ea.		14.20		14.20	
Install	Ea.	18.90	17.25		36.15	
Demolish and Install	Ea.	18.90	31.45		50.35	
Reinstall	Ea.		13.81		13.81	
Minimum Charge	Job		207		207	
4' Wide						Includes material and labor to install header, double studs each side of opening, cripples, blocking, nails and sub-sills for opening up to 4' in a 2" x 4" stud wall 8' high.
Demolish	Ea.		14.20		14.20	
Install	Ea.	21	17.25		38.25	
Demolish and Install	Ea.	21	31.45		52.45	
Reinstall	Ea.		13.81		13.81	
Minimum Charge	Job		207		207	
5' Wide						Includes material and labor to install header, double studs each side of opening, cripples, blocking, nails and sub-sills for opening up to 5' in a 2" x 4" stud wall 8' high.
Demolish	Ea.		14.20		14.20	
Install	Ea.	25	17.25		42.25	
Demolish and Install	Ea.	25	31.45		56.45	
Reinstall	Ea.		13.81		13.81	
Minimum Charge	Job		207		207	
6' Wide						Includes material and labor to install header, double studs each side of opening, cripples, blocking, nails and sub-sills for opening up to 6' in a 2" x 4" stud wall 8' high.
Demolish	Ea.		14.20		14.20	
Install	Ea.	27.50	17.25		44.75	
Demolish and Install	Ea.	27.50	31.45		58.95	
Reinstall	Ea.		13.81		13.81	
Minimum Charge	Job		207		207	
7' Wide						Includes material and labor to install header, double studs each side of opening, cripples, blocking, nails and sub-sills for opening up to 7' in a 2" x 4" stud wall 8' high.
Demolish	Ea.		14.20		14.20	
Install	Ea.	34	17.25		51.25	
Demolish and Install	Ea.	34	31.45		65.45	
Reinstall	Ea.		13.81		13.81	
Minimum Charge	Job		207		207	
8' Wide						Includes material and labor to install header, double studs each side of opening, cripples, blocking, nails and sub-sills for opening up to 8' in a 2" x 4" stud wall 8' high.
Demolish	Ea.		15.45		15.45	
Install	Ea.	37.50	18.85		56.35	
Demolish and Install	Ea.	37.50	34.30		71.80	
Reinstall	Ea.		15.07		15.07	
Minimum Charge	Job		207		207	

Rough Frame / Structure

Rough-in Opening

	Unit	Material	Labor	Equip.	Total	Specification
10' Wide						
Demolish	Ea.		15.45		15.45	Includes material and labor to install
Install	Ea.	49	18.85		67.85	header, double studs each side of
Demolish and Install	Ea.	49	34.30		83.30	opening, cripples, blocking, nails and
Reinstall	Ea.		15.07		15.07	sub-sills for opening up to 10' in a 2"
Minimum Charge	Job		207		207	x 4" stud wall 8' high.
12' Wide						
Demolish	Ea.		15.45		15.45	Includes material and labor to install
Install	Ea.	68	18.85		86.85	header, double studs each side of
Demolish and Install	Ea.	68	34.30		102.30	opening, cripples, blocking, nails and
Reinstall	Ea.		15.07		15.07	sub-sills for opening up to 12' in a 2"
Minimum Charge	Job		207		207	x 4" stud wall 8' high.

Window w / 2" x 6" Lumber

	Unit	Material	Labor	Equip.	Total	Specification
2' Wide						
Demolish	Ea.		14.20		14.20	Includes material and labor to install
Install	Ea.	25.50	17.25		42.75	header, double studs each side of
Demolish and Install	Ea.	25.50	31.45		56.95	opening, cripples, blocking, nails and
Reinstall	Ea.		13.81		13.81	sub-sills for opening up to 2' in a 2" x
Minimum Charge	Job		207		207	6" stud wall 8' high.
3' Wide						
Demolish	Ea.		14.20		14.20	Includes material and labor to install
Install	Ea.	28.50	17.25		45.75	header, double studs each side of
Demolish and Install	Ea.	28.50	31.45		59.95	opening, cripples, blocking, nails and
Reinstall	Ea.		13.81		13.81	sub-sills for opening up to 3' in a 2" x
Minimum Charge	Job		207		207	6" stud wall 8' high.
4' Wide						
Demolish	Ea.		14.20		14.20	Includes material and labor to install
Install	Ea.	30.50	17.25		47.75	header, double studs each side of
Demolish and Install	Ea.	30.50	31.45		61.95	opening, cripples, blocking, nails and
Reinstall	Ea.		13.81		13.81	sub-sills for opening up to 4' in a 2" x
Minimum Charge	Job		207		207	6" stud wall 8' high.
5' Wide						
Demolish	Ea.		14.20		14.20	Includes material and labor to install
Install	Ea.	34.50	17.25		51.75	header, double studs each side of
Demolish and Install	Ea.	34.50	31.45		65.95	opening, cripples, blocking, nails and
Reinstall	Ea.		13.81		13.81	sub-sills for opening up to 5' in a 2" x
Minimum Charge	Job		207		207	6" stud wall 8' high.
6' Wide						
Demolish	Ea.		14.20		14.20	Includes material and labor to install
Install	Ea.	38	17.25		55.25	header, double studs each side of
Demolish and Install	Ea.	38	31.45		69.45	opening, cripples, blocking, nails and
Reinstall	Ea.		13.81		13.81	sub-sills for opening up to 6' in a 2" x
Minimum Charge	Job		207		207	6" stud wall 8' high.
7' Wide						
Demolish	Ea.		14.20		14.20	Includes material and labor to install
Install	Ea.	45	17.25		62.25	header, double studs each side of
Demolish and Install	Ea.	45	31.45		76.45	opening, cripples, blocking, nails and
Reinstall	Ea.		13.81		13.81	sub-sills for opening up to 7' in a 2" x
Minimum Charge	Job		207		207	6" stud wall 8' high.

Rough Frame / Structure

Rough-in Opening

	Unit	Material	Labor	Equip.	Total	Specification
8' Wide						Includes material and labor to install
Demolish	Ea.		15.45		15.45	header, double studs each side of
Install	Ea.	49.50	18.85		68.35	opening, cripples, blocking, nails and
Demolish and Install	Ea.	49.50	34.30		83.80	sub-sills for opening up to 8' in a 2" x
Reinstall	Ea.		15.07		15.07	6" stud wall 8' high.
Minimum Charge	Job		207		207	
10' Wide						Includes material and labor to install
Demolish	Ea.		15.45		15.45	header, double studs each side of
Install	Ea.	61.50	18.85		80.35	opening, cripples, blocking, nails and
Demolish and Install	Ea.	61.50	34.30		95.80	sub-sills for opening up to 10' in a 2"
Reinstall	Ea.		15.07		15.07	x 6" stud wall 8' high.
Minimum Charge	Job		207		207	
12' Wide						Includes material and labor to install
Demolish	Ea.		15.45		15.45	header, double studs each side of
Install	Ea.	82	18.85		100.85	opening, cripples, blocking, nails and
Demolish and Install	Ea.	82	34.30		116.30	sub-sills for opening up to 12' in a 2"
Reinstall	Ea.		15.07		15.07	x 6" stud wall 8' high.
Minimum Charge	Job		207		207	

Glue-Laminated Beams

	Unit	Material	Labor	Equip.	Total	Specification
3-1/2" x 6"						Includes material and labor to install
Demolish	L.F.		2.55		2.55	glue-laminated wood beam.
Install	L.F.	5.65	3.13	1.12	9.90	
Demolish and Install	L.F.	5.65	5.68	1.12	12.45	
Reinstall	L.F.		2.51	.90	3.41	
Clean	L.F.	.15	.38		.53	
Paint	L.F.	.35	1.04		1.39	
Minimum Charge	Job		207		207	
3-1/2" x 9"						Includes material and labor to install
Demolish	L.F.		2.55		2.55	glue-laminated wood beam.
Install	L.F.	7.60	3.13	1.12	11.85	
Demolish and Install	L.F.	7.60	5.68	1.12	14.40	
Reinstall	L.F.		2.51	.90	3.41	
Clean	L.F.	.21	.40		.61	
Paint	L.F.	.45	1.36		1.81	
Minimum Charge	Job		207		207	
3-1/2" x 12"						Includes material and labor to install
Demolish	L.F.		3.82		3.82	glue-laminated wood beam.
Install	L.F.	10.10	3.13	1.12	14.35	
Demolish and Install	L.F.	10.10	6.95	1.12	18.17	
Reinstall	L.F.		2.51	.90	3.41	
Clean	L.F.	.25	.41		.66	
Paint	L.F.	.56	1.69		2.25	
Minimum Charge	Job		207		207	
3-1/2" x 15"						Includes material and labor to install
Demolish	L.F.		3.82		3.82	glue-laminated wood beam.
Install	L.F.	12.65	3.24	1.16	17.05	
Demolish and Install	L.F.	12.65	7.06	1.16	20.87	
Reinstall	L.F.		2.59	.93	3.52	
Clean	L.F.	.30	.42		.72	
Paint	L.F.	.66	1.97		2.63	
Minimum Charge	Job		207		207	

Rough Frame / Structure

Glue-Laminated Beams

	Unit	Material	Labor	Equip.	Total	Specification
3-1/2" x 18"						
Demolish	L.F.		4.78		4.78	Includes material and labor to install
Install	L.F.	17.05	3.24	1.16	21.45	glue-laminated wood beam.
Demolish and Install	L.F.	17.05	8.02	1.16	26.23	
Reinstall	L.F.		2.59	.93	3.52	
Clean	L.F.	.35	.44		.79	
Paint	L.F.	.78	2.29		3.07	
Minimum Charge	Job		207		207	
5-1/8" x 6"						
Demolish	L.F.		3.82		3.82	Includes material and labor to install
Install	L.F.	8.30	3.13	1.12	12.55	glue-laminated wood beam.
Demolish and Install	L.F.	8.30	6.95	1.12	16.37	
Reinstall	L.F.		2.51	.90	3.41	
Clean	L.F.	.18	.38		.56	
Paint	L.F.	.37	1.15		1.52	
Minimum Charge	Job		207		207	
5-1/8" x 9"						
Demolish	L.F.		4.78		4.78	Includes material and labor to install
Install	L.F.	12.50	3.13	1.12	16.75	glue-laminated wood beam.
Demolish and Install	L.F.	12.50	7.91	1.12	21.53	
Reinstall	L.F.		2.51	.90	3.41	
Clean	L.F.	.22	.40		.62	
Paint	L.F.	.48	1.47		1.95	
Minimum Charge	Job		207		207	
5-1/8" x 12"						
Demolish	L.F.		5.70		5.70	Includes material and labor to install
Install	L.F.	16.60	3.13	1.12	20.85	glue-laminated wood beam.
Demolish and Install	L.F.	16.60	8.83	1.12	26.55	
Reinstall	L.F.		2.51	.90	3.41	
Clean	L.F.	.28	.41		.69	
Paint	L.F.	.59	1.78		2.37	
Minimum Charge	Job		207		207	
5-1/8" x 18"						
Demolish	L.F.		9.55		9.55	Includes material and labor to install
Install	L.F.	25	3.24	1.16	29.40	glue-laminated wood beam.
Demolish and Install	L.F.	25	12.79	1.16	38.95	
Reinstall	L.F.		2.59	.93	3.52	
Clean	L.F.	.36	.44		.80	
Paint	L.F.	.69	2.40		3.09	
Minimum Charge	Job		207		207	
6-3/4" x 12"						
Demolish	L.F.		5.70		5.70	Includes material and labor to install
Install	L.F.	22	3.24	1.16	26.40	glue-laminated wood beam.
Demolish and Install	L.F.	22	8.94	1.16	32.10	
Reinstall	L.F.		2.59	.93	3.52	
Clean	L.F.	.30	.42		.72	
Paint	L.F.	.66	1.97		2.63	
Minimum Charge	Job		207		207	
6-3/4" x 15"						
Demolish	L.F.		9.55		9.55	Includes material and labor to install
Install	L.F.	27.50	3.24	1.16	31.90	glue-laminated wood beam.
Demolish and Install	L.F.	27.50	12.79	1.16	41.45	
Reinstall	L.F.		2.59	.93	3.52	
Clean	L.F.	.35	.44		.79	
Paint	L.F.	.78	2.29		3.07	
Minimum Charge	Job		207		207	

Rough Frame / Structure

Glue-Laminated Beams		Unit	Material	Labor	Equip.	Total	Specification
6-3/4″ x 18″							
	Demolish	L.F.		9.55		9.55	Includes material and labor to install
	Install	L.F.	33	3.36	1.20	37.56	glue-laminated wood beam.
	Demolish and Install	L.F.	33	12.91	1.20	47.11	
	Reinstall	L.F.		2.68	.96	3.64	
	Clean	L.F.	.40	.45		.85	
	Paint	L.F.	.88	2.61		3.49	
	Minimum Charge	Job		207		207	
Hardware							
5-1/4″ Glue-Lam Seat							
	Install	Ea.	211	2.30		213.30	Includes labor and material to install
	Minimum Charge	Job		207		207	beam hangers.
6-3/4″ Glue-Lam Seat							
	Install	Ea.	217	2.30		219.30	Includes labor and material to install
	Minimum Charge	Job		207		207	beam hangers.
Earthquake Strapping							
	Install	Ea.	2.99	2.59		5.58	Includes labor and material to replace
	Minimum Charge	Job		207		207	an earthquake strap.
Hurricane Clips							
	Install	Ea.	1.12	2.86		3.98	Includes labor and material to install a
	Minimum Charge	Job		207		207	hurricane clip.

Metal Stud Framing		Unit	Material	Labor	Equip.	Total	Specification
16″ O.C. System							
4″, 16 Ga.							
	Demolish	S.F.		1.25		1.25	Includes material and labor to install
	Install	S.F.	1.47	1.28		2.75	load bearing cold rolled metal stud
	Demolish and Install	S.F.	1.47	2.53		4	walls, to 10′ high, including studs, top
	Reinstall	S.F.		1.02		1.02	and bottom track and screws.
	Minimum Charge	Job		207		207	
6″, 16 Ga.							
	Demolish	S.F.		1.25		1.25	Includes material and labor to install
	Install	S.F.	1.83	1.30		3.13	load bearing cold rolled metal stud
	Demolish and Install	S.F.	1.83	2.55		4.38	walls, to 10′ high, including studs, top
	Reinstall	S.F.		1.04		1.04	and bottom track and screws.
	Minimum Charge	Job		207		207	
4″, 25 Ga.							
	Demolish	S.F.		.87		.87	Includes material and labor to install
	Install	S.F.	.47	.87		1.34	cold rolled metal stud walls, to 10′
	Demolish and Install	S.F.	.47	1.74		2.21	high, including studs, top and bottom
	Reinstall	S.F.		.70		.70	track and screws.
	Minimum Charge	Job		207		207	
6″, 25 Ga.							
	Demolish	S.F.		.87		.87	Includes material and labor to install
	Install	S.F.	.61	.88		1.49	cold rolled metal stud walls, to 10′
	Demolish and Install	S.F.	.61	1.75		2.36	high, including studs, top and bottom
	Reinstall	S.F.		.71		.71	track and screws.
	Minimum Charge	Job		207		207	
24″ O.C. System							
4″, 25 Ga.							
	Demolish	S.F.		.74		.74	Includes material and labor to install
	Install	S.F.	.34	.56		.90	cold rolled metal stud walls, to 10′
	Demolish and Install	S.F.	.34	1.30		1.64	high, including studs, top and bottom
	Reinstall	S.F.		.45		.45	track and screws.
	Minimum Charge	Job		207		207	

Rough Frame / Structure

Metal Stud Framing

		Unit	Material	Labor	Equip.	Total	Specification
6", 25 Ga.							
	Demolish	S.F.		.74		.74	Includes material and labor to install
	Install	S.F.	.44	.57		1.01	cold rolled metal stud walls, to 10'
	Demolish and Install	S.F.	.44	1.31		1.75	high, including studs, top and bottom
	Reinstall	S.F.		.46		.46	track and screws.
	Minimum Charge	Job		207		207	
4", 16 Ga.							
	Demolish	L.F.		8.40		8.40	Includes material and labor to install
	Install	S.F.	1.07	.92		1.99	load bearing cold rolled metal stud
	Demolish and Install	S.F.	1.07	9.32		10.39	walls, to 10' high, including studs, top
	Reinstall	S.F.		.74		.74	and bottom track and screws.
	Minimum Charge	Job		207		207	
6", 16 Ga.							
	Demolish	L.F.		8.40		8.40	Includes material and labor to install
	Install	S.F.	1.33	.94		2.27	load bearing cold rolled metal stud
	Demolish and Install	S.F.	1.33	9.34		10.67	walls, to 10' high, including studs, top
	Reinstall	S.F.		.75		.75	and bottom track and screws.
	Minimum Charge	Job		207		207	

Metal Joist

		Unit	Material	Labor	Equip.	Total	Specification
Bar Joist							
18K9							
	Demolish	L.F.		1.01	.39	1.40	Includes material, labor and
	Install	L.F.	8.60	2.27	.96	11.83	equipment to install open web joist.
	Demolish and Install	L.F.	8.60	3.28	1.35	13.23	
	Reinstall	L.F.		1.82	.77	2.59	
	Minimum Charge	Job		1875	675	2550	
16K6							
	Demolish	L.F.		1.01	.39	1.40	Includes material, labor and
	Install	L.F.	5.65	1.53	.10	7.28	equipment to install open web joist.
	Demolish and Install	L.F.	5.65	2.54	.49	8.68	
	Reinstall	L.F.		1.23	.08	1.31	
	Minimum Charge	Job		1875	675	2550	

Exterior Sheathing

		Unit	Material	Labor	Equip.	Total	Specification
CDX Plywood							
5/16"							
	Demolish	S.F.		.58		.58	Cost includes material and labor to
	Install	S.F.	.61	.52		1.13	install 5/16" CDX plywood sheathing.
	Demolish and Install	S.F.	.61	1.10		1.71	
	Minimum Charge	Job		207		207	
3/8"							
	Demolish	S.F.		.59		.59	Cost includes material and labor to
	Install	S.F.	.52	.69		1.21	install 3/8" CDX plywood sheathing.
	Demolish and Install	S.F.	.52	1.28		1.80	
	Minimum Charge	Job		207		207	
1/2"							
	Demolish	S.F.		.61		.61	Cost includes material and labor to
	Install	S.F.	.52	.74		1.26	install 1/2" CDX plywood sheathing.
	Demolish and Install	S.F.	.52	1.35		1.87	
	Minimum Charge	Job		207		207	

Rough Frame / Structure

Exterior Sheathing		Unit	Material	Labor	Equip.	Total	Specification
5/8"							
	Demolish	S.F.		.62		.62	Cost includes material and labor to
	Install	S.F.	.68	.79		1.47	install 5/8" CDX plywood sheathing.
	Demolish and Install	S.F.	.68	1.41		2.09	
	Minimum Charge	Job		207		207	
3/4"							
	Demolish	S.F.		.63		.63	Cost includes material and labor to
	Install	S.F.	.77	.85		1.62	install 3/4" CDX plywood sheathing.
	Demolish and Install	S.F.	.77	1.48		2.25	
	Minimum Charge	Job		207		207	
OSB							
1/2"							
	Demolish	S.F.		.61		.61	Cost includes material and labor to
	Install	S.F.	.43	.63		1.06	install 4' x 8' x 1/2" OSB sheathing.
	Demolish and Install	S.F.	.43	1.24		1.67	
	Minimum Charge	Job		207		207	
5/8"							
	Demolish	S.F.		.62		.62	Cost includes material and labor to
	Install	S.F.	.43	.50		.93	install 4' x 8' x 5/8" OSB sheathing.
	Demolish and Install	S.F.	.43	1.12		1.55	
	Minimum Charge	Job		207		207	
Vapor Barrier							
Black Paper							
	Install	S.F.	.07	.11		.18	Includes material and labor to install
	Minimum Charge	Job		207		207	#15 felt building paper.

Plywood Sheathing		Unit	Material	Labor	Equip.	Total	Specification
Finish Plywood							
5/16"							
	Demolish	S.F.		.58		.58	Includes material and labor to install
	Install	S.F.	.80	.26		1.06	exterior 5/16" AC plywood on walls.
	Demolish and Install	S.F.	.80	.84		1.64	
	Minimum Charge	Job		207		207	
3/8"							
	Demolish	S.F.		.59		.59	Includes material and labor to install
	Install	S.F.	.80	.35		1.15	exterior 3/8" AC plywood on walls.
	Demolish and Install	S.F.	.80	.94		1.74	
	Minimum Charge	Job		207		207	
1/2"							
	Demolish	S.F.		.61		.61	Includes material and labor to install
	Install	S.F.	.85	.37		1.22	exterior 1/2" AC plywood on walls.
	Demolish and Install	S.F.	.85	.98		1.83	
	Minimum Charge	Job		207		207	
5/8"							
	Demolish	S.F.		.62		.62	Includes material and labor to install
	Install	S.F.	1.06	.37		1.43	exterior 5/8" AC plywood on walls.
	Demolish and Install	S.F.	1.06	.99		2.05	
	Reinstall	S.F.		.37		.37	
	Minimum Charge	Job		207		207	
3/4"							
	Demolish	S.F.		.63		.63	Includes material and labor to install
	Install	S.F.	1.29	.37		1.66	exterior 3/4" AC plywood on walls.
	Demolish and Install	S.F.	1.29	1		2.29	
	Reinstall	S.F.		.37		.37	
	Minimum Charge	Job		207		207	

Rough Frame / Structure

Stairs

Stairs	Unit	Material	Labor	Equip.	Total	Specification
Job-built						
Treads and Risers						
Demolish	Ea.		42.50		42.50	Includes material and labor to install
Install	Ea.	585	415		1000	three 2" x 12" stringers, treads and
Demolish and Install	Ea.	585	457.50		1042.50	risers of 3/4" CDX plywood, installed
Clean	Flight	4.77	26.50		31.27	in a straight or "L" shaped run
Paint	Ea.	.11	71		71.11	including carpet.
Minimum Charge	Job		207		207	
Landing						
Demolish	S.F.		.34		.34	Includes material and labor to install
Install	S.F.	68	2.88		70.88	landing framing, 3/4" CDX plywood
Demolish and Install	S.F.	68	3.22		71.22	surface and carpet.
Clean	S.F.		.38		.38	
Paint	S.F.	.44	.88		1.32	
Minimum Charge	Job		207		207	

Ceiling Framing

Ceiling Framing	Unit	Material	Labor	Equip.	Total	Specification
16" O.C. System						
2" x 6" Joists						
Demolish	S.F.		.53		.53	Cost includes material and labor to
Install	S.F.	.45	.68		1.13	install 2" x 6" joists including end and
Demolish and Install	S.F.	.45	1.21		1.66	header joist installed 16" O.C. Does
Reinstall	S.F.		.55		.55	not include beams, ledger strips,
Minimum Charge	Job		207		207	blocking or bridging.
2" x 8" Joists						
Demolish	S.F.		.54		.54	Cost includes material and labor to
Install	S.F.	.63	.84		1.47	install 2" x 8" joists including end and
Demolish and Install	S.F.	.63	1.38		2.01	header joist installed 16" O.C. Does
Reinstall	S.F.		.67		.67	not include beams, ledger strips,
Minimum Charge	Job		207		207	blocking or bridging.
2" x 10" Joists						
Demolish	S.F.		.56		.56	Cost includes material and labor to
Install	S.F.	.84	.99		1.83	install 2" x 10" joists including end
Demolish and Install	S.F.	.84	1.55		2.39	and header joist installed 16" O.C.
Reinstall	S.F.		.79		.79	Does not include beams, ledger strips,
Minimum Charge	Job		207		207	blocking or bridging.
2" x 12" Joists						
Demolish	S.F.		.58		.58	Cost includes material and labor to
Install	S.F.	1.07	1.21		2.28	install 2" x 12" joists including end
Demolish and Install	S.F.	1.07	1.79		2.86	and header joist installed 16" O.C.
Reinstall	S.F.		.97		.97	Does not include beams, ledger strips,
Minimum Charge	Job		207		207	blocking or bridging.
Block / Bridge						
Demolish	Ea.		1.06		1.06	Includes material and labor to install
Install	Ea.	1.49	2.33		3.82	set of cross bridging or per block of
Demolish and Install	Ea.	1.49	3.39		4.88	solid bridging for 2" x 10" joists cut to
Minimum Charge	Job		207		207	size on site.

Rough Frame / Structure

Ceiling Framing		Unit	Material	Labor	Equip.	Total	Specification
24″ O.C. System							
2″ x 6″ Joists							
	Demolish	S.F.		.35		.35	Cost includes material and labor to
	Install	S.F.	.30	.45		.75	install 2″ x 6″ joists including end and
	Demolish and Install	S.F.	.30	.80		1.10	header joist installed 24″ O.C. Does
	Reinstall	S.F.		.36		.36	not include beams, ledger strips,
	Minimum Charge	Job		207		207	blocking or bridging.
2″ x 8″ Joists							
	Demolish	S.F.		.36		.36	Cost includes material and labor to
	Install	S.F.	.42	.56		.98	install 2″ x 8″ joists including end and
	Demolish and Install	S.F.	.42	.92		1.34	header joist installed 24″ O.C. Does
	Reinstall	S.F.		.45		.45	not include beams, ledger strips,
	Minimum Charge	Job		207		207	blocking or bridging.
2″ x 10″ Joists							
	Demolish	S.F.		.37		.37	Cost includes material and labor to
	Install	S.F.	.56	.66		1.22	install 2″ x 10″ joists including end
	Demolish and Install	S.F.	.56	1.03		1.59	and header joist installed 24″ O.C.
	Reinstall	S.F.		.53		.53	Does not include beams, ledger strips,
	Minimum Charge	Job		207		207	blocking or bridging.
2″ x 12″ Joists							
	Demolish	S.F.		.39		.39	Cost includes material and labor to
	Install	S.F.	.72	.81		1.53	install 2″ x 12″ joists including end
	Demolish and Install	S.F.	.72	1.20		1.92	and header joist installed 24″ O.C.
	Reinstall	S.F.		.65		.65	Does not include beams, ledger strips,
	Minimum Charge	Job		207		207	blocking or bridging.
Block / Bridge							
	Demolish	Ea.		1.06		1.06	Includes material and labor to install
	Install	Ea.	1.49	2.33		3.82	set of cross bridging or per block of
	Demolish and Install	Ea.	1.49	3.39		4.88	solid bridging for 2″ x 10″ joists cut to
	Minimum Charge	Job		207		207	size on site.
Ledger Strips							
1″ x 2″							
	Demolish	L.F.		.28		.28	Cost includes material and labor to
	Install	L.F.	.28	1.20		1.48	install 1″ x 2″ ledger strip nailed to the
	Demolish and Install	L.F.	.28	1.48		1.76	face of studs, beams or joist.
	Minimum Charge	Job		207		207	
1″ x 3″							
	Demolish	L.F.		.28		.28	Includes material and labor to install
	Install	L.F.	.45	1.38		1.83	up to 1″ x 4″ ledger strip nailed to the
	Demolish and Install	L.F.	.45	1.66		2.11	face of studs, beams or joist.
	Minimum Charge	Job		207		207	
1″ x 4″							
	Demolish	L.F.		.28		.28	Includes material and labor to install
	Install	L.F.	.45	1.38		1.83	up to 1″ x 4″ ledger strip nailed to the
	Demolish and Install	L.F.	.45	1.66		2.11	face of studs, beams or joist.
	Minimum Charge	Job		207		207	
2″ x 2″							
	Demolish	L.F.		.31		.31	Cost includes material and labor to
	Install	L.F.	.36	1.26		1.62	install 2″ x 2″ ledger strip nailed to the
	Demolish and Install	L.F.	.36	1.57		1.93	face of studs, beams or joist.
	Minimum Charge	Job		207		207	
2″ x 4″							
	Demolish	L.F.		.34		.34	Cost includes material and labor to
	Install	L.F.	.36	1.66		2.02	install 2″ x 4″ ledger strip nailed to the
	Demolish and Install	L.F.	.36	2		2.36	face of studs, beams or joist.
	Reinstall	L.F.		1.33		1.33	
	Minimum Charge	Job		207		207	

Rough Frame / Structure

Ceiling Framing

		Unit	Material	Labor	Equip.	Total	Specification
Ledger Boards							
	Demolish	L.F.		.34		.34	Cost includes material and labor to
	Install	L.F.	4.58	2.30		6.88	install 2" x 4" ledger board fastened to
	Demolish and Install	L.F.	4.58	2.64		7.22	a wall, joists or studs.
	Reinstall	L.F.		1.84		1.84	
	Minimum Charge	Job		207		207	
4" x 6"							
	Demolish	L.F.		.57		.57	Cost includes material and labor to
	Install	L.F.	8.10	2.59		10.69	install 4" x 6" ledger board fastened to
	Demolish and Install	L.F.	8.10	3.16		11.26	a wall, joists or studs.
	Reinstall	L.F.		2.07		2.07	
	Minimum Charge	Job		207		207	
4" x 8"							
	Demolish	L.F.		.76		.76	Cost includes material and labor to
	Install	L.F.	9.10	2.59		11.69	install 4" x 8" ledger board fastened to
	Demolish and Install	L.F.	9.10	3.35		12.45	a wall, joists or studs.
	Reinstall	L.F.		2.07		2.07	
	Minimum Charge	Job		207		207	
Earthquake Strapping							
	Install	Ea.	2.99	2.59		5.58	Includes labor and material to replace
	Minimum Charge	Job		207		207	an earthquake strap.
Hurricane Clips							
	Install	Ea.	1.12	2.86		3.98	Includes labor and material to install a
	Minimum Charge	Job		207		207	hurricane clip.

Roof Framing

		Unit	Material	Labor	Equip.	Total	Specification
16" O.C. System							
2" x 4" Rafters							
	Demolish	S.F.		.77		.77	Cost includes material and labor to
	Install	S.F.	.28	.74		1.02	install 2" x 4", 16" O.C. rafter framing
	Demolish and Install	S.F.	.28	1.51		1.79	for flat, shed or gable roofs, 25' span,
	Reinstall	S.F.		.59		.59	up to 5/12 slope, per S.F. of roof.
	Minimum Charge	Job		207		207	
2" x 6" Rafters							
	Demolish	S.F.		.81		.81	Cost includes material and labor to
	Install	S.F.	.44	.78		1.22	install 2" x 6", 16" O.C. rafter framing
	Demolish and Install	S.F.	.44	1.59		2.03	for flat, shed or gable roofs, 25' span,
	Reinstall	S.F.		.62		.62	up to 5/12 slope, per S.F. of roof.
	Minimum Charge	Job		207		207	
2" x 8" Rafters							
	Demolish	S.F.		.83		.83	Cost includes material and labor to
	Install	S.F.	.62	.83		1.45	install 2" x 8", 16" O.C. rafter framing
	Demolish and Install	S.F.	.62	1.66		2.28	for flat, shed or gable roofs, 25' span,
	Reinstall	S.F.		.66		.66	up to 5/12 slope, per S.F. of roof.
	Minimum Charge	Job		207		207	
2" x 10" Rafters							
	Demolish	S.F.		.83		.83	Cost includes material and labor to
	Install	S.F.	.83	1.26		2.09	install 2" x 10", 16" O.C. rafter
	Demolish and Install	S.F.	.83	2.09		2.92	framing for flat, shed or gable roofs,
	Reinstall	S.F.		1		1	25' span, up to 5/12 slope, per S.F.
	Minimum Charge	Job		207		207	of roof.

Rough Frame / Structure

Roof Framing		Unit	Material	Labor	Equip.	Total	Specification
2" x 12" Rafters							Cost includes material and labor to
	Demolish	S.F.		.84		.84	install 2" x 12", 16" O.C. rafter
	Install	S.F.	1.06	1.37		2.43	framing for flat, shed or gable roofs,
	Demolish and Install	S.F.	1.06	2.21		3.27	25' span, up to 5/12 slope, per S.F.
	Reinstall	S.F.		1.09		1.09	of roof.
	Minimum Charge	Job		207		207	
24" O.C. System							
2" x 4" Rafters							Cost includes material and labor to
	Demolish	S.F.		.58		.58	install 2" x 4", 24" O.C. rafter framing
	Install	S.F.	.18	.56		.74	for flat, shed or gable roofs, 25' span,
	Demolish and Install	S.F.	.18	1.14		1.32	up to 5/12 slope, per S.F. of roof.
	Reinstall	S.F.		.44		.44	
	Minimum Charge	Job		207		207	
2" x 6" Rafters							Cost includes material and labor to
	Demolish	S.F.		.61		.61	install 2" x 6", 24" O.C. rafter framing
	Install	S.F.	.30	.58		.88	for flat, shed or gable roofs, 25' span,
	Demolish and Install	S.F.	.30	1.19		1.49	up to 5/12 slope, per S.F. of roof.
	Reinstall	S.F.		.47		.47	
	Minimum Charge	Job		207		207	
2" x 8" Rafters							Cost includes material and labor to
	Demolish	S.F.		.62		.62	install 2" x 8", 24" O.C. rafter framing
	Install	S.F.	.42	.62		1.04	for flat, shed or gable roofs, 25' span,
	Demolish and Install	S.F.	.42	1.24		1.66	up to 5/12 slope, per S.F. of roof.
	Reinstall	S.F.		.50		.50	
	Minimum Charge	Job		207		207	
2" x 10" Rafters							Cost includes material and labor to
	Demolish	S.F.		.62		.62	install 2" x 10", 24" O.C. rafter
	Install	S.F.	.55	.94		1.49	framing for flat, shed or gable roofs,
	Demolish and Install	S.F.	.55	1.56		2.11	25' span, up to 5/12 slope, per S.F.
	Reinstall	S.F.		.76		.76	of roof.
	Minimum Charge	Job		207		207	
2" x 12" Rafters							Cost includes material and labor to
	Demolish	S.F.		.63		.63	install 2" x 12", 24" O.C. rafter
	Install	S.F.	.70	1.03		1.73	framing for flat, shed or gable roofs,
	Demolish and Install	S.F.	.70	1.66		2.36	25' span, up to 5/12 slope, per S.F.
	Reinstall	S.F.		.82		.82	of roof.
	Minimum Charge	Job		207		207	
Rafter							
2" x 4"							Cost includes material and labor to
	Demolish	L.F.		.79		.79	install 2" x 4" rafters for flat, shed or
	Install	L.F.	.36	1.04		1.40	gable roofs, up to 5/12 slope, 25'
	Demolish and Install	L.F.	.36	1.83		2.19	span, per L.F.
	Reinstall	L.F.		.83		.83	
	Minimum Charge	Job		207		207	
2" x 6"							Cost includes material and labor to
	Demolish	L.F.		.80		.80	install 2" x 6" rafters for flat, shed or
	Install	L.F.	.58	1.04		1.62	gable roofs, up to 5/12 slope, 25'
	Demolish and Install	L.F.	.58	1.84		2.42	span, per L.F.
	Reinstall	L.F.		.83		.83	
	Minimum Charge	Job		207		207	
2" x 8"							Cost includes material and labor to
	Demolish	L.F.		.81		.81	install 2" x 8" rafters for flat, shed or
	Install	L.F.	.83	1.10		1.93	gable roofs, up to 5/12 slope, 25'
	Demolish and Install	L.F.	.83	1.91		2.74	span, per L.F.
	Reinstall	L.F.		.88		.88	
	Minimum Charge	Job		207		207	

Rough Frame / Structure

Roof Framing

	Unit	Material	Labor	Equip.	Total	Specification
2" x 10"						
Demolish	L.F.		.83		.83	Cost includes material and labor to
Install	L.F.	1.11	1.67		2.78	install 2" x 10" rafters for flat, shed or
Demolish and Install	L.F.	1.11	2.50		3.61	gable roofs, up to 5/12 slope, 25'
Reinstall	L.F.		1.34		1.34	span, per L.F.
Minimum Charge	Job		207		207	
2" x 12"						
Demolish	L.F.		.84		.84	Cost includes material and labor to
Install	L.F.	1.41	1.82		3.23	install 2" x 12" rafters for flat, shed or
Demolish and Install	L.F.	1.41	2.66		4.07	gable roofs, up to 5/12 slope, 25'
Reinstall	L.F.		1.46		1.46	span, per L.F.
Minimum Charge	Job		207		207	
2" x 4" Valley / Jack						
Demolish	L.F.		.79		.79	Includes material and labor to install
Install	L.F.	.58	1.74		2.32	up to 2" x 6" valley/jack rafters for
Demolish and Install	L.F.	.58	2.53		3.11	flat, shed or gable roofs, up to 5/12
Reinstall	L.F.		1.40		1.40	slope, 25' span, per L.F.
Minimum Charge	Job		207		207	
2" x 6" Valley / Jack						
Demolish	L.F.		.80		.80	Includes material and labor to install
Install	L.F.	.58	1.74		2.32	up to 2" x 6" valley/jack rafters for
Demolish and Install	L.F.	.58	2.54		3.12	flat, shed or gable roofs, up to 5/12
Reinstall	L.F.		1.40		1.40	slope, 25' span, per L.F.
Minimum Charge	Job		207		207	
Ridgeboard						
2" x 4"						
Demolish	L.F.		.76		.76	Cost includes material and labor to
Install	L.F.	.36	1.51		1.87	install 2" x 4" ridgeboard for flat, shed
Demolish and Install	L.F.	.36	2.27		2.63	or gable roofs, up to 5/12 slope, 25'
Reinstall	L.F.		1.21		1.21	span, per L.F.
Minimum Charge	Job		207		207	
2" x 6"						
Demolish	L.F.		.78		.78	Cost includes material and labor to
Install	L.F.	.58	1.66		2.24	install 2" x 6" ridgeboard for flat, shed
Demolish and Install	L.F.	.58	2.44		3.02	or gable roofs, up to 5/12 slope, 25'
Reinstall	L.F.		1.33		1.33	span, per L.F.
Minimum Charge	Job		207		207	
2" x 8"						
Demolish	L.F.		.80		.80	Cost includes material and labor to
Install	L.F.	.83	1.84		2.67	install 2" x 8" ridgeboard for flat, shed
Demolish and Install	L.F.	.83	2.64		3.47	or gable roofs, up to 5/12 slope, 25'
Reinstall	L.F.		1.47		1.47	span, per L.F.
Minimum Charge	Job		207		207	
2" x 10"						
Demolish	L.F.		.83		.83	Cost includes material and labor to
Install	L.F.	1.11	2.07		3.18	install 2" x 10" ridgeboard for flat,
Demolish and Install	L.F.	1.11	2.90		4.01	shed or gable roofs, up to 5/12
Reinstall	L.F.		1.66		1.66	slope, 25' span, per L.F.
Minimum Charge	Job		207		207	
2" x 12"						
Demolish	L.F.		.85		.85	Cost includes material and labor to
Install	L.F.	1.41	1.18		2.59	install 2" x 12" ridgeboard for flat,
Demolish and Install	L.F.	1.41	2.03		3.44	shed or gable roofs, up to 5/12
Reinstall	L.F.		.95		.95	slope, 25' span, per L.F.
Minimum Charge	Job		207		207	

Rough Frame / Structure

Roof Framing		Unit	Material	Labor	Equip.	Total	Specification
Collar Beam							
1″ x 6″							
	Demolish	L.F.		.60		.60	Cost includes material and labor to
	Install	L.F.	.79	.52		1.31	install 1″ x 6″ collar beam or tie for
	Demolish and Install	L.F.	.79	1.12		1.91	roof framing.
	Reinstall	L.F.		.41		.41	
	Minimum Charge	Job		207		207	
2″ x 6″							
	Demolish	L.F.		.70		.70	Cost includes material and labor to
	Install	L.F.	.58	.52		1.10	install 2″ x 6″ collar beam or tie for
	Demolish and Install	L.F.	.58	1.22		1.80	roof framing.
	Reinstall	L.F.		.41		.41	
	Minimum Charge	Job		207		207	
Purlins							
	Demolish	L.F.		.68		.68	Cost includes material and labor to
	Install	L.F.	.58	.46		1.04	install 2″ x 6″ purlins below roof
	Demolish and Install	L.F.	.58	1.14		1.72	rafters.
	Reinstall	L.F.		.37		.37	
	Minimum Charge	Job		207		207	
2″ x 8″							
	Demolish	L.F.		.69		.69	Cost includes material and labor to
	Install	L.F.	.83	.47		1.30	install 2″ x 8″ purlins below roof
	Demolish and Install	L.F.	.83	1.16		1.99	rafters.
	Reinstall	L.F.		.37		.37	
	Minimum Charge	Job		207		207	
2″ x 10″							
	Demolish	L.F.		.69		.69	Cost includes material and labor to
	Install	L.F.	1.11	.47		1.58	install 2″ x 10″ purlins below roof
	Demolish and Install	L.F.	1.11	1.16		2.27	rafters.
	Reinstall	L.F.		.38		.38	
	Minimum Charge	Job		207		207	
2″ x 12″							
	Demolish	L.F.		.70		.70	Cost includes material and labor to
	Install	L.F.	1.41	.48		1.89	install 2″ x 12″ purlins below roof
	Demolish and Install	L.F.	1.41	1.18		2.59	rafters.
	Reinstall	L.F.		.38		.38	
	Minimum Charge	Job		207		207	
4″ x 6″							
	Demolish	L.F.		.70		.70	Cost includes material and labor to
	Install	L.F.	2.75	.48		3.23	install 4″ x 6″ purlins below roof
	Demolish and Install	L.F.	2.75	1.18		3.93	rafters.
	Reinstall	L.F.		.38		.38	
	Minimum Charge	Job		207		207	
4″ x 8″							
	Demolish	L.F.		.71		.71	Cost includes material and labor to
	Install	L.F.	3.74	.49		4.23	install 4″ x 8″ purlins below roof
	Demolish and Install	L.F.	3.74	1.20		4.94	rafters.
	Reinstall	L.F.		.39		.39	
	Minimum Charge	Job		207		207	
Ledger Board							
2″ x 6″							
	Demolish	L.F.		.34		.34	Cost includes material and labor to
	Install	L.F.	.58	1.87		2.45	install 2″ x 6″ ledger board nailed to
	Demolish and Install	L.F.	.58	2.21		2.79	the face of a rafter.
	Reinstall	L.F.		1.49		1.49	
	Minimum Charge	Job		207		207	

Rough Frame / Structure

Roof Framing		Unit	Material	Labor	Equip.	Total	Specification
4" x 6"							
	Demolish	L.F.		.57		.57	Cost includes material and labor to
	Install	L.F.	2.75	2.74		5.49	install 4" x 6" ledger board nailed to
	Demolish and Install	L.F.	2.75	3.31		6.06	the face of a rafter.
	Reinstall	L.F.		2.20		2.20	
	Minimum Charge	Job		207		207	
4" x 8"							
	Demolish	L.F.		.76		.76	Cost includes material and labor to
	Install	L.F.	3.74	3.16		6.90	install 4" x 8" ledger board nailed to
	Demolish and Install	L.F.	3.74	3.92		7.66	the face of a rafter.
	Reinstall	L.F.		2.53		2.53	
	Minimum Charge	Job		207		207	
Outriggers							
2" x 4"							
	Demolish	L.F.		.23		.23	Cost includes material and labor to
	Install	L.F.	.36	1.66		2.02	install 2" x 4" outrigger rafters for flat,
	Demolish and Install	L.F.	.36	1.89		2.25	shed or gabled roofs, up to 5/12
	Reinstall	L.F.		1.33		1.33	slope, per L.F.
	Minimum Charge	Job		207		207	
2" x 6"							
	Demolish	L.F.		.35		.35	Cost includes material and labor to
	Install	L.F.	.58	1.66		2.24	install 2" x 6" outrigger rafters for flat,
	Demolish and Install	L.F.	.58	2.01		2.59	shed or gabled roofs, up to 5/12
	Reinstall	L.F.		1.33		1.33	slope, per L.F.
	Minimum Charge	Job		207		207	
Lookout Rafter							
2" x 4"							
	Demolish	L.F.		.79		.79	Cost includes material and labor to
	Install	L.F.	.36	.69		1.05	install 2" x 4" lookout rafters for flat,
	Demolish and Install	L.F.	.36	1.48		1.84	shed or gabled roofs, up to 5/12
	Reinstall	L.F.		.55		.55	slope, per L.F.
	Minimum Charge	Job		207		207	
2" x 6"							
	Demolish	L.F.		.80		.80	Cost includes material and labor to
	Install	L.F.	.58	.70		1.28	install 2" x 6" lookout rafters for flat,
	Demolish and Install	L.F.	.58	1.50		2.08	shed or gabled roofs, up to 5/12
	Reinstall	L.F.		.56		.56	slope, per L.F.
	Minimum Charge	Job		207		207	
Fly Rafter							
2" x 4"							
	Demolish	L.F.		.79		.79	Cost includes material and labor to
	Install	L.F.	.36	.69		1.05	install 2" x 4" fly rafters for flat, shed
	Demolish and Install	L.F.	.36	1.48		1.84	or gabled roofs, up to 5/12 slope,
	Reinstall	L.F.		.55		.55	per L.F.
	Minimum Charge	Job		207		207	
2" x 6"							
	Demolish	L.F.		.80		.80	Cost includes material and labor to
	Install	L.F.	.58	.70		1.28	install 2" x 6" fly rafters for flat, shed
	Demolish and Install	L.F.	.58	1.50		2.08	or gabled roofs, up to 5/12 slope,
	Reinstall	L.F.		.56		.56	per L.F.
	Minimum Charge	Job		207		207	

Residential Trusses	Unit	Material	Labor	Equip.	Total	Specification
W or Fink Truss						
24' Span						
Demolish	Ea.		31.50	11.35	42.85	Includes material, labor and
Install	Ea.	84.50	31.50	11.20	127.20	equipment to install wood gang-nailed
Demolish and Install	Ea.	84.50	63	22.55	170.05	residential truss, up to 24' span.
Reinstall	Ea.		31.28	11.22	42.50	
Minimum Charge	Job		207		207	
28' Span						
Demolish	Ea.		33.50	12.05	45.55	Includes material, labor and
Install	Ea.	102	35.50	12.70	150.20	equipment to install wood gang-nailed
Demolish and Install	Ea.	102	69	24.75	195.75	residential truss, up to 28' span.
Reinstall	Ea.		35.41	12.70	48.11	
Minimum Charge	Job		207		207	
32' Span						
Demolish	Ea.		37.50	13.35	50.85	Includes material, labor and
Install	Ea.	120	37.50	13.45	170.95	equipment to install wood gang-nailed
Demolish and Install	Ea.	120	75	26.80	221.80	residential truss, up to 32' span.
Reinstall	Ea.		37.54	13.46	51	
Minimum Charge	Job		207		207	
36' Span						
Demolish	Ea.		40	14.40	54.40	Includes material, labor and
Install	Ea.	146	41	14.65	201.65	equipment to install wood gang-nailed
Demolish and Install	Ea.	146	81	29.05	256.05	residential truss, up to 36' span.
Reinstall	Ea.		40.80	14.63	55.43	
Minimum Charge	Job		207		207	
Gable End						
24' Span						
Demolish	Ea.		31.50	11.35	42.85	Includes material, labor and
Install	Ea.	118	33.50	12	163.50	equipment to install wood gang-nailed
Demolish and Install	Ea.	118	65	23.35	206.35	residential gable end truss, up to 24'
Reinstall	Ea.		33.51	12.02	45.53	span.
Clean	Ea.	1.99	41		42.99	
Paint	Ea.	4.40	47.50		51.90	
Minimum Charge	Job		207		207	
28' Span						
Demolish	Ea.		33.50	12.05	45.55	Includes material, labor and
Install	Ea.	145	40	14.30	199.30	equipment to install wood gang-nailed
Demolish and Install	Ea.	145	73.50	26.35	244.85	residential gable end truss, up to 30'
Reinstall	Ea.		39.93	14.32	54.25	span.
Clean	Ea.	2.08	55.50		57.58	
Paint	Ea.	4.59	64.50		69.09	
Minimum Charge	Job		207		207	
32' Span						
Demolish	Ea.		37.50	13.35	50.85	Includes material, labor and
Install	Ea.	160	41	14.65	215.65	equipment to install wood gang-nailed
Demolish and Install	Ea.	160	78.50	28	266.50	residential gable end truss, up to 32'
Reinstall	Ea.		40.80	14.63	55.43	span.
Clean	Ea.	2.17	73		75.17	
Paint	Ea.	4.80	84.50		89.30	
Minimum Charge	Job		207		207	
36' Span						
Demolish	Ea.		40	14.40	54.40	Includes material, labor and
Install	Ea.	206	47	16.85	269.85	equipment to install wood gang-nailed
Demolish and Install	Ea.	206	87	31.25	324.25	residential gable end truss, up to 36'
Reinstall	Ea.		46.92	16.83	63.75	span.
Clean	Ea.	2.28	92		94.28	
Paint	Ea.	5.05	107		112.05	
Minimum Charge	Job		207		207	

Rough Frame / Structure

Residential Trusses

	Unit	Material	Labor	Equip.	Total	Specification
Truss Hardware						
5-1/4″ Glue-Lam Seat						
Install	Ea.	211	2.30		213.30	Includes labor and material to install
Minimum Charge	Job		207		207	beam hangers.
6-3/4″ Glue-Lam Seat						
Install	Ea.	217	2.30		219.30	Includes labor and material to install
Minimum Charge	Job		207		207	beam hangers.
2″ x 4″ Joist Hanger						
Install	Ea.	.74	2.37		3.11	Includes labor and material to install
Minimum Charge	Job		207		207	joist and beam hangers.
2″ x 12″ Joist Hanger						
Install	Ea.	1.41	2.51		3.92	Cost includes labor and material to
Minimum Charge	Job		207		207	install 2″ x 12″ joist hanger.

Commercial Trusses

	Unit	Material	Labor	Equip.	Total	Specification
Engineered Lumber, Truss / Joist						
9-1/2″						
Demolish	S.F.		.56		.56	Includes material and labor to install
Install	S.F.	1.60	.41		2.01	engineered lumber truss / joists per
Demolish and Install	S.F.	1.60	.97		2.57	S.F. of floor area based on joists 16″
Reinstall	S.F.		.33		.33	O.C. Beams, supports and bridging
Minimum Charge	Job		207		207	are not included.
11-7/8″						
Demolish	S.F.		.58		.58	Includes material and labor to install
Install	S.F.	1.80	.42		2.22	engineered lumber truss / joists per
Demolish and Install	S.F.	1.80	1		2.80	S.F. of floor area based on joists 16″
Reinstall	S.F.		.34		.34	O.C. Beams, supports and bridging
Minimum Charge	Job		207		207	are not included.
14″						
Demolish	S.F.		.60		.60	Includes material and labor to install
Install	S.F.	2.49	.45		2.94	engineered lumber truss / joists per
Demolish and Install	S.F.	2.49	1.05		3.54	S.F. of floor area based on joists 16″
Reinstall	S.F.		.36		.36	O.C. Beams, supports and bridging
Minimum Charge	Job		207		207	are not included.
16″						
Demolish	S.F.		.62		.62	Includes material and labor to install
Install	S.F.	3.08	.48		3.56	engineered lumber truss / joists per
Demolish and Install	S.F.	3.08	1.10		4.18	S.F. of floor area based on joists 16″
Reinstall	S.F.		.38		.38	O.C. Beams, supports and bridging
Minimum Charge	Job		207		207	are not included.
Bowstring Truss						
100′ Clear Span						
Demolish	SF Flr.		.57	.47	1.04	Includes material, labor and
Install	SF Flr.	7.50	.47	.30	8.27	equipment to install bow string truss
Demolish and Install	SF Flr.	7.50	1.04	.77	9.31	system up to 100′ clear span per S.F.
Minimum Charge	Job		207		207	of floor area.
120′ Clear Span						
Demolish	SF Flr.		.64	.53	1.17	Includes material, labor and
Install	SF Flr.	8	.52	.34	8.86	equipment to install bow string truss
Demolish and Install	SF Flr.	8	1.16	.87	10.03	system up to 120′ clear span per S.F.
Minimum Charge	Job		207		207	of floor area.

Rough Frame / Structure

Roof Sheathing		Unit	Material	Labor	Equip.	Total	Specification
Plywood							
3/8"							
	Demolish	S.F.		.44		.44	Cost includes material and labor to
	Install	S.F.	.52	.54		1.06	install 3/8" CDX plywood roof
	Demolish and Install	S.F.	.52	.98		1.50	sheathing.
	Reinstall	S.F.		.54		.54	
	Minimum Charge	Job		207		207	
1/2"							
	Demolish	S.F.		.44		.44	Cost includes material and labor to
	Install	S.F.	.52	.59		1.11	install 1/2" CDX plywood roof
	Demolish and Install	S.F.	.52	1.03		1.55	sheathing.
	Minimum Charge	Job		207		207	
5/8"							
	Demolish	S.F.		.44		.44	Cost includes material and labor to
	Install	S.F.	.68	.64		1.32	install 5/8" CDX plywood roof
	Demolish and Install	S.F.	.68	1.08		1.76	sheathing.
	Minimum Charge	Job		207		207	
3/4"							
	Demolish	S.F.		.44		.44	Cost includes material and labor to
	Install	S.F.	.77	.69		1.46	install 3/4" CDX plywood roof
	Demolish and Install	S.F.	.77	1.13		1.90	sheathing.
	Minimum Charge	Job		207		207	
OSB							
1/2"							
	Demolish	S.F.		.44		.44	Cost includes material and labor to
	Install	S.F.	.43	.63		1.06	install 4' x 8' x 1/2" OSB sheathing.
	Demolish and Install	S.F.	.43	1.07		1.50	
	Minimum Charge	Job		207		207	
5/8"							
	Demolish	S.F.		.44		.44	Cost includes material and labor to
	Install	S.F.	.43	.50		.93	install 4' x 8' x 5/8" OSB sheathing.
	Demolish and Install	S.F.	.43	.94		1.37	
	Minimum Charge	Job		207		207	
Plank							
	Demolish	S.F.		.44		.44	Cost includes material and labor to
	Install	S.F.	1.76	1.14		2.90	install 1" x 6" or 1" x 8" utility T&G
	Demolish and Install	S.F.	1.76	1.58		3.34	board sheathing laid diagonal.
	Reinstall	S.F.		1.14		1.14	
	Minimum Charge	Job		207		207	
Skip-type							
1" x 4"							
	Demolish	S.F.		.68		.68	Includes material and labor to install
	Install	S.F.	.56	.35		.91	sheathing board material 1" x 4", 7"
	Demolish and Install	S.F.	.56	1.03		1.59	O.C.
	Minimum Charge	Job		207		207	
1" x 6"							
	Demolish	S.F.		.68		.68	Includes material and labor to install
	Install	S.F.	.79	.29		1.08	sheathing board material 1" x 6", 7"
	Demolish and Install	S.F.	.79	.97		1.76	or 9" O.C.
	Minimum Charge	Job		207		207	

Rough Frame / Structure

Wood Deck	Unit	Material	Labor	Equip.	Total	Specification
Treated						
Demolish	S.F.		1.42		1.42	Includes material and labor to install
Install	S.F.	3.54	10.35		13.89	unfinished deck using 2" x 4" treated
Demolish and Install	S.F.	3.54	11.77		15.31	decking, with 2" x 6" double beams
Reinstall	S.F.		8.29		8.29	24" O.C., 4" x 4" posts 5' O.C. set in
Clean	S.F.	.10	.31		.41	concrete.
Paint	S.F.	.13	.27		.40	
Minimum Charge	Job		207		207	
Redwood						
Demolish	S.F.		1.42		1.42	Includes material and labor to install
Install	S.F.	10.50	10.35		20.85	unfinished deck using 2" x 4" select
Demolish and Install	S.F.	10.50	11.77		22.27	redwood decking, with 2" x 6" double
Reinstall	S.F.		8.29		8.29	beams 24" O.C., 4" x 4" posts 5'
Clean	S.F.	.10	.31		.41	O.C. set in concrete.
Paint	S.F.	.13	.27		.40	
Minimum Charge	Job		207		207	
Cedar						
Demolish	S.F.		1.42		1.42	Includes material and labor to install
Install	S.F.	9.80	10.35		20.15	unfinished deck using 2" x 4" select
Demolish and Install	S.F.	9.80	11.77		21.57	cedar decking, with 2" x 6" double
Reinstall	S.F.		8.29		8.29	beams 24" O.C., 4" x 4" posts 5'
Clean	S.F.	.10	.31		.41	O.C. set in concrete.
Paint	S.F.	.13	.27		.40	
Minimum Charge	Job		207		207	
Stairs						
Demolish	Ea.		400		400	Includes material and labor to install
Install	Ea.	130	720		850	wood steps. 5 - 7 risers included.
Demolish and Install	Ea.	130	1120		1250	
Reinstall	Ea.		577.15		577.15	
Clean	Flight	4.77	26.50		31.27	
Paint	Flight	21	47.50		68.50	
Minimum Charge	Job		207		207	
Railing						
Demolish	L.F.		5.25		5.25	Includes material and labor to install
Install	L.F.	28	18.85		46.85	porch rail with balusters.
Demolish and Install	L.F.	28	24.10		52.10	
Clean	L.F.	.96	1.92		2.88	
Paint	L.F.	.80	2.96		3.76	
Minimum Charge	Job		207		207	
Bench Seating						
Demolish	L.F.		5.65		5.65	Includes material and labor to install
Install	L.F.	1.76	20.50		22.26	pressure treated bench seating.
Demolish and Install	L.F.	1.76	26.15		27.91	
Reinstall	L.F.		16.58		16.58	
Clean	L.F.	.19	1.53		1.72	
Paint	L.F.	.63	2.84		3.47	
Minimum Charge	Job		207		207	
Privacy Wall						
Demolish	SF Flr.		1.36		1.36	Includes material, labor and
Install	SF Flr.	1.45	.70	.18	2.33	equipment to install privacy wall.
Demolish and Install	SF Flr.	1.45	2.06	.18	3.69	
Reinstall	SF Flr.		.56	.14	.70	
Clean	SF Flr.	.10	.31		.41	
Paint	S.F.	.13	.27		.40	
Minimum Charge	Job		207		207	

Rough Frame / Structure

Porch

	Unit	Material	Labor	Equip.	Total	Specification
Treated						
Demolish	S.F.		2.84		2.84	Includes material and labor to install
Install	S.F.	4.61	20.50		25.11	floor and roof frame and decking
Demolish and Install	S.F.	4.61	23.34		27.95	using 2" x 4" treated decking, with 2"
Reinstall	S.F.		16.58		16.58	x 6" double beams 24" O.C., 4" x 4"
Clean	S.F.	.19	.63		.82	posts 5' O.C. set in concrete.
Paint	S.F.	.21	.71		.92	
Minimum Charge	Job		207		207	
Redwood						
Demolish	S.F.		2.84		2.84	Includes material and labor to install
Install	S.F.	11.75	20.50		32.25	floor and roof frame and decking
Demolish and Install	S.F.	11.75	23.34		35.09	using 2" x 4" redwood decking, with
Reinstall	S.F.		16.58		16.58	2" x 6" double beams 24" O.C., 4" x
Clean	S.F.	.19	.63		.82	4" posts 5' O.C. set in concrete.
Paint	S.F.	.21	.71		.92	
Minimum Charge	Job		207		207	
Cedar						
Demolish	S.F.		2.84		2.84	Includes material and labor to install
Install	S.F.	11.10	20.50		31.60	floor and roof frame and cedar
Demolish and Install	S.F.	11.10	23.34		34.44	decking using 2" x 4" select cedar,
Reinstall	S.F.		16.58		16.58	with 2" x 6" double beams 24" O.C.,
Clean	S.F.	.19	.63		.82	4" x 4" posts 5' O.C. set in concrete.
Paint	S.F.	.21	.71		.92	
Minimum Charge	Job		207		207	
Stairs						
Demolish	Ea.		400		400	Includes material and labor to install
Install	Ea.	130	720		850	wood steps. 5 - 7 risers included.
Demolish and Install	Ea.	130	1120		1250	
Reinstall	Ea.		577.15		577.15	
Clean	Flight	4.77	26.50		31.27	
Paint	Flight	21	47.50		68.50	
Minimum Charge	Job		207		207	
Railing						
Demolish	L.F.		5.25		5.25	Includes material and labor to install
Install	L.F.	28	18.85		46.85	porch rail with balusters.
Demolish and Install	L.F.	28	24.10		52.10	
Clean	L.F.	.96	2.39		3.35	
Paint	L.F.	.80	2.96		3.76	
Minimum Charge	Job		207		207	
Bench Seating						
Demolish	L.F.		5.65		5.65	Includes material and labor to install
Install	L.F.	1.76	20.50		22.26	pressure treated bench seating.
Demolish and Install	L.F.	1.76	26.15		27.91	
Reinstall	L.F.		16.58		16.58	
Clean	L.F.	.19	1.53		1.72	
Paint	L.F.	.63	2.84		3.47	
Minimum Charge	Job		207		207	
Privacy Wall						
Demolish	SF Flr.		1.36		1.36	Includes material, labor and
Install	SF Flr.	1.45	.70	.18	2.33	equipment to install privacy wall.
Demolish and Install	SF Flr.	1.45	2.06	.18	3.69	
Reinstall	SF Flr.		.56	.14	.70	
Clean	SF Flr.	.10	.31		.41	
Paint	S.F.	.13	.27		.40	
Minimum Charge	Job		207		207	

Rough Frame / Structure

Porch

	Unit	Material	Labor	Equip.	Total	Specification
Wood Board Ceiling						
Demolish	S.F.		.57		.57	Includes material and labor to install
Install	S.F.	3.15	1.84		4.99	wood board on ceiling.
Demolish and Install	S.F.	3.15	2.41		5.56	
Clean	S.F.	.04	.18		.22	
Paint	S.F.	.18	.44		.62	
Minimum Charge	Job		207		207	
Re-screen						
Install	S.F.	1.74	1.66		3.40	Includes labor and material to
Minimum Charge	Job		207		207	re-screen wood frame.

Exterior Trim

Exterior Trim	Unit	Material	Labor	Equip.	Total	Specification
Stock Lumber						
1″ x 2″						
Demolish	L.F.		.28		.28	Cost includes material and labor to
Install	L.F.	.28	1.26		1.54	install 1″ x 2″ pine trim.
Demolish and Install	L.F.	.28	1.54		1.82	
Clean	L.F.	.01	.20		.21	
Paint	L.F.	.02	.56		.58	
Minimum Charge	Job		207		207	
1″ x 3″						
Demolish	L.F.		.28		.28	Cost includes material and labor to
Install	L.F.	.28	1.43		1.71	install 1″ x 3″ pine trim.
Demolish and Install	L.F.	.28	1.71		1.99	
Clean	L.F.	.01	.20		.21	
Paint	L.F.	.02	.56		.58	
Minimum Charge	Job		207		207	
1″ x 4″						
Demolish	L.F.		.28		.28	Cost includes material and labor to
Install	L.F.	.45	1.66		2.11	install 1″ x 4″ pine trim.
Demolish and Install	L.F.	.45	1.94		2.39	
Clean	L.F.	.01	.20		.21	
Paint	L.F.	.02	.56		.58	
Minimum Charge	Job		207		207	
1″ x 6″						
Demolish	L.F.		.28		.28	Cost includes material and labor to
Install	L.F.	.79	1.66		2.45	install 1″ x 6″ pine trim.
Demolish and Install	L.F.	.79	1.94		2.73	
Clean	L.F.	.02	.20		.22	
Paint	L.F.	.08	.56		.64	
Minimum Charge	Job		207		207	
1″ x 8″						
Demolish	L.F.		.31		.31	Cost includes material and labor to
Install	L.F.	1.10	2.07		3.17	install 1″ x 8″ pine trim.
Demolish and Install	L.F.	1.10	2.38		3.48	
Reinstall	L.F.		1.66		1.66	
Clean	L.F.	.03	.22		.25	
Paint	L.F.	.08	.56		.64	
Minimum Charge	Job		207		207	

Exterior Trim

Exterior Trim		Unit	Material	Labor	Equip.	Total	Specification
1" x 10"							
	Demolish	L.F.		.47		.47	Cost includes material and labor to
	Install	L.F.	1.43	2.30		3.73	install 1" x 10" pine trim.
	Demolish and Install	L.F.	1.43	2.77		4.20	
	Minimum Charge	Job		207		207	
1" x 12"							
	Demolish	L.F.		.47		.47	Cost includes material and labor to
	Install	L.F.	1.79	2.30		4.09	install 1" x 12" pine trim.
	Demolish and Install	L.F.	1.79	2.77		4.56	
	Minimum Charge	Job		207		207	

Fascia		Unit	Material	Labor	Equip.	Total	Specification
Aluminum							
	Demolish	L.F.		.59		.59	Includes material and labor to install
	Install	S.F.	2.16	1.97		4.13	aluminum fascia.
	Demolish and Install	S.F.	2.16	2.56		4.72	
	Reinstall	S.F.		1.58		1.58	
	Clean	L.F.		.38		.38	
	Minimum Charge	Job		207		207	
Vinyl							
	Demolish	L.F.		.59		.59	Cost includes material and labor to
	Install	L.F.	4.79	2.37		7.16	install 6" vinyl fascia with 12" vinyl
	Demolish and Install	L.F.	4.79	2.96		7.75	soffit and J-channel.
	Reinstall	L.F.		1.89		1.89	
	Clean	L.F.		.38		.38	
	Minimum Charge	Job		207		207	
Plywood							
	Demolish	L.F.		.59		.59	Cost includes material and labor to
	Install	L.F.	1.29	.92		2.21	install 12" wide plywood fascia.
	Demolish and Install	L.F.	1.29	1.51		2.80	
	Reinstall	L.F.		.74		.74	
	Clean	L.F.	.06	.26		.32	
	Paint	L.F.	.17	.89		1.06	
	Minimum Charge	Job		207		207	
Cedar							
	Demolish	L.F.		.59		.59	Cost includes material and labor to
	Install	L.F.	2.96	.92		3.88	install 12" wide cedar fascia.
	Demolish and Install	L.F.	2.96	1.51		4.47	
	Reinstall	L.F.		.74		.74	
	Clean	L.F.	.06	.26		.32	
	Paint	L.F.	.17	.89		1.06	
	Minimum Charge	Job		207		207	
Redwood							
1" x 6"							
	Demolish	L.F.		.46		.46	Cost includes material and labor to
	Install	L.F.	1.91	1.66		3.57	install 1" x 6" redwood fascia board.
	Demolish and Install	L.F.	1.91	2.12		4.03	
	Reinstall	L.F.		1.33		1.33	
	Minimum Charge	Job		207		207	
1" x 8"							
	Demolish	L.F.		.51		.51	Cost includes material and labor to
	Install	L.F.	2.54	1.80		4.34	install 1" x 8" redwood fascia board.
	Demolish and Install	L.F.	2.54	2.31		4.85	
	Reinstall	L.F.		1.44		1.44	
	Minimum Charge	Job		207		207	

Exterior Trim

Fascia		Unit	Material	Labor	Equip.	Total	Specification
2" x 6"							
	Demolish	L.F.		.46		.46	Cost includes material and labor to
	Install	L.F.	.58	3.32		3.90	install 2" x 6" hem-fir exterior trim
	Demolish and Install	L.F.	.58	3.78		4.36	board.
	Reinstall	L.F.		2.65		2.65	
	Minimum Charge	Job		207		207	
2" x 8"							
	Demolish	L.F.		.51		.51	Cost includes material and labor to
	Install	L.F.	.83	3.68		4.51	install 2" x 8" hem-fir exterior trim
	Demolish and Install	L.F.	.83	4.19		5.02	board.
	Reinstall	L.F.		2.95		2.95	
	Minimum Charge	Job		207		207	

Hem-fir Std & Better

		Unit	Material	Labor	Equip.	Total	Specification
2" x 6"							
	Demolish	L.F.		.46		.46	Cost includes material and labor to
	Install	L.F.	.58	3.32		3.90	install 2" x 6" hem-fir exterior trim
	Demolish and Install	L.F.	.58	3.78		4.36	board.
	Reinstall	L.F.		2.65		2.65	
	Clean	L.F.	.02	.26		.28	
	Paint	L.F.	.17	.89		1.06	
	Minimum Charge	Job		207		207	
2" x 8"							
	Demolish	L.F.		.51		.51	Cost includes material and labor to
	Install	L.F.	.83	3.68		4.51	install 2" x 8" hem-fir exterior trim
	Demolish and Install	L.F.	.83	4.19		5.02	board.
	Reinstall	L.F.		2.95		2.95	
	Clean	L.F.	.03	.26		.29	
	Paint	L.F.	.17	.89		1.06	
	Minimum Charge	Job		207		207	
2" x 10"							
	Demolish	L.F.		.59		.59	Cost includes material and labor to
	Install	L.F.	1.11	4.60		5.71	install 2" x 10" hem-fir exterior trim
	Demolish and Install	L.F.	1.11	5.19		6.30	board.
	Reinstall	L.F.		3.68		3.68	
	Clean	L.F.	.06	.28		.34	
	Paint	L.F.	.17	.89		1.06	
	Minimum Charge	Job		207		207	

Barge Rafter

		Unit	Material	Labor	Equip.	Total	Specification
2" x 6"							
	Demolish	L.F.		.91		.91	Cost includes material and labor to
	Install	L.F.	.58	.46		1.04	install 2" x 6" barge rafters.
	Demolish and Install	L.F.	.58	1.37		1.95	
	Reinstall	L.F.		.37		.37	
	Clean	L.F.	.02	.26		.28	
	Paint	L.F.	.17	.89		1.06	
	Minimum Charge	Job		207		207	
2" x 8"							
	Demolish	L.F.		.92		.92	Cost includes material and labor to
	Install	L.F.	.83	.49		1.32	install 2" x 8" barge rafters.
	Demolish and Install	L.F.	.83	1.41		2.24	
	Reinstall	L.F.		.39		.39	
	Clean	L.F.	.03	.26		.29	
	Paint	L.F.	.17	.89		1.06	
	Minimum Charge	Job		207		207	

Exterior Trim

Fascia

	Unit	Material	Labor	Equip.	Total	Specification
2″ x 10″						
Demolish	L.F.		.94		.94	Cost includes material and labor to
Install	L.F.	1.11	.50		1.61	install 2″ x 10″ barge rafters.
Demolish and Install	L.F.	1.11	1.44		2.55	
Reinstall	L.F.		.40		.40	
Clean	L.F.	.06	.28		.34	
Paint	L.F.	.17	.89		1.06	
Minimum Charge	Job		207		207	

Soffit

	Unit	Material	Labor	Equip.	Total	Specification
Aluminum						
12″ w / Fascia						
Demolish	L.F.		.59		.59	Cost includes material and labor to
Install	L.F.	4.79	2.37		7.16	install 12″ aluminum soffit with 6″
Demolish and Install	L.F.	4.79	2.96		7.75	fascia and J-channel.
Reinstall	L.F.		1.89		1.89	
Clean	L.F.		.38		.38	
Paint	L.F.	.21	.89		1.10	
Minimum Charge	Job		207		207	
18″ w / Fascia						
Demolish	L.F.		.59		.59	Cost includes material and labor to
Install	L.F.	5.90	2.76		8.66	install 18″ aluminum soffit with 6″
Demolish and Install	L.F.	5.90	3.35		9.25	fascia and J-channel.
Reinstall	L.F.		2.21		2.21	
Clean	L.F.		.38		.38	
Paint	L.F.	.21	.89		1.10	
Minimum Charge	Job		207		207	
24″ w / Fascia						
Demolish	L.F.		.59		.59	Cost includes material and labor to
Install	L.F.	6.95	3.07		10.02	install 24″ aluminum soffit with 6″
Demolish and Install	L.F.	6.95	3.66		10.61	fascia and J-channel.
Reinstall	L.F.		2.46		2.46	
Clean	L.F.		.56		.56	
Paint	L.F.	.21	.89		1.10	
Minimum Charge	Job		207		207	
Vinyl						
Demolish	L.F.		.59		.59	Cost includes material and labor to
Install	L.F.	4.79	2.37		7.16	install 6″ vinyl fascia with 12″ vinyl
Demolish and Install	L.F.	4.79	2.96		7.75	soffit and J-channel.
Reinstall	L.F.		1.89		1.89	
Clean	L.F.		.38		.38	
Paint	L.F.	.21	.89		1.10	
Minimum Charge	Job		207		207	
Plywood						
Demolish	L.F.		.65		.65	Cost includes material and labor to
Install	L.F.	1.29	1.18		2.47	install 12″ wide plywood soffit.
Demolish and Install	L.F.	1.29	1.83		3.12	
Reinstall	L.F.		.95		.95	
Clean	L.F.	.06	.26		.32	
Paint	L.F.	.17	.89		1.06	
Minimum Charge	Job		207		207	

Exterior Trim

Soffit		Unit	Material	Labor	Equip.	Total	Specification
Redwood							
	Demolish	L.F.		.65		.65	Cost includes material and labor to
	Install	L.F.	5.15	1.18		6.33	install 12" wide redwood soffit.
	Demolish and Install	L.F.	5.15	1.83		6.98	
	Reinstall	L.F.		.95		.95	
	Clean	L.F.	.06	.26		.32	
	Paint	L.F.	.17	.89		1.06	
	Minimum Charge	Job		207		207	
Cedar							
	Demolish	L.F.		.65		.65	Cost includes material and labor to
	Install	L.F.	2.96	1.18		4.14	install 12" wide cedar soffit.
	Demolish and Install	L.F.	2.96	1.83		4.79	
	Reinstall	L.F.		.95		.95	
	Clean	L.F.	.06	.26		.32	
	Paint	L.F.	.17	.89		1.06	
	Minimum Charge	Job		207		207	
Douglas Fir							
	Demolish	L.F.		.65		.65	Cost includes material and labor to
	Install	L.F.	1.79	1.18		2.97	install 12" wide Douglas fir soffit.
	Demolish and Install	L.F.	1.79	1.83		3.62	
	Reinstall	L.F.		.95		.95	
	Clean	L.F.	.06	.26		.32	
	Paint	L.F.	.17	.89		1.06	
	Minimum Charge	Job		207		207	

Roofing

Roofing and Flashing

Tile Roofing

Metal Flashing		Unit	Material	Labor	Equip.	Total	Specification
Galvanized							
6″							
	Demolish	L.F.		.23		.23	Includes material and labor to install
	Install	L.F.	.78	.94		1.72	flat galvanized steel flashing, 6″ wide.
	Demolish and Install	L.F.	.78	1.17		1.95	
	Paint	L.F.	.11	.44		.55	
	Minimum Charge	Job		188		188	
14″							
	Demolish	L.F.		.23		.23	Includes material and labor to install
	Install	L.F.	1.83	.94		2.77	flat galvanized steel flashing, 14″
	Demolish and Install	L.F.	1.83	1.17		3	wide.
	Paint	L.F.	.11	.44		.55	
	Minimum Charge	Job		188		188	
20″							
	Demolish	L.F.		.23		.23	Includes material and labor to install
	Install	L.F.	2.62	.94		3.56	flat galvanized steel flashing, 20″
	Demolish and Install	L.F.	2.62	1.17		3.79	wide.
	Paint	L.F.	.11	.44		.55	
	Minimum Charge	Job		188		188	
Aluminum							
6″							
	Demolish	L.F.		.23		.23	Includes material and labor to install
	Install	L.F.	.40	.94		1.34	flat aluminum flashing, 6″ wide.
	Demolish and Install	L.F.	.40	1.17		1.57	
	Paint	L.F.	.11	.44		.55	
	Minimum Charge	Job		188		188	
14″							
	Demolish	L.F.		.23		.23	Includes material and labor to install
	Install	L.F.	.67	.94		1.61	flat aluminum flashing, 14″ wide.
	Demolish and Install	L.F.	.67	1.17		1.84	
	Paint	L.F.	.11	.44		.55	
	Minimum Charge	Job		188		188	
20″							
	Demolish	L.F.		.23		.23	Includes material and labor to install
	Install	L.F.	.98	.94		1.92	flat aluminum flashing, 20″ wide.
	Demolish and Install	L.F.	.98	1.17		2.15	
	Paint	L.F.	.11	.44		.55	
	Minimum Charge	Job		188		188	

Metal Flashing	Unit	Material	Labor	Equip.	Total	Specification
Copper						
6"						
Demolish	L.F.		.23		.23	Includes material and labor to install
Install	L.F.	4.33	1.25		5.58	flat copper flashing, 6" wide.
Demolish and Install	L.F.	4.33	1.48		5.81	
Minimum Charge	Job		229		229	
14"						
Demolish	L.F.		.23		.23	Includes material and labor to install
Install	L.F.	10.10	1.25		11.35	flat copper flashing, 14" wide.
Demolish and Install	L.F.	10.10	1.48		11.58	
Minimum Charge	Job		229		229	
18"						
Demolish	L.F.		.23		.23	Includes material and labor to install
Install	L.F.	14.45	1.25		15.70	flat copper flashing, 18" wide.
Demolish and Install	L.F.	14.45	1.48		15.93	
Minimum Charge	Job		229		229	
Aluminum Valley						
Demolish	L.F.		.23		.23	Includes material and labor to install
Install	L.F.	3.19	2.44		5.63	aluminum valley flashing, .024" thick.
Demolish and Install	L.F.	3.19	2.67		5.86	
Paint	L.F.	.11	.44		.55	
Minimum Charge	Job		207		207	
Gravel Stop						
Demolish	L.F.		.21		.21	Includes material and labor to install
Install	L.F.	6.60	3.16		9.76	aluminum gravel stop, .050" thick, 4"
Demolish and Install	L.F.	6.60	3.37		9.97	high, mill finish.
Reinstall	L.F.		2.53		2.53	
Paint	L.F.	.18	.44		.62	
Minimum Charge	Job		207		207	
Drip Edge						
Demolish	L.F.		.21		.21	Includes material and labor to install
Install	L.F.	.42	1.04		1.46	aluminum drip edge, .016" thick, 5"
Demolish and Install	L.F.	.42	1.25		1.67	wide, mill finish.
Reinstall	L.F.		.83		.83	
Paint	L.F.	.18	.44		.62	
Minimum Charge	Job		207		207	
End Wall						
Demolish	L.F.		1.05		1.05	Includes material and labor to install
Install	L.F.	1.96	2.44		4.40	aluminum end wall flashing, .024"
Demolish and Install	L.F.	1.96	3.49		5.45	thick.
Minimum Charge	Job		207		207	
Side Wall						
Demolish	L.F.		.20		.20	Includes material and labor to install
Install	L.F.	1.96	2.44		4.40	aluminum side wall flashing, .024"
Demolish and Install	L.F.	1.96	2.64		4.60	thick.
Minimum Charge	Job		207		207	
Coping and Wall Cap						
Demolish	L.F.		1.42		1.42	Includes material and labor to install
Install	L.F.	2.35	2.59		4.94	aluminum flashing, mill finish, 0.40
Demolish and Install	L.F.	2.35	4.01		6.36	thick, 12" wide.
Clean	L.F.	.12	.96		1.08	
Minimum Charge	Job		188		188	

Roofing

Roof Shingles

	Unit	Material	Labor	Equip.	Total	Specification
Underlayment						
15#						
Demolish	Sq.		11.35		11.35	Includes material and labor to install
Install	Sq.	6.20	5.85		12.05	#15 felt underlayment.
Demolish and Install	Sq.	6.20	17.20		23.40	
Minimum Charge	Job		188		188	
30#						
Demolish	Sq.		11.35		11.35	Includes material and labor to install
Install	Sq.	12.45	6.45		18.90	#30 felt underlayment.
Demolish and Install	Sq.	12.45	17.80		30.25	
Minimum Charge	Job		188		188	
Self Adhering						
Demolish	Sq.		28.50		28.50	Includes material and labor to install
Install	Sq.	81.50	17.05		98.55	self adhering ice barrier roofing
Demolish and Install	Sq.	81.50	45.55		127.05	underlayment.
Minimum Charge	Job		188		188	

Rolled Roofing

	Unit	Material	Labor	Equip.	Total	Specification
90 lb						
Demolish	Sq.		28.50		28.50	Cost includes material and labor to
Install	Sq.	38	31.50		69.50	install 90 lb mineral surface rolled
Demolish and Install	Sq.	38	60		98	roofing.
Minimum Charge	Job		188		188	

Composition Shingles

	Unit	Material	Labor	Equip.	Total	Specification
Fiberglass (3-tab)						
225 lb, 20 Year						
Demolish	Sq.		31		31	Cost includes material and labor to
Install	Sq.	76	73		149	install 225 lb, 20 year fiberglass
Demolish and Install	Sq.	76	104		180	shingles.
Minimum Charge	Job		188		188	
300 lb, 25 Year						
Demolish	Sq.		31		31	Cost includes material and labor to
Install	Sq.	75	73		148	install 300 lb, 25 year fiberglass
Demolish and Install	Sq.	75	104		179	shingles.
Minimum Charge	Job		188		188	
Emergency Repairs						
Install	Ea.	149	188		337	Includes labor and material for
Minimum Charge	Job		188		188	emergency repairs.
Architectural						
Laminated, 25 Year						
Demolish	Sq.		31		31	Cost includes material and labor to
Install	Sq.	117	73		190	install 25 year fiberglass roof shingles.
Demolish and Install	Sq.	117	104		221	
Minimum Charge	Job		188		188	
Laminated, 30 Year						
Demolish	Sq.		31		31	Cost includes material and labor to
Install	Sq.	99.50	73		172.50	install 30 year fiberglass roof shingles.
Demolish and Install	Sq.	99.50	104		203.50	
Minimum Charge	Job		188		188	

Roofing

Composition Shingles		Unit	Material	Labor	Equip.	Total	Specification
Laminated, 40 Year							
	Demolish	Sq.		31		31	Cost includes material and labor to
	Install	Sq.	139	73		212	install 40 year fiberglass roof shingles.
	Demolish and Install	Sq.	139	104		243	
	Minimum Charge	Job		188		188	
Laminated Shake, 40 Year							
	Demolish	Sq.		31		31	Cost includes material and labor to
	Install	Sq.	138	97.50		235.50	install 40 year fiberglass roof shakes.
	Demolish and Install	Sq.	138	128.50		266.50	
	Minimum Charge	Job		188		188	
Emergency Repairs							
	Install	Ea.	149	188		337	Includes labor and material for
	Minimum Charge	Job		188		188	emergency repairs.
Roof Jack							
	Demolish	Ea.		6.20		6.20	Includes material and labor to install
	Install	Ea.	25	41.50		66.50	residential roof jack, w/bird screen,
	Demolish and Install	Ea.	25	47.70		72.70	backdraft damper, 3" & 4" dia. round
	Paint	Ea.	.06	4.44		4.50	duct.
	Minimum Charge	Job		226		226	
Ridge Vent							
	Demolish	L.F.		1.10		1.10	Includes material and labor to install a
	Install	L.F.	3.25	2.95		6.20	mill finish aluminum ridge vent strip.
	Demolish and Install	L.F.	3.25	4.05		7.30	
	Minimum Charge	Job		207		207	
Shingle Molding							
1" x 2"							
	Demolish	L.F.		.21		.21	Cost includes material and labor to
	Install	L.F.	.28	1.26		1.54	install 1" x 2" pine trim.
	Demolish and Install	L.F.	.28	1.47		1.75	
	Paint	L.F.	.02	.56		.58	
	Minimum Charge	Job		207		207	
1" x 3"							
	Demolish	L.F.		.21		.21	Cost includes material and labor to
	Install	L.F.	.28	1.43		1.71	install 1" x 3" pine trim.
	Demolish and Install	L.F.	.28	1.64		1.92	
	Paint	L.F.	.02	.56		.58	
	Minimum Charge	Job		207		207	
1" x 4"							
	Demolish	L.F.		.21		.21	Cost includes material and labor to
	Install	L.F.	.45	1.66		2.11	install 1" x 4" pine trim.
	Demolish and Install	L.F.	.45	1.87		2.32	
	Paint	L.F.	.02	.56		.58	
	Minimum Charge	Job		207		207	
Add for Steep Pitch							
	Install	Sq.		23.50		23.50	Includes labor and material added for
Add for Additional Story							2nd story or steep roofs.
	Install	Sq.		23.50		23.50	Includes labor and material added for
							2nd story or steep roofs.

Roofing

Wood Shingles		Unit	Material	Labor	Equip.	Total	Specification
Cedar Wood Shingles							
16" Red Label (#2)							
	Demolish	Sq.		75.50		75.50	Includes material and labor to install
	Install	Sq.	164	166		330	wood shingles/shakes.
	Demolish and Install	Sq.	164	241.50		405.50	
	Minimum Charge	Job		207		207	
16" Blue Label (#1)							
	Demolish	Sq.		75.50		75.50	Includes material and labor to install
	Install	Sq.	229	128		357	wood shingles/shakes.
	Demolish and Install	Sq.	229	203.50		432.50	
	Minimum Charge	Job		207		207	
18" Red Label (#2)							
	Demolish	Sq.		75.50		75.50	Includes material and labor to install
	Install	Sq.	286	106		392	wood shingles/shakes.
	Demolish and Install	Sq.	286	181.50		467.50	
	Minimum Charge	Job		207		207	
18" Blue Label (#1)							
	Demolish	Sq.		75.50		75.50	Includes material and labor to install
	Install	Sq.	251	116		367	wood shingles/shakes.
	Demolish and Install	Sq.	251	191.50		442.50	
	Minimum Charge	Job		207		207	
Replace Shingle							
	Install	Ea.	37.50	10.35		47.85	Includes labor and material to replace
	Minimum Charge	Job		207		207	individual wood shingle/shake. Cost is per shingle.
Cedar Shake							
18" Medium Handsplit							
	Demolish	Sq.		75.50		75.50	Includes material and labor to install
	Install	Sq.	175	159		334	wood shingles/shakes.
	Demolish and Install	Sq.	175	234.50		409.50	
	Minimum Charge	Job		207		207	
18" Heavy Handsplit							
	Demolish	Sq.		75.50		75.50	Includes material and labor to install
	Install	Sq.	175	177		352	wood shingles/shakes.
	Demolish and Install	Sq.	175	252.50		427.50	
	Minimum Charge	Job		207		207	
24" Heavy Handsplit							
	Demolish	Sq.		75.50		75.50	Includes material and labor to install
	Install	Sq.	256	142		398	wood shingles/shakes.
	Demolish and Install	Sq.	256	217.50		473.50	
	Minimum Charge	Job		207		207	
24" Medium Handsplit							
	Demolish	Sq.		75.50		75.50	Includes material and labor to install
	Install	Sq.	256	128		384	wood shingles/shakes.
	Demolish and Install	Sq.	256	203.50		459.50	
	Minimum Charge	Job		207		207	
24" Straight Split							
	Demolish	Sq.		75.50		75.50	Includes material and labor to install
	Install	Sq.	264	188		452	wood shingles/shakes.
	Demolish and Install	Sq.	264	263.50		527.50	
	Minimum Charge	Job		207		207	
24" Tapersplit							
	Demolish	Sq.		75.50		75.50	Includes material and labor to install
	Install	Sq.	320	188		508	wood shingles/shakes.
	Demolish and Install	Sq.	320	263.50		583.50	
	Minimum Charge	Job		207		207	

Roofing

Wood Shingles

Wood Shingles		Unit	Material	Labor	Equip.	Total	Specification
18″ Straight Split							
	Demolish	Sq.		75.50		75.50	Includes material and labor to install
	Install	Sq.	256	188		444	wood shingles/shakes.
	Demolish and Install	Sq.	256	263.50		519.50	
	Minimum Charge	Job		207		207	
Replace Shingle							
	Install	Ea.	37.50	10.35		47.85	Includes labor and material to replace
	Minimum Charge	Job		207		207	individual wood shingle/shake. Cost is per shingle.

Slate Tile Roofing

Slate Tile Roofing		Unit	Material	Labor	Equip.	Total	Specification
Unfading Green							
	Demolish	Sq.		68		68	Includes material and labor to install
	Install	Sq.	530	215		745	clear Vermont slate tile.
	Demolish and Install	Sq.	530	283		813	
	Reinstall	Sq.		172.07		172.07	
	Minimum Charge	Job		188		188	
Unfading Purple							
	Demolish	Sq.		68		68	Includes material and labor to install
	Install	Sq.	470	215		685	clear Vermont slate tile.
	Demolish and Install	Sq.	470	283		753	
	Reinstall	Sq.		172.07		172.07	
	Minimum Charge	Job		188		188	
Replace Slate Tiles							
	Install	Ea.	6.50	19.80		26.30	Includes labor and material to replace
	Minimum Charge	Job		188		188	individual slate tiles. Cost is per tile.
Variegated Purple							
	Demolish	Sq.		68		68	Includes material and labor to install
	Install	Sq.	455	215		670	clear Vermont slate tile.
	Demolish and Install	Sq.	455	283		738	
	Reinstall	Sq.		172.07		172.07	
	Minimum Charge	Job		188		188	
Unfading Grey / Black							
	Demolish	Sq.		68		68	Includes material and labor to install
	Install	Sq.	505	215		720	clear Vermont slate tile.
	Demolish and Install	Sq.	505	283		788	
	Reinstall	Sq.		172.07		172.07	
	Minimum Charge	Job		188		188	
Unfading Red							
	Demolish	Sq.		68		68	Includes material and labor to install
	Install	Sq.	1300	215		1515	clear Vermont slate tile.
	Demolish and Install	Sq.	1300	283		1583	
	Reinstall	Sq.		172.07		172.07	
	Minimum Charge	Job		188		188	
Weathering Black							
	Demolish	Sq.		68		68	Includes material and labor to install
	Install	Sq.	540	215		755	clear Pennsylvania slate tile.
	Demolish and Install	Sq.	540	283		823	
	Reinstall	Sq.		172.07		172.07	
	Minimum Charge	Job		188		188	

Roofing

Slate Tile Roofing

Slate Tile Roofing		Unit	Material	Labor	Equip.	Total	Specification
Weathering Green							
	Demolish	Sq.		68		68	Includes material and labor to install
	Install	Sq.	385	215		600	clear Vermont slate tile.
	Demolish and Install	Sq.	385	283		668	
	Reinstall	Sq.		172.07		172.07	
	Minimum Charge	Job		188		188	

Flat Clay Tile Roofing

Flat Clay Tile Roofing		Unit	Material	Labor	Equip.	Total	Specification
Glazed							
	Demolish	Sq.		75.50		75.50	Includes material and labor to install
	Install	Sq.	360	188		548	tile roofing. Cost based on terra cotta
	Demolish and Install	Sq.	360	263.50		623.50	red flat clay tile and includes ridge
	Reinstall	Sq.		150.56		150.56	and rake tiles.
	Minimum Charge	Job		188		188	
Terra Cotta Red							
	Demolish	Sq.		75.50		75.50	Includes material and labor to install
	Install	Sq.	360	188		548	tile roofing. Cost based on terra cotta
	Demolish and Install	Sq.	360	263.50		623.50	red flat clay tile and includes ridge
	Reinstall	Sq.		150.56		150.56	and rake tiles.
	Minimum Charge	Job		188		188	

Mission Tile Roofing

Mission Tile Roofing		Unit	Material	Labor	Equip.	Total	Specification
Glazed Red							
	Demolish	Sq.		75.50		75.50	Includes material and labor to install
	Install	Sq.	835	205		1040	tile roofing. Cost based on glazed red
	Demolish and Install	Sq.	835	280.50		1115.50	tile and includes birdstop, ridge and
	Reinstall	Sq.		164.25		164.25	rake tiles.
	Minimum Charge	Job		188		188	
Unglazed Red							
	Demolish	Sq.		75.50		75.50	Includes material and labor to install
	Install	Sq.	835	205		1040	tile roofing. Cost based on unglazed
	Demolish and Install	Sq.	835	280.50		1115.50	red tile and includes birdstop, ridge
	Reinstall	Sq.		164.25		164.25	and rake tiles.
	Minimum Charge	Job		188		188	
Glazed Blue							
	Demolish	Sq.		75.50		75.50	Includes material and labor to install
	Install	Sq.	835	205		1040	tile roofing. Cost based on glazed
	Demolish and Install	Sq.	835	280.50		1115.50	blue tile and includes birdstop, ridge
	Reinstall	Sq.		164.25		164.25	and rake tiles.
	Minimum Charge	Job		188		188	
Glazed White							
	Demolish	Sq.		75.50		75.50	Includes material and labor to install
	Install	Sq.	835	205		1040	tile roofing. Cost based on glazed
	Demolish and Install	Sq.	835	280.50		1115.50	white tile and includes birdstop, ridge
	Reinstall	Sq.		164.25		164.25	and rake tiles.
	Minimum Charge	Job		188		188	
Unglazed White							
	Demolish	Sq.		75.50		75.50	Includes material and labor to install
	Install	Sq.	835	205		1040	tile roofing. Cost based on unglazed
	Demolish and Install	Sq.	835	280.50		1115.50	white tile and includes birdstop, ridge
	Reinstall	Sq.		164.25		164.25	and rake tiles.
	Minimum Charge	Job		188		188	

Roofing

Mission Tile Roofing

Mission Tile Roofing	Unit	Material	Labor	Equip.	Total	Specification
Color Blend						Includes material and labor to install tile roofing. Cost based on color blend tile and includes birdstop, ridge and rake tiles.
Demolish	Sq.		75.50		75.50	
Install	Sq.	835	205		1040	
Demolish and Install	Sq.	835	280.50		1115.50	
Reinstall	Sq.		164.25		164.25	
Minimum Charge	Job		188		188	
Accessories / Extras						
Add for Cap Furring Strips						Includes labor and material to install vertically placed wood furring strips under cap tiles.
Install	Sq.	98	235		333	
Add for Tile Adhesive						Includes material and labor for adhesive material placed between tiles.
Install	Sq.	23	13.75		36.75	
Add for Wire Attachment						Includes labor and material to install single wire anchors for attaching tile.
Install	Sq.	15.15	164		179.15	
Add for Braided Runners						Includes labor and material to install braided wire runners for secure attachment in high wind areas.
Install	Sq.	38	157		195	
Add for Stainless Steel Nails						Includes material only for stainless steel nails.
Install	Sq.	25.50			25.50	
Add for Brass Nails						Includes material only for brass nails.
Install	Sq.	44			44	
Add for Hurricane Clips						Includes material and labor for Hurricane or wind clips for high wind areas.
Install	Sq.	22.50	221		243.50	
Add for Copper Nails						Includes material only for copper nails.
Install	Sq.	44			44	
Add for Vertical Furring Strips						Includes labor and material to install vertically placed wood furring strips under tiles.
Install	Sq.	19.30	44		63.30	
Add for Horizontal Furring Strips						Includes labor and material to install horizontally placed wood furring strips under tiles.
Install	Sq.	12.45	19.60		32.05	

Spanish Tile Roofing

Spanish Tile Roofing	Unit	Material	Labor	Equip.	Total	Specification
Glazed Red						Includes material and labor to install tile roofing. Cost based on glazed red tile and includes birdstop, ridge and rake tiles.
Demolish	Sq.		75.50		75.50	
Install	Sq.	695	157		852	
Demolish and Install	Sq.	695	232.50		927.50	
Reinstall	Sq.		125.47		125.47	
Minimum Charge	Job		188		188	

Roofing

Spanish Tile Roofing		Unit	Material	Labor	Equip.	Total	Specification
Glazed White							
	Demolish	Sq.		75.50		75.50	Includes material and labor to install
	Install	Sq.	695	209		904	tile roofing. Cost based on glazed
	Demolish and Install	Sq.	695	284.50		979.50	white tile and includes birdstop, ridge
	Reinstall	Sq.		167.29		167.29	and rake tiles.
	Minimum Charge	Job		188		188	
Glazed Blue							
	Demolish	Sq.		75.50		75.50	Includes material and labor to install
	Install	Sq.	695	157		852	tile roofing. Cost based on glazed
	Demolish and Install	Sq.	695	232.50		927.50	blue tile and includes birdstop, ridge
	Reinstall	Sq.		125.47		125.47	and rake tiles.
	Minimum Charge	Job		188		188	
Unglazed Red							
	Demolish	Sq.		75.50		75.50	Includes material and labor to install
	Install	Sq.	540	157		697	tile roofing. Cost based on unglazed
	Demolish and Install	Sq.	540	232.50		772.50	red tile and includes birdstop, ridge
	Reinstall	Sq.		125.47		125.47	and rake tiles.
	Minimum Charge	Job		188		188	
Unglazed White							
	Demolish	Sq.		75.50		75.50	Includes material and labor to install
	Install	Sq.	605	157		762	tile roofing. Cost based on unglazed
	Demolish and Install	Sq.	605	232.50		837.50	white tile and includes birdstop, ridge
	Reinstall	Sq.		125.47		125.47	and rake tiles.
	Minimum Charge	Job		188		188	
Color Blend							
	Demolish	Sq.		75.50		75.50	Includes material and labor to install
	Install	Sq.	605	157		762	tile roofing. Cost based on color blend
	Demolish and Install	Sq.	605	232.50		837.50	tile and includes birdstop, ridge and
	Reinstall	Sq.		125.47		125.47	rake tiles.
	Minimum Charge	Job		188		188	
Accessories / Extras							
Add for Vertical Furring Strips							
	Install	Sq.	19.30	44		63.30	Includes labor and material to install vertically placed wood furring strips under tiles.
Add for Wire Attachment							
	Install	Sq.	7.75	125		132.75	Includes labor and material to install single wire ties.
Add for Braided Runners							
	Install	Sq.	29	108		137	Includes labor and material to install braided wire runners for secure attachment in high wind areas.
Add for Stainless Steel Nails							
	Install	Sq.	19			19	Includes material only for stainless steel nails.
Add for Copper Nails							
	Install	Sq.	33			33	Includes material only for copper nails.
Add for Brass Nails							
	Install	Sq.	32.50			32.50	Includes material only for brass nails.
Add for Hurricane Clips							
	Install	Sq.	11.60	130		141.60	Includes material and labor to install hurricane or wind clips for high wind areas.

Spanish Tile Roofing		Unit	Material	Labor	Equip.	Total	Specification
Add for Mortar Set Tiles							
	Install	Sq.	48	188		236	Includes material and labor to install setting tiles by using mortar material placed between tiles.
Add for Tile Adhesive							
	Install	Sq.	11.75	12.20		23.95	Includes material and labor for adhesive placed between tiles.
Add for Cap Furring Strips							
	Install	Sq.	98	235		333	Includes labor and material to install vertically placed wood furring strips under cap tiles.
Add for Horizontal Furring Strips							
	Install	Sq.	12.45	19.60		32.05	Includes labor and material to install horizontally placed wood furring strips under tiles.

Concrete Tile Roofing		Unit	Material	Labor	Equip.	Total	Specification
Corrugated Red / Brown							
	Demolish	Sq.		75.50		75.50	Includes material and labor to install tile roofing. Cost includes birdstop, booster, ridge and rake tiles.
	Install	Sq.	107	279		386	
	Demolish and Install	Sq.	107	354.50		461.50	
	Reinstall	Sq.		223.05		223.05	
	Minimum Charge	Job		188		188	
Corrugated Gray							
	Demolish	Sq.		75.50		75.50	Includes material and labor to install tile roofing. Cost includes birdstop, booster, ridge and rake tiles.
	Install	Sq.	107	279		386	
	Demolish and Install	Sq.	107	354.50		461.50	
	Reinstall	Sq.		223.05		223.05	
	Minimum Charge	Job		188		188	
Corrugated Bright Red							
	Demolish	Sq.		75.50		75.50	Includes material and labor to install tile roofing. Cost includes birdstop, booster, ridge and rake tiles.
	Install	Sq.	111	279		390	
	Demolish and Install	Sq.	111	354.50		465.50	
	Reinstall	Sq.		223.05		223.05	
	Minimum Charge	Job		188		188	
Corrugated Black							
	Demolish	Sq.		75.50		75.50	Includes material and labor to install tile roofing. Cost includes birdstop, booster, ridge and rake tiles.
	Install	Sq.	111	279		390	
	Demolish and Install	Sq.	111	354.50		465.50	
	Reinstall	Sq.		223.05		223.05	
	Minimum Charge	Job		188		188	
Corrugated Green							
	Demolish	Sq.		75.50		75.50	Includes material and labor to install tile roofing. Cost includes birdstop, booster, ridge and rake tiles.
	Install	Sq.	111	279		390	
	Demolish and Install	Sq.	111	354.50		465.50	
	Reinstall	Sq.		223.05		223.05	
	Minimum Charge	Job		188		188	
Corrugated Blue							
	Demolish	Sq.		75.50		75.50	Includes material and labor to install tile roofing. Cost includes birdstop, booster, ridge and rake tiles.
	Install	Sq.	111	279		390	
	Demolish and Install	Sq.	111	354.50		465.50	
	Reinstall	Sq.		223.05		223.05	
	Minimum Charge	Job		188		188	

Roofing

Concrete Tile Roofing

Concrete Tile Roofing	Unit	Material	Labor	Equip.	Total	Specification
Flat Natural Gray						
Demolish	Sq.		75.50		75.50	Includes material and labor to install
Install	Sq.	101	279		380	tile roofing. Cost includes birdstop,
Demolish and Install	Sq.	101	354.50		455.50	booster, ridge and rake tiles.
Reinstall	Sq.		223.05		223.05	
Minimum Charge	Job		188		188	
Flat Red / Brown						
Demolish	Sq.		75.50		75.50	Includes material and labor to install
Install	Sq.	101	279		380	tile roofing. Cost includes birdstop,
Demolish and Install	Sq.	101	354.50		455.50	booster, ridge and rake tiles.
Reinstall	Sq.		223.05		223.05	
Minimum Charge	Job		188		188	
Flat Bright Red						
Demolish	Sq.		75.50		75.50	Includes material and labor to install
Install	Sq.	101	279		380	tile roofing. Cost includes birdstop,
Demolish and Install	Sq.	101	354.50		455.50	booster, ridge and rake tiles.
Reinstall	Sq.		223.05		223.05	
Minimum Charge	Job		188		188	
Flat Green						
Demolish	Sq.		75.50		75.50	Includes material and labor to install
Install	Sq.	101	279		380	tile roofing. Cost includes birdstop,
Demolish and Install	Sq.	101	354.50		455.50	booster, ridge and rake tiles.
Minimum Charge	Job		188		188	
Flat Blue						
Demolish	Sq.		75.50		75.50	Includes material and labor to install
Install	Sq.	101	279		380	tile roofing. Cost includes birdstop,
Demolish and Install	Sq.	101	354.50		455.50	booster, ridge and rake tiles.
Reinstall	Sq.		223.05		223.05	
Minimum Charge	Job		188		188	
Flat Black						
Demolish	Sq.		75.50		75.50	Includes material and labor to install
Install	Sq.	101	279		380	tile roofing. Cost includes birdstop,
Demolish and Install	Sq.	101	354.50		455.50	booster, ridge and rake tiles.
Reinstall	Sq.		223.05		223.05	
Minimum Charge	Job		188		188	

Aluminum Sheet

Aluminum Sheet	Unit	Material	Labor	Equip.	Total	Specification
Corrugated						
.019" Thick Natural						
Demolish	S.F.		.81		.81	Includes material and labor to install
Install	S.F.	1.42	1.91		3.33	aluminum sheet metal roofing.
Demolish and Install	S.F.	1.42	2.72		4.14	
Reinstall	S.F.		1.53		1.53	
Minimum Charge	Job		460		460	
.016" Thick Natural						
Demolish	S.F.		.81		.81	Includes material and labor to install
Install	S.F.	1.08	1.91		2.99	aluminum sheet metal roofing.
Demolish and Install	S.F.	1.08	2.72		3.80	
Reinstall	S.F.		1.53		1.53	
Minimum Charge	Job		460		460	
.016" Colored Finish						
Demolish	S.F.		.81		.81	Includes material and labor to install
Install	S.F.	1.57	1.91		3.48	aluminum sheet metal roofing.
Demolish and Install	S.F.	1.57	2.72		4.29	
Reinstall	S.F.		1.53		1.53	
Minimum Charge	Job		460		460	

Aluminum Sheet		Unit	Material	Labor	Equip.	Total	Specification
.019" Colored Finish							
	Demolish	S.F.		.81		.81	Includes material and labor to install
	Install	S.F.	1.74	1.91		3.65	aluminum sheet metal roofing.
	Demolish and Install	S.F.	1.74	2.72		4.46	
	Reinstall	S.F.		1.53		1.53	
	Minimum Charge	Job		460		460	
Ribbed							
.019" Thick Natural							
	Demolish	S.F.		.81		.81	Includes material and labor to install
	Install	S.F.	1.42	1.91		3.33	aluminum sheet metal roofing.
	Demolish and Install	S.F.	1.42	2.72		4.14	
	Reinstall	S.F.		1.53		1.53	
	Minimum Charge	Job		460		460	
.016" Thick Natural							
	Demolish	S.F.		.81		.81	Includes material and labor to install
	Install	S.F.	1.08	1.91		2.99	aluminum sheet metal roofing.
	Demolish and Install	S.F.	1.08	2.72		3.80	
	Reinstall	S.F.		1.53		1.53	
	Minimum Charge	Job		460		460	
.050" Colored Finish							
	Demolish	S.F.		.81		.81	Includes material and labor to install
	Install	S.F.	4.85	1.91		6.76	aluminum sheet metal roofing.
	Demolish and Install	S.F.	4.85	2.72		7.57	
	Reinstall	S.F.		1.53		1.53	
	Minimum Charge	Job		460		460	
.032" Thick Natural							
	Demolish	S.F.		.81		.81	Includes material and labor to install
	Install	S.F.	2.75	1.91		4.66	aluminum sheet metal roofing.
	Demolish and Install	S.F.	2.75	2.72		5.47	
	Reinstall	S.F.		1.53		1.53	
	Minimum Charge	Job		460		460	
.040" Thick Natural							
	Demolish	S.F.		.81		.81	Includes material and labor to install
	Install	S.F.	3.34	1.91		5.25	aluminum sheet metal roofing.
	Demolish and Install	S.F.	3.34	2.72		6.06	
	Reinstall	S.F.		1.53		1.53	
	Minimum Charge	Job		460		460	
.050" Thick Natural							
	Demolish	S.F.		.81		.81	Includes material and labor to install
	Install	S.F.	4.02	1.91		5.93	aluminum sheet metal roofing.
	Demolish and Install	S.F.	4.02	2.72		6.74	
	Reinstall	S.F.		1.53		1.53	
	Minimum Charge	Job		460		460	
.016" Colored Finish							
	Demolish	S.F.		.81		.81	Includes material and labor to install
	Install	S.F.	1.57	1.91		3.48	aluminum sheet metal roofing.
	Demolish and Install	S.F.	1.57	2.72		4.29	
	Reinstall	S.F.		1.53		1.53	
	Minimum Charge	Job		460		460	
.019" Colored Finish							
	Demolish	S.F.		.81		.81	Includes material and labor to install
	Install	S.F.	1.74	1.91		3.65	aluminum sheet metal roofing.
	Demolish and Install	S.F.	1.74	2.72		4.46	
	Reinstall	S.F.		1.53		1.53	
	Minimum Charge	Job		460		460	

Roofing

Aluminum Sheet

Aluminum Sheet	Unit	Material	Labor	Equip.	Total	Specification
.032" Colored Finish						
Demolish	S.F.		.81		.81	Includes material and labor to install
Install	S.F.	3.38	1.91		5.29	aluminum sheet metal roofing.
Demolish and Install	S.F.	3.38	2.72		6.10	
Reinstall	S.F.		1.53		1.53	
Minimum Charge	Job		460		460	
.040" Colored Finish						
Demolish	S.F.		.81		.81	Includes material and labor to install
Install	S.F.	4.03	1.91		5.94	aluminum sheet metal roofing.
Demolish and Install	S.F.	4.03	2.72		6.75	
Reinstall	S.F.		1.53		1.53	
Minimum Charge	Job		460		460	

Fiberglass Sheet

Fiberglass Sheet	Unit	Material	Labor	Equip.	Total	Specification
12 Ounce Corrugated						
Demolish	S.F.		1.44		1.44	Cost includes material and labor to
Install	S.F.	3.78	1.53		5.31	install 12 ounce corrugated fiberglass
Demolish and Install	S.F.	3.78	2.97		6.75	sheet roofing.
Reinstall	S.F.		1.22		1.22	
Minimum Charge	Job		188		188	
8 Ounce Corrugated						
Demolish	S.F.		1.44		1.44	Cost includes material and labor to
Install	S.F.	2.09	1.53		3.62	install 8 ounce corrugated fiberglass
Demolish and Install	S.F.	2.09	2.97		5.06	roofing.
Reinstall	S.F.		1.22		1.22	
Minimum Charge	Job		188		188	

Galvanized Steel

Galvanized Steel	Unit	Material	Labor	Equip.	Total	Specification
Corrugated						
24 Gauge						
Demolish	S.F.		.81		.81	Includes material and labor to install
Install	S.F.	3.33	1.61		4.94	galvanized steel sheet metal roofing.
Demolish and Install	S.F.	3.33	2.42		5.75	Cost based on 24 gauge corrugated
Reinstall	S.F.		1.29		1.29	or ribbed steel roofing.
Minimum Charge	Job		188		188	
26 Gauge						
Demolish	S.F.		.81		.81	Includes material and labor to install
Install	S.F.	2.11	1.53		3.64	galvanized steel sheet metal roofing.
Demolish and Install	S.F.	2.11	2.34		4.45	Cost based on 26 gauge corrugated
Reinstall	S.F.		1.22		1.22	or ribbed steel roofing.
Minimum Charge	Job		188		188	
28 Gauge						
Demolish	S.F.		.81		.81	Includes material and labor to install
Install	S.F.	2.05	1.46		3.51	galvanized steel sheet metal roofing.
Demolish and Install	S.F.	2.05	2.27		4.32	Cost based on 28 gauge corrugated
Reinstall	S.F.		1.16		1.16	or ribbed steel roofing.
Minimum Charge	Job		188		188	
30 Gauge						
Demolish	S.F.		.81		.81	Includes material and labor to install
Install	S.F.	1.93	1.39		3.32	galvanized steel sheet metal roofing.
Demolish and Install	S.F.	1.93	2.20		4.13	Cost based on 30 gauge corrugated
Reinstall	S.F.		1.11		1.11	or ribbed steel roofing.
Minimum Charge	Job		188		188	

Roofing

Galvanized Steel		Unit	Material	Labor	Equip.	Total	Specification
Ribbed							
24 Gauge							
	Demolish	S.F.		.81		.81	Includes material and labor to install
	Install	S.F.	3.33	1.61		4.94	galvanized steel sheet metal roofing.
	Demolish and Install	S.F.	3.33	2.42		5.75	Cost based on 24 gauge corrugated
	Reinstall	S.F.		1.29		1.29	or ribbed steel roofing.
	Minimum Charge	Job		188		188	
26 Gauge							
	Demolish	S.F.		.81		.81	Includes material and labor to install
	Install	S.F.	2.11	1.53		3.64	galvanized steel sheet metal roofing.
	Demolish and Install	S.F.	2.11	2.34		4.45	Cost based on 26 gauge corrugated
	Reinstall	S.F.		1.22		1.22	or ribbed steel roofing.
	Minimum Charge	Job		188		188	
28 Gauge							
	Demolish	S.F.		.81		.81	Includes material and labor to install
	Install	S.F.	2.05	1.46		3.51	galvanized steel sheet metal roofing.
	Demolish and Install	S.F.	2.05	2.27		4.32	Cost based on 28 gauge corrugated
	Reinstall	S.F.		1.16		1.16	or ribbed steel roofing.
	Minimum Charge	Job		188		188	
30 Gauge							
	Demolish	S.F.		.81		.81	Includes material and labor to install
	Install	S.F.	1.93	1.39		3.32	galvanized steel sheet metal roofing.
	Demolish and Install	S.F.	1.93	2.20		4.13	Cost based on 30 gauge corrugated
	Reinstall	S.F.		1.11		1.11	or ribbed steel roofing.
	Minimum Charge	Job		188		188	

Standing Seam		Unit	Material	Labor	Equip.	Total	Specification
Copper							
16 Ounce							
	Demolish	Sq.		80.50		80.50	Includes material and labor to install
	Install	Sq.	1075	350		1425	copper standing seam metal roofing.
	Demolish and Install	Sq.	1075	430.50		1505.50	Cost based on 16 ounce copper
	Reinstall	Sq.		281.85		281.85	roofing.
	Minimum Charge	Job		229		229	
18 Ounce							
	Demolish	Sq.		80.50		80.50	Includes material and labor to install
	Install	Sq.	1200	380		1580	copper standing seam metal roofing.
	Demolish and Install	Sq.	1200	460.50		1660.50	Cost based on 18 ounce copper
	Reinstall	Sq.		305.33		305.33	roofing.
	Minimum Charge	Job		229		229	
20 Ounce							
	Demolish	Sq.		80.50		80.50	Includes material and labor to install
	Install	Sq.	1350	415		1765	copper standing seam metal roofing.
	Demolish and Install	Sq.	1350	495.50		1845.50	Cost based on 20 ounce copper
	Reinstall	Sq.		333.09		333.09	roofing.
Stainless Steel							
26 Gauge							
	Demolish	Sq.		80.50		80.50	Cost includes material and labor to
	Install	Sq.	695	400		1095	install 26 gauge stainless steel
	Demolish and Install	Sq.	695	480.50		1175.50	standing seam metal roofing.
	Reinstall	Sq.		318.61		318.61	
	Minimum Charge	Job		229		229	

Roofing

Standing Seam	Unit	Material	Labor	Equip.	Total	Specification
28 Gauge						
Demolish	Sq.		80.50		80.50	Includes material and labor to install
Install	Sq.	690	380		1070	standing seam metal roofing. Cost
Demolish and Install	Sq.	690	460.50		1150.50	based on 28 gauge stainless steel
Reinstall	Sq.		305.33		305.33	roofing.
Minimum Charge	Job		229		229	

Elastomeric Roofing	Unit	Material	Labor	Equip.	Total	Specification
Neoprene						
1/16″						
Demolish	Sq.		28		28	Includes material and labor to install
Install	Sq.	259	179	36	474	neoprene membrane, fully adhered,
Demolish and Install	Sq.	259	207	36	502	1/16″ thick.
Minimum Charge	Job		855	98.50	953.50	
GRM Membrane						
Demolish	Sq.		28		28	Includes material and labor to install
Install	Sq.	279	285	33	597	coal tar based elastomeric roofing
Demolish and Install	Sq.	279	313	33	625	membrane, polyester fiber reinforced.
Minimum Charge	Job		855	98.50	953.50	
Cant Strips						
3″						
Demolish	L.F.		.87		.87	Includes material and labor to install
Install	L.F.	1.11	1.15		2.26	cants 3″ x 3″, treated timber, cut
Demolish and Install	L.F.	1.11	2.02		3.13	diagonally.
Minimum Charge	Job		94		94	
4″						
Demolish	L.F.		.87		.87	Includes material and labor to install
Install	L.F.	2.22	1.15		3.37	cants 4″ x 4″, treated timber, cut
Demolish and Install	L.F.	2.22	2.02		4.24	diagonally.
Minimum Charge	Job		94		94	
Polyvinyl Chloride (PVC)						
45 mil (loose laid)						
Demolish	Sq.		28		28	Cost includes material and labor to
Install	Sq.	94.50	33.50	3.87	131.87	install 45 mil PVC elastomeric roofing,
Demolish and Install	Sq.	94.50	61.50	3.87	159.87	loose-laid with stone.
Minimum Charge	Job		855	98.50	953.50	
48 mil (loose laid)						
Demolish	Sq.		28		28	Cost includes material and labor to
Install	Sq.	110	33.50	3.87	147.37	install 48 mil PVC elastomeric roofing,
Demolish and Install	Sq.	110	61.50	3.87	175.37	loose-laid with stone.
Minimum Charge	Job		855	98.50	953.50	
60 mil (loose laid)						
Demolish	Sq.		28		28	Cost includes material and labor to
Install	Sq.	112	33.50	3.87	149.37	install 60 mil PVC elastomeric roofing,
Demolish and Install	Sq.	112	61.50	3.87	177.37	loose-laid with stone.
Minimum Charge	Job		855	98.50	953.50	
45 mil (attached)						
Demolish	Sq.		44.50		44.50	Cost includes material and labor to
Install	Sq.	85.50	66	7.60	159.10	install 45 mil PVC elastomeric roofing
Demolish and Install	Sq.	85.50	110.50	7.60	203.60	fully attached to roof deck.
Minimum Charge	Job		855	98.50	953.50	

Elastomeric Roofing		Unit	Material	Labor	Equip.	Total	Specification
48 mil (attached)							Cost includes material and labor to
	Demolish	Sq.		44.50		44.50	install 48 mil PVC elastomeric roofing
	Install	Sq.	138	66	7.60	211.60	fully attached to roof deck.
	Demolish and Install	Sq.	138	110.50	7.60	256.10	
	Minimum Charge	Job		855	98.50	953.50	
60 mil (attached)							Cost includes material and labor to
	Demolish	Sq.		44.50		44.50	install 60 mil PVC elastomeric roofing
	Install	Sq.	140	66	7.60	213.60	fully attached to roof deck.
	Demolish and Install	Sq.	140	110.50	7.60	258.10	
	Minimum Charge	Job		855	98.50	953.50	
CSPE Type							
45 mil (loose laid w / stone)							Cost includes material and labor to
	Demolish	Sq.		28		28	install 45 mil CSPE (chlorosulfonated
	Install	Sq.	217	33.50	3.87	254.37	polyethylene-hypalon) roofing material
	Demolish and Install	Sq.	217	61.50	3.87	282.37	loose laid on deck and ballasted with
	Minimum Charge	Job		855	98.50	953.50	stone.
45 mil (attached at seams)							Cost includes material and labor to
	Demolish	Sq.		33.50		33.50	install 45 mil CSPE (chlorosulfonated
	Install	Sq.	209	49	5.65	263.65	polyethylene-hypalon) roofing material
	Demolish and Install	Sq.	209	82.50	5.65	297.15	attached to deck at seams with batten
	Minimum Charge	Job		855	98.50	953.50	strips.
45 mil (fully attached)							Cost includes material and labor to
	Demolish	Sq.		44.50		44.50	install 45 mil CSPE (chlorosulfonated
	Install	Sq.	208	66	7.60	281.60	polyethylene-hypalon) roofing material
	Demolish and Install	Sq.	208	110.50	7.60	326.10	fully attached to deck.
	Minimum Charge	Job		855	98.50	953.50	
EPDM Type							
45 mil (attached at seams)							Cost includes material and labor to
	Demolish	Sq.		33.50		33.50	install 45 mil EPDM (ethylene
	Install	Sq.	70	49	5.65	124.65	propylene diene monomer) roofing
	Demolish and Install	Sq.	70	82.50	5.65	158.15	material attached to deck at seams.
	Minimum Charge	Job		855	98.50	953.50	
45 mil (fully attached)							Cost includes material and labor to
	Demolish	Sq.		44.50		44.50	install 45 mil EPDM (ethylene
	Install	Sq.	109	66	7.60	182.60	propylene diene monomer) roofing
	Demolish and Install	Sq.	109	110.50	7.60	227.10	material fully attached to deck.
	Minimum Charge	Job		855	98.50	953.50	
45 mil (loose laid w / stone)							Cost includes material and labor to
	Demolish	Sq.		28		28	install 45 mil EPDM (ethylene
	Install	Sq.	74.50	33.50	3.87	111.87	propylene diene monomer) roofing
	Demolish and Install	Sq.	74.50	61.50	3.87	139.87	material loose laid on deck and
	Minimum Charge	Job		855	98.50	953.50	ballasted with stones (approx. 1/2 ton
							of stone per square).
60 mil (attached at seams)							Cost includes material and labor to
	Demolish	Sq.		33.50		33.50	install 60 mil EPDM (ethylene
	Install	Sq.	80.50	49	5.65	135.15	propylene diene monomer) roofing
	Demolish and Install	Sq.	80.50	82.50	5.65	168.65	material attached to deck at seams.
	Minimum Charge	Job		855	98.50	953.50	
60 mil (fully attached)							Cost includes material and labor to
	Demolish	Sq.		44.50		44.50	install 60 mil EPDM (ethylene
	Install	Sq.	120	66	7.60	193.60	propylene diene monomer) roofing
	Demolish and Install	Sq.	120	110.50	7.60	238.10	material fully attached to deck.
	Minimum Charge	Job		855	98.50	953.50	

Roofing

Elastomeric Roofing

Elastomeric Roofing	Unit	Material	Labor	Equip.	Total	Specification
60 mil (loose laid w / stone)						Cost includes material and labor to
Demolish	Sq.		28		28	install 60 mil EPDM (ethylene
Install	Sq.	86	33.50	3.87	123.37	propylene diene monomer) roofing
Demolish and Install	Sq.	86	61.50	3.87	151.37	material loose laid on deck and
Minimum Charge	Job		855	98.50	953.50	ballasted with stones (approx. 1/2 ton of stone per square).

Modified Bitumen Roofing

Modified Bitumen Roofing	Unit	Material	Labor	Equip.	Total	Specification
Fully Attached						
120 mil						
Demolish	Sq.		66.50		66.50	Cost includes material and labor to
Install	Sq.	92	8.35	1.69	102.04	install 120 mil modified bitumen
Demolish and Install	Sq.	92	74.85	1.69	168.54	roofing, fully attached to deck by
Minimum Charge	Job		94		94	torch.
150 mil						
Demolish	Sq.		66.50		66.50	Cost includes material and labor to
Install	Sq.	132	20.50	4.15	156.65	install 150 mil modified bitumen
Demolish and Install	Sq.	132	87	4.15	223.15	roofing, fully attached to deck by
Minimum Charge	Job		94		94	torch.
160 mil						
Demolish	Sq.		66.50		66.50	Cost includes material and labor to
Install	Sq.	106	21.50	4.33	131.83	install 160 mil modified bitumen
Demolish and Install	Sq.	106	88	4.33	198.33	roofing, fully attached to deck by
Minimum Charge	Job		94		94	torch.

Built-up Roofing

Built-up Roofing	Unit	Material	Labor	Equip.	Total	Specification
Emergency Repairs						
Install	Ea.	242	1750	355	2347	Minimum charge for work requiring
Minimum Charge	Job		1225	249	1474	hot asphalt.
Asphalt						
3-ply Asphalt						
Demolish	Sq.		69.50		69.50	Cost includes material and labor to
Install	Sq.	72.50	103	20.50	196	install 3-ply asphalt built-up roof
Demolish and Install	Sq.	72.50	172.50	20.50	265.50	including one 30 lb and two 15 lb
Minimum Charge	Job		1225	249	1474	layers of felt.
4-ply Asphalt						
Demolish	Sq.		82.50		82.50	Cost includes material and labor to
Install	Sq.	97	112	22.50	231.50	install 4-ply asphalt built-up roof
Demolish and Install	Sq.	97	194.50	22.50	314	including one 30 lb and three 15 lb
Minimum Charge	Job		1225	249	1474	layers of felt.
5-ply Asphalt						
Demolish	Sq.		108		108	Cost includes material and labor to
Install	Sq.	134	123	25	282	install 5-ply asphalt built-up roof
Demolish and Install	Sq.	134	231	25	390	including one 30 lb and four 15 lb
Minimum Charge	Job		1225	249	1474	layers of felt.

Roofing

Built-up Roofing		Unit	Material	Labor	Equip.	Total	Specification
Components / Accessories							
Flood Coat							
	Install	Sq.	26	57.50		83.50	Includes labor and material to install flood coat.
R / R Gravel and Flood Coat							
	Install	Sq.	31	188		219	Includes labor and material to install flood coat and gravel.
Aluminum UV Coat							
	Install	Sq.	28.50	214	24.50	267	Includes labor and material to install aluminum-based UV coating.
Gravel Coat							
	Demolish	Sq.		34.50		34.50	Includes labor and material to install gravel coat.
	Install	Sq.	4.93	31.50		36.43	
	Demolish and Install	Sq.	4.93	66		70.93	
Mineral Surface Cap Sheet							
	Install	Sq.	49.50	6.45		55.95	Cost includes labor and material to install 50 # mineral surfaced cap sheet.
Fibrated Aluminum UV Coating							
	Install	Sq.	35	57.50		92.50	Includes labor and material to install fibered aluminum-based UV coating.
Impregnated Walk							
1″							
	Install	S.F.	3.09	2		5.09	Cost includes labor and material to install 1″ layer of asphalt coating.
1/2″							
	Install	S.F.	2.21	1.58		3.79	Cost includes labor and material to install 1/2″ layer of asphalt coating.
3/4″							
	Install	S.F.	2.76	1.67		4.43	Cost includes labor and material to install 3/4″ layer of asphalt coating.

| Doors | Roof Window | Double Hung Window |

Exterior Type Door		Unit	Material	Labor	Equip.	Total	Specification
Entry							
Flush (1-3/4")							
	Demolish	Ea.		38.50		38.50	Cost includes material and labor to
	Install	Ea.	229	26		255	install 3' x 6' 8" pre-hung 1-3/4"
	Demolish and Install	Ea.	229	64.50		293.50	door, including casing and stop,
	Reinstall	Ea.		25.90		25.90	hinges, jamb, aluminum sill,
	Clean	Ea.	4.77	12.75		17.52	weatherstripped.
	Paint	Ea.	9.20	50.50		59.70	
	Minimum Charge	Job		207		207	
Raised Panel							
	Demolish	Ea.		38.50		38.50	Cost includes material and labor to
	Install	Ea.	480	23		503	install 3' x 6' 8" pre-hung 1-3/4"
	Demolish and Install	Ea.	480	61.50		541.50	door, jamb, including casing and
	Reinstall	Ea.		23.02		23.02	stop, hinges, aluminum sill,
	Clean	Ea.	4.77	12.75		17.52	weatherstripping.
	Paint	Ea.	9.20	50.50		59.70	
	Minimum Charge	Job		207		207	
Entry w / Lights							
Good Quality							
	Demolish	Ea.		38.50		38.50	Cost includes material and labor to
	Install	Ea.	350	52		402	install 3' x 6' 8" pre-hung 1-3/4"
	Demolish and Install	Ea.	350	90.50		440.50	door, solid wood lower panel, with up
	Reinstall	Ea.		51.80		51.80	to 9-light glass panels, casing, sill,
	Clean	Ea.	4.77	12.75		17.52	weatherstripped.
	Paint	Ea.	6.60	23.50		30.10	
	Minimum Charge	Job		207		207	
Better Quality							
	Demolish	Ea.		38.50		38.50	Cost includes material and labor to
	Install	Ea.	360	52		412	install 3' x 6' 8" pre-hung 1-3/4" Ash
	Demolish and Install	Ea.	360	90.50		450.50	door, solid wood, raised panel door
	Reinstall	Ea.		51.80		51.80	without glass panels.
	Clean	Ea.	4.77	12.75		17.52	
	Paint	Ea.	9.20	50.50		59.70	
	Minimum Charge	Job		207		207	
Premium Quality							
	Demolish	Ea.		38.50		38.50	Cost includes material and labor to
	Install	Ea.	965	24.50		989.50	install 3' x 6' 8" pre-hung 1-3/4" Oak
	Demolish and Install	Ea.	965	63		1028	door, solid wood, raised panel door
	Reinstall	Ea.		24.38		24.38	without glass panels.
	Clean	Ea.	4.77	12.75		17.52	
	Paint	Ea.	9.20	50.50		59.70	
	Minimum Charge	Job		207		207	

Exterior Type Door		Unit	Material	Labor	Equip.	Total	Specification
Custom Quality							
	Demolish	Ea.		38.50		38.50	Cost includes material and labor to
	Install	Ea.	365	55.50		420.50	install 3' x 6' 8" pre-hung 1-3/4"
	Demolish and Install	Ea.	365	94		459	hand-made, solid wood, raised panel
	Reinstall	Ea.		55.25		55.25	door with custom stained glass.
	Clean	Ea.	.33	12.75		13.08	
	Paint	Ea.	2.34	118		120.34	
	Minimum Charge	Job		207		207	
Miami Style							
	Demolish	Ea.		38.50		38.50	Cost includes material and labor to
	Install	Ea.	216	24.50		240.50	install 3' x 6' 8" pre-hung 1-3/4"
	Demolish and Install	Ea.	216	63		279	lauan door of solid wood.
	Reinstall	Ea.		24.38		24.38	
	Clean	Ea.	.33	12.75		13.08	
	Paint	Ea.	9.20	50.50		59.70	
	Minimum Charge	Job		207		207	
French Style							
1-Light							
	Demolish	Ea.		38.50		38.50	Cost includes material and labor to
	Install	Ea.	660	69		729	install 3' x 6' 8" pre-hung 1-3/4"
	Demolish and Install	Ea.		107.50		767.50	French style door with 1 light.
	Reinstall	Ea.		69.07		69.07	
	Clean	Ea.	2.99	19.15		22.14	
	Paint	Ea.	10.30	89		99.30	
	Minimum Charge	Job		207		207	
9-Light							
	Demolish	Ea.		38.50		38.50	Cost includes material and labor to
	Install	Ea.	725	29.50		754.50	install 3' x 6' 8" pre-hung 1-3/4"
	Demolish and Install	Ea.	725	68		793	French style door with 9 lights.
	Reinstall	Ea.		29.60		29.60	
	Clean	Ea.	.66	25.50		26.16	
	Paint	Ea.	10.30	89		99.30	
	Minimum Charge	Job		207		207	
15-Light							
	Demolish	Ea.		42.50		42.50	Cost includes material and labor to
	Install	Ea.	700	59		759	install 3' x 6' 8" pre-hung 1-3/4"
	Demolish and Install	Ea.	700	101.50		801.50	French style door with 15 lights.
	Reinstall	Ea.		59.20		59.20	
	Clean	Ea.	.66	25.50		26.16	
	Paint	Ea.	10.30	89		99.30	
	Minimum Charge	Job		207		207	
Jamb							
Wood							
	Demolish	Ea.		23		23	Includes material and labor to install
	Install	Ea.	100	11.20		111.20	flat pine jamb with square cut heads
	Demolish and Install	Ea.	100	34.20		134.20	and rabbeted sides for 6' 8" high and
	Clean	Ea.	.15	7.65		7.80	3-9/16" door including trim sets for
	Paint	Ea.	6.60	23.50		30.10	both sides.
	Minimum Charge	Job		207		207	
Metal 6' 8" High							
	Demolish	Ea.		23		23	Cost includes material and labor to
	Install	Ea.	167	26		193	install 18 gauge hollow metal door
	Demolish and Install	Ea.	167	49		216	frame to fit a 4-1/2" jamb 6' 8" high
	Reinstall	Ea.		25.90		25.90	and up to 3' 6" opening.
	Clean	Ea.	1	6.40		7.40	
	Paint	Ea.	1.79	7.10		8.89	
	Minimum Charge	Job		207		207	

Exterior Doors and Windows

Exterior Type Door		Unit	Material	Labor	Equip.	Total	Specification
Metal 7' High							
	Demolish	Ea.		23		23	Cost includes material and labor to
	Install	Ea.	173	27.50		200.50	install 18 gauge hollow metal door
	Demolish and Install	Ea.	173	50.50		223.50	frame to fit a 4-1/2" jamb 7' high and
	Reinstall	Ea.		27.63		27.63	up to 3' 6" opening.
	Clean	Ea.	1	6.40		7.40	
	Paint	Ea.	1.79	7.10		8.89	
	Minimum Charge	Job		207		207	
Metal 8' High							
	Demolish	Ea.		23		23	Cost includes material and labor to
	Install	Ea.	212	34.50		246.50	install 18 gauge hollow metal door
	Demolish and Install	Ea.	212	57.50		269.50	frame to fit a 4-1/2" jamb 8' high and
	Reinstall	Ea.		34.53		34.53	up to 3' 6" opening.
	Clean	Ea.	1.41	7.65		9.06	
	Paint	Ea.	2	7.90		9.90	
	Minimum Charge	Job		207		207	
Metal 9' High							
	Demolish	Ea.		23		23	Cost includes material and labor to
	Install	Ea.	277	41.50		318.50	install 18 gauge hollow metal door
	Demolish and Install	Ea.	277	64.50		341.50	frame to fit a 4-1/2" jamb 9' high and
	Reinstall	Ea.		41.44		41.44	up to 3' 6" opening.
	Clean	Ea.	1.41	7.65		9.06	
	Paint	Ea.	2	7.90		9.90	
	Minimum Charge	Job		207		207	
Casing Trim							
Single Width							
	Demolish	Ea.		7.30		7.30	Cost includes material and labor to
	Install	Opng.	25	34.50		59.50	install 11/16" x 2-1/2" pine ranch
	Demolish and Install	Opng.	25	41.80		66.80	style casing for one side of a standard
	Reinstall	Opng.		27.63		27.63	door opening.
	Clean	Opng.	.68	3.06		3.74	
	Paint	Ea.	5.25	7.10		12.35	
	Minimum Charge	Job		207		207	
Double Width							
	Demolish	Ea.		8.70		8.70	Cost includes material and labor to
	Install	Opng.	28.50	41.50		70	install 11/16" x 2-1/2" pine ranch
	Demolish and Install	Opng.	28.50	50.20		78.70	style door casing for one side of a
	Reinstall	Opng.		33.15		33.15	double door opening.
	Clean	Opng.	.79	6.15		6.94	
	Paint	Ea.	5.25	8.05		13.30	
	Minimum Charge	Job		207		207	

Residential Metal Door		Unit	Material	Labor	Equip.	Total	Specification
Pre-hung, Steel-clad							
2' 8" x 6' 8"							
	Demolish	Ea.		38.50		38.50	Cost includes material and labor to
	Install	Ea.	330	49		379	install 2' x 6'8" pre-hung 1-3/4" 24
	Demolish and Install	Ea.	330	87.50		417.50	gauge steel clad door with 4-1/2"
	Reinstall	Ea.		48.75		48.75	wood frame, trims, hinges, aluminum
	Clean	Ea.	4.77	12.75		17.52	sill, weatherstripped.
	Paint	Ea.	10.30	50.50		60.80	
	Minimum Charge	Job		207		207	

Exterior Doors and Windows

Residential Metal Door

3' x 6' 8"	Unit	Material	Labor	Equip.	Total	Specification
Demolish	Ea.		38.50		38.50	Cost includes material and labor to
Install	Ea.	273	55.50		328.50	install 3' x 6' 8" pre-hung 1-3/4" 24
Demolish and Install	Ea.	273	94		367	gauge steel clad door with 4-1/2"
Reinstall	Ea.		55.25		55.25	wood frame, trims, hinges, aluminum
Clean	Ea.	4.77	12.75		17.52	sill, weatherstripped.
Paint	Ea.	10.30	50.50		60.80	
Minimum Charge	Job		207		207	

Metal Door

2' 8" x 6' 8", 18 Gauge	Unit	Material	Labor	Equip.	Total	Specification
Demolish	Ea.		8.20		8.20	Cost includes material and labor to
Install	Ea.	545	26		571	install 18 gauge 2' 8" x 6' 8" steel
Demolish and Install	Ea.	545	34.20		579.20	door only, 1-3/4" thick, hinges.
Reinstall	Ea.		25.90		25.90	
Clean	Ea.	1.99	9.60		11.59	
Paint	Ea.	6.50	29.50		36	
Minimum Charge	Job		207		207	
3' x 6' 8", 18 Gauge						
Demolish	Ea.		8.20		8.20	Cost includes material and labor to
Install	Ea.	535	27.50		562.50	install 18 gauge 3' x 6' 8" steel door
Demolish and Install	Ea.	535	35.70		570.70	only, 1-3/4" thick, hinges.
Reinstall	Ea.		27.63		27.63	
Clean	Ea.	1.99	9.60		11.59	
Paint	Ea.	6.50	29.50		36	
Minimum Charge	Job		207		207	
2' 8" x 7', 18 Gauge						
Demolish	Ea.		8.20		8.20	Cost includes material and labor to
Install	Ea.	560	27.50		587.50	install 18 gauge 2' 8" x 7' steel door
Demolish and Install	Ea.	560	35.70		595.70	only, 1-3/4" thick, hinges.
Reinstall	Ea.		27.63		27.63	
Clean	Ea.	1.99	9.60		11.59	
Paint	Ea.	6.50	29.50		36	
Minimum Charge	Job		207		207	
3' x 7', 18 Gauge						
Demolish	Ea.		8.20		8.20	Cost includes material and labor to
Install	Ea.	660	29.50		689.50	install 18 gauge 3' x 7' steel door
Demolish and Install	Ea.	660	37.70		697.70	only, 1-3/4" thick, hinges.
Reinstall	Ea.		29.60		29.60	
Clean	Ea.	1.99	9.60		11.59	
Paint	Ea.	6.50	29.50		36	
Minimum Charge	Job		207		207	
3' 6" x 7', 18 Gauge						
Demolish	Ea.		8.20		8.20	Cost includes material and labor to
Install	Ea.	640	32		672	install 18 gauge 3' 6" x 7' steel door
Demolish and Install	Ea.	640	40.20		680.20	only, 1-3/4" thick, hinges.
Reinstall	Ea.		31.88		31.88	
Clean	Ea.	1.99	9.60		11.59	
Paint	Ea.	6.50	29.50		36	
Minimum Charge	Job		207		207	

Exterior Doors and Windows

Metal Door

	Unit	Material	Labor	Equip.	Total	Specification
Casing Trim						
Single Width						
Demolish	Ea.		7.30		7.30	Cost includes material and labor to
Install	Opng.	25	34.50		59.50	install 11/16" x 2-1/2" pine ranch
Demolish and Install	Opng.	25	41.80		66.80	style casing for one side of a standard
Reinstall	Opng.		27.63		27.63	door opening.
Clean	Opng.	.68	3.06		3.74	
Paint	Ea.	5.25	7.10		12.35	
Minimum Charge	Job		207		207	
Double Width						
Demolish	Ea.		8.70		8.70	Cost includes material and labor to
Install	Opng.	28.50	41.50		70	install 11/16" x 2-1/2" pine ranch
Demolish and Install	Opng.	28.50	50.20		78.70	style door casing for one side of a
Reinstall	Opng.		33.15		33.15	double door opening.
Clean	Opng.	.79	6.15		6.94	
Paint	Ea.	5.25	8.05		13.30	
Minimum Charge	Job		207		207	

Solid Core Door

	Unit	Material	Labor	Equip.	Total	Specification
Exterior Type						
Flush (1-3/4")						
Demolish	Ea.		38.50		38.50	Cost includes material and labor to
Install	Ea.	365	52		417	install 3' x 6' 8" pre-hung 1-3/4"
Demolish and Install	Ea.	365	90.50		455.50	door, including casing and stop,
Reinstall	Ea.		51.80		51.80	hinges, jamb, aluminum sill,
Clean	Ea.	4.77	12.75		17.52	weatherstripped.
Paint	Ea.	10.30	50.50		60.80	
Minimum Charge	Job		207		207	
Raised Panel						
Demolish	Ea.		38.50		38.50	Cost includes material and labor to
Install	Ea.	480	23		503	install 3' x 6' 8" pre-hung 1-3/4"
Demolish and Install	Ea.	480	61.50		541.50	door, jamb, including casing and
Reinstall	Ea.		23.02		23.02	stop, hinges, aluminum sill,
Clean	Ea.	4.77	12.75		17.52	weatherstripping.
Paint	Ea.	10.30	118		128.30	
Minimum Charge	Job		207		207	
Entry w / Lights						
Demolish	Ea.		38.50		38.50	Cost includes material and labor to
Install	Ea.	350	52		402	install 3' x 6' 8" pre-hung 1-3/4"
Demolish and Install	Ea.	350	90.50		440.50	door, solid wood lower panel, with up
Reinstall	Ea.		51.80		51.80	to 9-light glass panels, casing, sill,
Clean	Ea.	4.77	12.75		17.52	weatherstripped.
Paint	Ea.	2.34	118		120.34	
Minimum Charge	Job		207		207	
Custom Entry						
Demolish	Ea.		38.50		38.50	Cost includes material and labor to
Install	Ea.	1925	83		2008	install prehung, fir, single glazed with
Demolish and Install	Ea.	1925	121.50		2046.50	lead caming, 1-3/4" x 6' 8" x 3'
Reinstall	Ea.		82.88		82.88	
Clean	Ea.	4.77	12.75		17.52	
Paint	Ea.	6.50	29.50		36	
Minimum Charge	Job		207		207	

Exterior Doors and Windows

Solid Core Door

	Unit	Material	Labor	Equip.	Total	Specification
Dutch Style						
Demolish	Ea.		38.50		38.50	Includes material and labor to install
Install	Ea.	785	69		854	dutch door, pine, 1-3/4" x 6' 8" x 2'
Demolish and Install	Ea.	785	107.50		892.50	8" wide.
Reinstall	Ea.		69.07		69.07	
Clean	Ea.	4.77	12.75		17.52	
Paint	Ea.	2.34	118		120.34	
Minimum Charge	Job		207		207	
Miami Style						
Demolish	Ea.		38.50		38.50	Cost includes material and labor to
Install	Ea.	216	24.50		240.50	install 3' x 6' 8" pre-hung 1-3/4"
Demolish and Install	Ea.	216	63		279	lauan door of solid wood.
Reinstall	Ea.		24.38		24.38	
Clean	Ea.	4.77	12.75		17.52	
Paint	Ea.	9.20	50.50		59.70	
Minimum Charge	Job		207		207	
French Style						
Demolish	Ea.		42.50		42.50	Cost includes material and labor to
Install	Ea.	700	59		759	install 3' x 6' 8" pre-hung 1-3/4"
Demolish and Install	Ea.	700	101.50		801.50	french style door with 15 lights.
Reinstall	Ea.		59.20		59.20	
Clean	Ea.	.33	12.75		13.08	
Paint	Ea.	6.90	178		184.90	
Minimum Charge	Job		207		207	
Double						
Demolish	Ea.		28.50		28.50	Includes material and labor to install a
Install	Ea.	1450	104		1554	pre-hung double entry door including
Demolish and Install	Ea.	1450	132.50		1582.50	frame and exterior trim.
Clean	Ea.	.18	45		45.18	
Paint	Ea.	20.50	178		198.50	
Minimum Charge	Job		104		104	
Commercial Grade						
3' x 6' 8"						
Demolish	Ea.		38.50		38.50	Includes material and labor to install
Install	Ea.	310	24.50		334.50	flush solid core 1-3/4" hardwood
Demolish and Install	Ea.	310	63		373	veneer 3' x 6' 8' door only.
Reinstall	Ea.		24.38		24.38	
Clean	Ea.	4.77	12.75		17.52	
Paint	Ea.	10.80	29.50		40.30	
Minimum Charge	Job		207		207	
3' 6" x 6' 8"						
Demolish	Ea.		38.50		38.50	Includes material and labor to install
Install	Ea.	385	24.50		409.50	flush solid core 1-3/4" hardwood
Demolish and Install	Ea.	385	63		448	veneer 3' 6" x 6' 8' door only.
Reinstall	Ea.		24.38		24.38	
Clean	Ea.	4.77	12.75		17.52	
Paint	Ea.	10.80	29.50		40.30	
Minimum Charge	Job		207		207	
3' x 7'						
Demolish	Ea.		38.50		38.50	Includes material and labor to install
Install	Ea.	325	59		384	flush solid core 1-3/4" hardwood
Demolish and Install	Ea.	325	97.50		422.50	veneer 3' x 7' door only.
Reinstall	Ea.		59.20		59.20	
Clean	Ea.	4.77	12.75		17.52	
Paint	Ea.	10.80	29.50		40.30	
Minimum Charge	Job		207		207	

Exterior Doors and Windows

Solid Core Door		Unit	Material	Labor	Equip.	Total	Specification
3' 6" x 7'							
	Demolish	Ea.		38.50		38.50	Includes material and labor to install
	Install	Ea.	445	29.50		474.50	flush solid core 1-3/4" hardwood
	Demolish and Install	Ea.	445	68		513	veneer 3' 6" x 7' door only.
	Reinstall	Ea.		29.60		29.60	
	Clean	Ea.	4.77	12.75		17.52	
	Paint	Ea.	10.80	29.50		40.30	
	Minimum Charge	Job		207		207	
3' x 8'							
	Demolish	Ea.		38.50		38.50	Includes material and labor to install
	Install	Ea.	390	52		442	flush solid core 1-3/4" hardwood
	Demolish and Install	Ea.	390	90.50		480.50	veneer 3' x 8' door only.
	Reinstall	Ea.		51.80		51.80	
	Clean	Ea.	5.70	19.15		24.85	
	Paint	Ea.	10.80	29.50		40.30	
	Minimum Charge	Job		207		207	
3' 6" x 8'							
	Demolish	Ea.		38.50		38.50	Includes material and labor to install
	Install	Ea.	475	52		527	flush solid core 1-3/4" hardwood
	Demolish and Install	Ea.	475	90.50		565.50	veneer 3' 6" x 8' door only.
	Reinstall	Ea.		51.80		51.80	
	Clean	Ea.	5.70	19.15		24.85	
	Paint	Ea.	10.80	29.50		40.30	
	Minimum Charge	Job		207		207	
3' x 9'							
	Demolish	Ea.		38.50		38.50	Includes material and labor to install
	Install	Ea.	540	59		599	flush solid core 1-3/4" hardwood
	Demolish and Install	Ea.	540	97.50		637.50	veneer 3' x 9' door only.
	Reinstall	Ea.		59.20		59.20	
	Clean	Ea.	5.70	19.15		24.85	
	Paint	Ea.	10.80	29.50		40.30	
	Minimum Charge	Job		207		207	
Stain							
	Install	Ea.	9.70	39.50		49.20	Includes labor and material to stain
	Minimum Charge	Job		178		178	exterior type door and trim on both sides.
Door Only (SC)							
2' 4" x 6' 8"							
	Demolish	Ea.		8.20		8.20	Cost includes material and labor to
	Install	Ea.	205	23		228	install 2' 4" x 6' 8" lauan solid core
	Demolish and Install	Ea.	205	31.20		236.20	door slab.
	Reinstall	Ea.		23.02		23.02	
	Clean	Ea.	1.99	9.60		11.59	
	Paint	Ea.	4.86	44.50		49.36	
	Minimum Charge	Job		207		207	
2' 8" x 6' 8"							
	Demolish	Ea.		8.20		8.20	Cost includes material and labor to
	Install	Ea.	212	23		235	install 2' 8" x 6' 8" lauan solid core
	Demolish and Install	Ea.	212	31.20		243.20	door slab.
	Reinstall	Ea.		23.02		23.02	
	Clean	Ea.	1.99	9.60		11.59	
	Paint	Ea.	4.86	44.50		49.36	
	Minimum Charge	Job		207		207	

Exterior Doors and Windows

Solid Core Door		Unit	Material	Labor	Equip.	Total	Specification
3' x 6' 8"							
	Demolish	Ea.		8.20		8.20	Cost includes material and labor to
	Install	Ea.	220	24.50		244.50	install 3' x 6' 8" lauan solid core door
	Demolish and Install	Ea.	220	32.70		252.70	slab.
	Reinstall	Ea.		24.38		24.38	
	Clean	Ea.	1.99	9.60		11.59	
	Paint	Ea.	4.86	44.50		49.36	
	Minimum Charge	Job		207		207	
3' 6" x 6' 8"							
	Demolish	Ea.		8.20		8.20	Cost includes material and labor to
	Install	Ea.	251	26		277	install 3' 6" x 6' 8" lauan solid core
	Demolish and Install	Ea.	251	34.20		285.20	door slab.
	Reinstall	Ea.		25.90		25.90	
	Clean	Ea.	1.99	9.60		11.59	
	Paint	Ea.	4.86	44.50		49.36	
	Minimum Charge	Job		207		207	
Panel							
	Demolish	Ea.		8.20		8.20	Cost includes material and labor to
	Install	Ea.	223	49		272	install 3' x 6' 8" six (6) panel interior
	Demolish and Install	Ea.	223	57.20		280.20	door.
	Reinstall	Ea.		48.75		48.75	
	Clean	Ea.	2.39	9.60		11.99	
	Paint	Ea.	4.86	44.50		49.36	
	Minimum Charge	Job		207		207	
Casing Trim							
Single Width							
	Demolish	Ea.		7.30		7.30	Cost includes material and labor to
	Install	Opng.	25	34.50		59.50	install 11/16" x 2-1/2" pine ranch
	Demolish and Install	Opng.	25	41.80		66.80	style casing for one side of a standard
	Reinstall	Opng.		27.63		27.63	door opening.
	Clean	Opng.	.68	3.06		3.74	
	Paint	Ea.	5.25	7.10		12.35	
	Minimum Charge	Job		207		207	
Double Width							
	Demolish	Ea.		8.70		8.70	Cost includes material and labor to
	Install	Opng.	28.50	41.50		70	install 11/16" x 2-1/2" pine ranch
	Demolish and Install	Opng.	28.50	50.20		78.70	style door casing for one side of a
	Reinstall	Opng.		33.15		33.15	double door opening.
	Clean	Opng.	.79	6.15		6.94	
	Paint	Ea.	5.25	8.05		13.30	
	Minimum Charge	Job		207		207	

Components		Unit	Material	Labor	Equip.	Total	Specification
Hardware							
Doorknob							
	Demolish	Ea.		16.45		16.45	Includes material and labor to install
	Install	Ea.	29	26		55	residential passage lockset, keyless
	Demolish and Install	Ea.	29	42.45		71.45	bored type.
	Reinstall	Ea.		20.72		20.72	
	Clean	Ea.	.47	9.60		10.07	
	Minimum Charge	Job		207		207	

Exterior Doors and Windows

Components		Unit	Material	Labor	Equip.	Total	Specification
Doorknob w / Lock							
	Demolish	Ea.		16.45		16.45	Includes material and labor to install
	Install	Ea.	44.50	26		70.50	privacy lockset.
	Demolish and Install	Ea.	44.50	42.45		86.95	
	Reinstall	Ea.		20.72		20.72	
	Clean	Ea.	.47	9.60		10.07	
	Minimum Charge	Job		207		207	
Lever Handle							
	Demolish	Ea.		16.45		16.45	Includes material and labor to install
	Install	Ea.	38	41.50		79.50	residential passage lockset, keyless
	Demolish and Install	Ea.	38	57.95		95.95	bored type with lever handle.
	Reinstall	Ea.		33.15		33.15	
	Clean	Ea.	.47	9.60		10.07	
	Minimum Charge	Job		207		207	
Deadbolt							
	Demolish	Ea.		14.40		14.40	Includes material and labor to install a
	Install	Ea.	70	29.50		99.50	deadbolt.
	Demolish and Install	Ea.	70	43.90		113.90	
	Reinstall	Ea.		23.68		23.68	
	Clean	Ea.	.47	9.60		10.07	
	Minimum Charge	Job		207		207	
Grip Handle Entry							
	Demolish	Ea.		13.15		13.15	Includes material and labor to install
	Install	Ea.	88	46		134	residential keyed entry lock set with
	Demolish and Install	Ea.	88	59.15		147.15	grip type handle.
	Reinstall	Ea.		36.84		36.84	
	Clean	Ea.	.47	9.60		10.07	
	Minimum Charge	Job		207		207	
Panic Device							
	Demolish	Ea.		34		34	Includes material and labor to install
	Install	Ea.	425	69		494	touch bar, low profile, exit only.
	Demolish and Install	Ea.	425	103		528	
	Reinstall	Ea.		55.25		55.25	
	Clean	Ea.	.24	17		17.24	
	Minimum Charge	Job		207		207	
Closer							
	Demolish	Ea.		8.65		8.65	Includes material and labor to install
	Install	Ea.	250	69		319	pneumatic heavy duty closer for
	Demolish and Install	Ea.	250	77.65		327.65	exterior type doors.
	Reinstall	Ea.		55.25		55.25	
	Clean	Ea.	.24	12.75		12.99	
	Minimum Charge	Job		207		207	
Peep-hole							
	Demolish	Ea.		7.55		7.55	Includes material and labor to install
	Install	Ea.	17.40	12.95		30.35	peep-hole for door.
	Demolish and Install	Ea.	17.40	20.50		37.90	
	Reinstall	Ea.		10.36		10.36	
	Clean	Ea.	.03	3.46		3.49	
	Minimum Charge	Job		207		207	
Exit Sign							
	Demolish	Ea.		23		23	Includes material and labor to install a
	Install	Ea.	113	56.50		169.50	wall mounted interior electric exit sign.
	Demolish and Install	Ea.	113	79.50		192.50	
	Reinstall	Ea.		45.20		45.20	
	Clean	Ea.	.03	7.05		7.08	
	Minimum Charge	Job		207		207	

Exterior Doors and Windows

Components		Unit	Material	Labor	Equip.	Total	Specification
Kickplate							
	Demolish	Ea.		12.80		12.80	Includes material and labor to install
	Install	Ea.	28.50	27.50		56	aluminum kickplate, 10" x 28".
	Demolish and Install	Ea.	28.50	40.30		68.80	
	Reinstall	Ea.		22.10		22.10	
	Clean	Ea.	.47	9.60		10.07	
	Minimum Charge	Job		207		207	
Threshold							
	Install	L.F.	3.92	4.14		8.06	Includes labor and material to install
	Minimum Charge	Job		104		104	oak threshold.
Weatherstripping							
	Install	L.F.	.48	1.04		1.52	Includes labor and material to install
	Minimum Charge	Job		104		104	rubber weatherstripping for door.
Metal Jamb							
6' 8" High							
	Demolish	Ea.		23		23	Cost includes material and labor to
	Install	Ea.	167	26		193	install 18 gauge hollow metal door
	Demolish and Install	Ea.	167	49		216	frame to fit a 4-1/2" jamb 6' 8" high
	Reinstall	Ea.		25.90		25.90	and up to 3' 6" opening.
	Clean	Ea.	1	6.40		7.40	
	Paint	Ea.	1.79	7.10		8.89	
	Minimum Charge	Job		207		207	
7' High							
	Demolish	Ea.		23		23	Cost includes material and labor to
	Install	Ea.	173	27.50		200.50	install 18 gauge hollow metal door
	Demolish and Install	Ea.	173	50.50		223.50	frame to fit a 4-1/2" jamb 7' high and
	Reinstall	Ea.		27.63		27.63	up to 3' 6" opening.
	Clean	Ea.	1	6.40		7.40	
	Paint	Ea.	1.79	7.10		8.89	
	Minimum Charge	Job		207		207	
8' High							
	Demolish	Ea.		23		23	Cost includes material and labor to
	Install	Ea.	212	34.50		246.50	install 18 gauge hollow metal door
	Demolish and Install	Ea.	212	57.50		269.50	frame to fit a 4-1/2" jamb 8' high and
	Reinstall	Ea.		34.53		34.53	up to 3' 6" opening.
	Clean	Ea.	1.41	7.65		9.06	
	Paint	Ea.	2	7.90		9.90	
	Minimum Charge	Job		207		207	
9' High							
	Demolish	Ea.		23		23	Cost includes material and labor to
	Install	Ea.	277	41.50		318.50	install 18 gauge hollow metal door
	Demolish and Install	Ea.	277	64.50		341.50	frame to fit a 4-1/2" jamb 9' high and
	Reinstall	Ea.		41.44		41.44	up to 3' 6" opening.
	Clean	Ea.	1.41	7.65		9.06	
	Paint	Ea.	2	7.90		9.90	
	Minimum Charge	Job		207		207	
Wood Jamb							
	Demolish	Ea.		29		29	Includes material and labor to install
	Install	Ea.	100	11.20		111.20	flat pine jamb with square cut heads
	Demolish and Install	Ea.	100	40.20		140.20	and rabbeted sides for 6' 8" high and
	Clean	Ea.	.15	7.65		7.80	3-9/16" door including trim sets for
	Paint	Ea.	6.60	23.50		30.10	both sides.
	Minimum Charge	Job		104		104	
Stain							
	Install	Ea.	6.65	29.50		36.15	Includes labor and material to stain
	Minimum Charge	Job		178		178	single door and trim on both sides.

Exterior Doors and Windows

Components	Unit	Material	Labor	Equip.	Total	Specification
Shave & Refit						
Install	Ea.		34.50		34.50	Includes labor to shave and rework
Minimum Charge	Job		104		104	door to fit opening at the job site.

Sliding Patio Door	Unit	Material	Labor	Equip.	Total	Specification
Aluminum						
6' Single Pane						
Demolish	Ea.		57.50		57.50	Cost includes material and labor to
Install	Ea.	500	207		707	install 6' x 6' 8" sliding anodized
Demolish and Install	Ea.	500	264.50		764.50	aluminum patio door with single pane
Reinstall	Ea.		165.76		165.76	tempered safety glass, anodized
Clean	Ea.	2.99	19.15		22.14	frame, screen, weatherstripped.
Minimum Charge	Job		207		207	
8' Single Pane						
Demolish	Ea.		57.50		57.50	Cost includes material and labor to
Install	Ea.	635	276		911	install 8' x 6' 8" sliding aluminum
Demolish and Install	Ea.	635	333.50		968.50	patio door with single pane tempered
Reinstall	Ea.		221.01		221.01	safety glass, anodized frame, screen,
Clean	Ea.	2.99	19.15		22.14	weatherstripped.
Minimum Charge	Job		207		207	
10' Single Pane						
Demolish	Ea.		57.50		57.50	Cost includes material and labor to
Install	Ea.	710	415		1125	install 10' x 6' 8" sliding aluminum
Demolish and Install	Ea.	710	472.50		1182.50	patio door with single pane tempered
Reinstall	Ea.		331.52		331.52	safety glass, anodized frame, screen,
Clean	Ea.	2.99	19.15		22.14	weatherstripped.
Minimum Charge	Job		207		207	
6' Insulated						
Demolish	Ea.		57.50		57.50	Cost includes material and labor to
Install	Ea.	1000	207		1207	install 6' x 6' 8" sliding aluminum
Demolish and Install	Ea.	1000	264.50		1264.50	patio door with double insulated
Reinstall	Ea.		165.76		165.76	tempered glass, baked-on enamel
Clean	Ea.	2.99	19.15		22.14	finish, screen, weatherstripped.
Minimum Charge	Job		207		207	
8' Insulated						
Demolish	Ea.		57.50		57.50	Cost includes material and labor to
Install	Ea.	1175	276		1451	install 8' x 6' 8" sliding aluminum
Demolish and Install	Ea.	1175	333.50		1508.50	patio door with insulated tempered
Reinstall	Ea.		221.01		221.01	glass, baked-on enamel finish, screen,
Clean	Ea.	2.99	19.15		22.14	weatherstripped.
Minimum Charge	Job		207		207	
10' Insulated						
Demolish	Ea.		57.50		57.50	Cost includes material and labor to
Install	Ea.	1450	415		1865	install 10' x 6' 8" sliding aluminum
Demolish and Install	Ea.	1450	472.50		1922.50	patio door with double insulated
Reinstall	Ea.		331.52		331.52	tempered glass, baked-on enamel
Clean	Ea.	2.99	19.15		22.14	finish, screen, weatherstripped.
Minimum Charge	Job		207		207	

Sliding Patio Door		Unit	Material	Labor	Equip.	Total	Specification
Vinyl							
6' Single Pane							
	Demolish	Ea.		57.50		57.50	Cost includes material and labor to
	Install	Ea.	460	207		667	install 6' x 6' 8" sliding vinyl patio
	Demolish and Install	Ea.	460	264.50		724.50	door with single pane tempered safety
	Reinstall	Ea.		165.76		165.76	glass, anodized frame, screen,
	Clean	Ea.	2.99	19.15		22.14	weatherstripped.
	Minimum Charge	Job		207		207	
8' Single Pane							
	Demolish	Ea.		57.50		57.50	Cost includes material and labor to
	Install	Ea.	645	276		921	install 8' x 6' 8" sliding vinyl patio
	Demolish and Install	Ea.	645	333.50		978.50	door with single pane tempered safety
	Reinstall	Ea.		221.01		221.01	glass, anodized frame, screen,
	Clean	Ea.	2.99	19.15		22.14	weatherstripped.
	Minimum Charge	Job		207		207	
10' Single Pane							
	Demolish	Ea.		57.50		57.50	Cost includes material and labor to
	Install	Ea.	700	415		1115	install 10' x 6' 8" sliding vinyl patio
	Demolish and Install	Ea.	700	472.50		1172.50	door with single pane tempered safety
	Reinstall	Ea.		331.52		331.52	glass, anodized frame, screen,
	Clean	Ea.	2.99	19.15		22.14	weatherstripped.
	Minimum Charge	Job		207		207	
6' Insulated							
	Demolish	Ea.		57.50		57.50	Cost includes material and labor to
	Install	Ea.	1250	207		1457	install 6' x 6' 8" sliding vinyl patio
	Demolish and Install	Ea.	1250	264.50		1514.50	door with double insulated tempered
	Reinstall	Ea.		165.76		165.76	glass, anodized frame, screen,
	Clean	Ea.	2.99	19.15		22.14	weatherstripped.
	Minimum Charge	Job		207		207	
8' Insulated							
	Demolish	Ea.		57.50		57.50	Cost includes material and labor to
	Install	Ea.	1025	276		1301	install 8' x 6' 8" sliding vinyl patio
	Demolish and Install	Ea.	1025	333.50		1358.50	door with double insulated tempered
	Reinstall	Ea.		221.01		221.01	glass, anodized frame, screen,
	Clean	Ea.	2.99	19.15		22.14	weatherstripped.
	Minimum Charge	Job		207		207	
10' Insulated							
	Demolish	Ea.		57.50		57.50	Cost includes material and labor to
	Install	Ea.	1850	207		2057	install 10' x 6' 8" sliding vinyl patio
	Demolish and Install	Ea.	1850	264.50		2114.50	door with double insulated tempered
	Reinstall	Ea.		165.76		165.76	glass, anodized frame, screen,
	Clean	Ea.	2.99	19.15		22.14	weatherstripped.
	Minimum Charge	Job		207		207	
Wood Framed							
6' Premium Insulated							
	Demolish	Ea.		57.50		57.50	Cost includes material and labor to
	Install	Ea.	1575	207		1782	install 6' x 6' 8" sliding wood patio
	Demolish and Install	Ea.	1575	264.50		1839.50	door with pine frame, double insulated
	Reinstall	Ea.		165.76		165.76	glass, screen, lock and dead bolt,
	Clean	Ea.	2.99	19.15		22.14	weatherstripped. Add for casing and
	Minimum Charge	Job		207		207	finishing.

Exterior Doors and Windows

Sliding Patio Door		Unit	Material	Labor	Equip.	Total	Specification
8' Premium Insulated							
	Demolish	Ea.		57.50		57.50	Cost includes material and labor to
	Install	Ea.	2000	276		2276	install 8' x 6' 8" sliding wood patio
	Demolish and Install	Ea.	2000	333.50		2333.50	door with pine frame, double insulated
	Reinstall	Ea.		221.01		221.01	glass, screen, lock and dead bolt,
	Clean	Ea.	2.99	19.15		22.14	weatherstripped. Add for casing and
	Minimum Charge	Job		207		207	finishing.
9' Premium Insulated							
	Demolish	Ea.		57.50		57.50	Cost includes material and labor to
	Install	Ea.	2000	276		2276	install 9' x 6' 8" sliding wood patio
	Demolish and Install	Ea.	2000	333.50		2333.50	door with pine frame, double insulated
	Reinstall	Ea.		221.01		221.01	glass, screen, lock and dead bolt,
	Clean	Ea.	2.99	19.15		22.14	weatherstripped. Add for casing and
	Minimum Charge	Job		207		207	finishing.
Stain							
	Install	Ea.	9.70	39.50		49.20	Includes labor and material to stain
	Minimum Charge	Job		178		178	exterior type door and trim on both
							sides.
Casing Trim							
	Demolish	Ea.		8.70		8.70	Cost includes material and labor to
	Install	Opng.	28.50	41.50		70	install 11/16" x 2-1/2" pine ranch
	Demolish and Install	Opng.	28.50	50.20		78.70	style door casing for one side of a
	Reinstall	Opng.		33.15		33.15	double door opening.
	Clean	Opng.	.79	6.15		6.94	
	Paint	Ea.	5.25	8.05		13.30	
	Minimum Charge	Job		207		207	
Sliding Screen							
	Demolish	Ea.		8.20		8.20	Includes material and labor to install
	Install	Ea.	134	20.50		154.50	sliding screen door, 6' 8" x 3'.
	Demolish and Install	Ea.	134	28.70		162.70	
	Reinstall	Ea.		16.58		16.58	
	Clean	Ea.	1	6.40		7.40	
	Minimum Charge	Job		207		207	

Screen Door		Unit	Material	Labor	Equip.	Total	Specification
Aluminum							
	Demolish	Ea.		38.50		38.50	Includes material and labor to install
	Install	Ea.	125	59		184	aluminum frame screen door with
	Demolish and Install	Ea.	125	97.50		222.50	fiberglass screen cloth, closer, hinges,
	Reinstall	Ea.		47.36		47.36	latch.
	Clean	Ea.	4.77	12.75		17.52	
	Paint	Ea.	5.05	14.20		19.25	
	Minimum Charge	Job		207		207	
Wood							
	Demolish	Ea.		38.50		38.50	Includes material and labor to install
	Install	Ea.	285	69		354	wood screen door with aluminum cloth
	Demolish and Install	Ea.	285	107.50		392.50	screen. Frame and hardware not
	Reinstall	Ea.		55.25		55.25	included.
	Clean	Ea.	4.77	12.75		17.52	
	Paint	Ea.	5.05	14.20		19.25	
	Minimum Charge	Job		207		207	
Shave & Refit							
	Install	Ea.		34.50		34.50	Includes labor to shave and rework
	Minimum Charge	Job		207		207	door to fit opening at the job site.

Exterior Doors and Windows

Storm Door		Unit	Material	Labor	Equip.	Total	Specification
Good Grade							
	Demolish	Ea.		38.50		38.50	Includes material and labor to install
	Install	Ea.	219	59		278	aluminum frame storm door with
	Demolish and Install	Ea.	219	97.50		316.50	fiberglass screen cloth, upper glass
	Reinstall	Ea.		47.36		47.36	panel, closer, hinges, latch.
	Clean	Ea.	4.77	12.75		17.52	
	Paint	Ea.	5.05	14.20		19.25	
	Minimum Charge	Job		207		207	
Better Grade							
	Demolish	Ea.		38.50		38.50	Includes material and labor to install
	Install	Ea.	270	59		329	aluminum frame storm door with
	Demolish and Install	Ea.	270	97.50		367.50	fiberglass screen cloth, upper and
	Reinstall	Ea.		47.36		47.36	lower glass panel, closer, latch.
	Clean	Ea.	4.77	12.75		17.52	
	Paint	Ea.	5.05	14.20		19.25	
	Minimum Charge	Job		207		207	
Premium Grade							
	Demolish	Ea.		38.50		38.50	Includes material and labor to install
	Install	Ea.	296	59		355	aluminum frame storm door with
	Demolish and Install	Ea.	296	97.50		393.50	fiberglass screen cloth, upper and
	Reinstall	Ea.		47.36		47.36	lower glass panel, closer, latch.
	Clean	Ea.	4.77	12.75		17.52	
	Paint	Ea.	5.05	14.20		19.25	
	Minimum Charge	Job		207		207	
Insulated							
	Demolish	Ea.		38.50		38.50	Includes material and labor to install
	Install	Ea.	272	29.50		301.50	aluminum frame storm door with
	Demolish and Install	Ea.	272	68		340	fiberglass screen cloth, upper and
	Reinstall	Ea.		23.68		23.68	lower glass panel, closer, latch.
	Clean	Ea.	4.77	12.75		17.52	
	Paint	Ea.	5.05	14.20		19.25	
	Minimum Charge	Job		207		207	

Garage Door		Unit	Material	Labor	Equip.	Total	Specification
9' One Piece Metal							
	Demolish	Ea.		97		97	Includes material and labor to install
	Install	Ea.	460	104		564	one piece steel garage door 9' x 7'
	Demolish and Install	Ea.	460	201		661	primed including hardware.
	Reinstall	Ea.		82.88		82.88	
	Clean	Ea.	6	38.50		44.50	
	Paint	Ea.	9.20	89		98.20	
	Minimum Charge	Job		207		207	
16' One Piece Metal							
	Demolish	Ea.		115		115	Includes material and labor to install
	Install	Ea.	755	138		893	one piece steel garage door 16' x 7'
	Demolish and Install	Ea.	755	253		1008	primed including hardware.
	Reinstall	Ea.		110.51		110.51	
	Clean	Ea.	11.95	51		62.95	
	Paint	Ea.	18.35	101		119.35	
	Minimum Charge	Job		207		207	

Exterior Doors and Windows

Garage Door		Unit	Material	Labor	Equip.	Total	Specification
9' Metal Sectional							
	Demolish	Ea.		97		97	Includes material and labor to install
	Install	Ea.	705	157		862	sectional metal garage door 9' x 7'
	Demolish and Install	Ea.	705	254		959	primed including hardware.
	Reinstall	Ea.		125.58		125.58	
	Clean	Ea.	6.10	44		50.10	
	Paint	Ea.	18.35	101		119.35	
	Minimum Charge	Job		207		207	
16' Metal Sectional							
	Demolish	Ea.		115		115	Includes material and labor to install
	Install	Ea.	855	276		1131	sectional metal garage door 16' x 7'
	Demolish and Install	Ea.	855	391		1246	primed including hardware.
	Reinstall	Ea.		221.01		221.01	
	Clean	Ea.	11.95	51		62.95	
	Paint	Ea.	18.35	101		119.35	
	Minimum Charge	Job		207		207	
Metal / Steel Roll Up							
8' x 8' Steel							
	Demolish	Ea.		132		132	Cost includes material and labor to
	Install	Ea.	1200	635		1835	install 8' x 8' steel overhead roll-up,
	Demolish and Install	Ea.	1200	767		1967	chain hoist operated service door.
	Reinstall	Ea.		509.60		509.60	
	Clean	Ea.	6.10	44		50.10	
	Paint	Ea.	19.65	118		137.65	
	Minimum Charge	Job		1025		1025	
10' x 10' Steel							
	Demolish	Ea.		153		153	Cost includes material and labor to
	Install	Ea.	2000	730		2730	install 10' x 10' steel overhead roll-up,
	Demolish and Install	Ea.	2000	883		2883	chain hoist operated service door.
	Reinstall	Ea.		582.40		582.40	
	Clean	Ea.	9.55	61.50		71.05	
	Paint	Ea.	31	118		149	
	Minimum Charge	Job		1025		1025	
12' x 12' Steel							
	Demolish	Ea.		184		184	Cost includes material and labor to
	Install	Ea.	2025	850		2875	install 12' x 12' steel overhead roll-up,
	Demolish and Install	Ea.	2025	1034		3059	chain hoist operated service door.
	Reinstall	Ea.		679.47		679.47	
	Clean	Ea.	13.75	68		81.75	
	Paint	Ea.	44	142		186	
	Minimum Charge	Job		1025		1025	
14' x 14' Steel							
	Demolish	Ea.		230		230	Cost includes material and labor to
	Install	Ea.	3300	1275		4575	install 14' x 14' steel overhead roll-up,
	Demolish and Install	Ea.	3300	1505		4805	chain hoist operated service door.
	Reinstall	Ea.		1019.20		1019.20	
	Clean	Ea.	18.75	87.50		106.25	
	Paint	Ea.	51.50	178		229.50	
	Minimum Charge	Job		1025		1025	
18' x 18' Steel							
	Demolish	Ea.		256		256	Cost includes material and labor to
	Install	Opng.	3550	1700		5250	install 18' x 18' steel overhead roll-up,
	Demolish and Install	Opng.	3550	1956		5506	chain hoist operated service door.
	Reinstall	Opng.		1358.93		1358.93	
	Clean	Ea.	18.75	51		69.75	
	Paint	Ea.	99	355		454	
	Minimum Charge	Job		1025		1025	
Automatic Motor							
	Install	Ea.	525	41.50		566.50	Includes labor and material to install
	Minimum Charge	Job		207		207	electric opener motor, 1/3 HP.

Exterior Doors and Windows

Garage Door		Unit	Material	Labor	Equip.	Total	Specification
9' One Piece Wood							
	Demolish	Ea.		97		97	Includes material and labor to install
	Install	Ea.	660	104		764	one piece wood garage door 9' x 7'
	Demolish and Install	Ea.	660	201		861	primed including hardware.
	Reinstall	Ea.		82.88		82.88	
	Clean	Ea.	6	38.50		44.50	
	Paint	Ea.	9.20	89		98.20	
	Minimum Charge	Job		207		207	
9' Wood Sectional							
	Demolish	Ea.		97		97	Includes material and labor to install
	Install	Ea.	990	104		1094	sectional wood garage door 9' x 7'
	Demolish and Install	Ea.	990	201		1191	unfinished including hardware.
	Reinstall	Ea.		82.88		82.88	
	Clean	Ea.	6	38.50		44.50	
	Paint	Ea.	9.20	89		98.20	
	Minimum Charge	Job		207		207	
16' Wood Sectional							
	Demolish	Ea.		115		115	Includes material and labor to install
	Install	Ea.	1700	138		1838	sectional fiberglass garage door 16' x
	Demolish and Install	Ea.	1700	253		1953	7' unfinished including hardware.
	Reinstall	Ea.		110.51		110.51	
	Clean	Ea.	11.95	51		62.95	
	Paint	Ea.	18.35	101		119.35	
	Minimum Charge	Job		207		207	
Electric Opener							
	Demolish	Ea.		68		68	Includes material and labor to install
	Install	Ea.	340	78		418	electric opener, 1/3 HP economy.
	Demolish and Install	Ea.	340	146		486	
	Reinstall	Ea.		62.20		62.20	
	Clean	Ea.	.24	17		17.24	
	Minimum Charge	Job		207		207	
Springs							
	Install	Pr.	83.50	104		187.50	Includes labor and material to replace
	Minimum Charge	Job		207		207	springs for garage door.

Commercial Metal Door		Unit	Material	Labor	Equip.	Total	Specification
Pre-hung Steel Door							
2' 8" x 6' 8"							
	Demolish	Ea.		57.50		57.50	Cost includes material and labor to
	Install	Ea.	720	26		746	install 2' 8" x 6' 8" pre-hung 1-3/4"
	Demolish and Install	Ea.	720	83.50		803.50	18 gauge steel door with steel frame,
	Reinstall	Ea.		25.90		25.90	hinges, aluminum sill,
	Clean	Ea.	4.77	12.75		17.52	weather-stripped.
	Paint	Ea.	6.50	29.50		36	
	Minimum Charge	Job		207		207	
3' x 6' 8"							
	Demolish	Ea.		57.50		57.50	Cost includes material and labor to
	Install	Ea.	675	27.50		702.50	install 3' x 6' 8" pre-hung 1-3/4" 18
	Demolish and Install	Ea.	675	85		760	gauge steel door with steel frame,
	Reinstall	Ea.		27.63		27.63	hinges, aluminum sill,
	Clean	Ea.	4.77	12.75		17.52	weather-stripped.
	Paint	Ea.	6.50	29.50		36	
	Minimum Charge	Job		207		207	

Commercial Metal Door		Unit	Material	Labor	Equip.	Total	Specification
3′ 6″ x 6′ 8″							
	Demolish	Ea.		57.50		57.50	Cost includes material and labor to
	Install	Ea.	770	32		802	install 3′ 6″ x 6′ 8″ pre-hung 1-3/4″
	Demolish and Install	Ea.	770	89.50		859.50	18 gauge steel door with steel frame,
	Reinstall	Ea.		31.88		31.88	hinges, aluminum sill,
	Clean	Ea.	4.77	12.75		17.52	weather-stripped.
	Paint	Ea.	6.50	29.50		36	
	Minimum Charge	Job		207		207	
4′ x 6′ 8″							
	Demolish	Ea.		57.50		57.50	Cost includes material and labor to
	Install	Ea.	840	41.50		881.50	install 4′ x 6′ 8″ pre-hung 1-3/4″ 18
	Demolish and Install	Ea.	840	99		939	gauge steel door with steel frame,
	Reinstall	Ea.		41.44		41.44	hinges, aluminum sill,
	Clean	Ea.	4.77	12.75		17.52	weather-stripped.
	Paint	Ea.	6.50	29.50		36	
	Minimum Charge	Job		207		207	
Metal Jamb							
6′ 8″ High							
	Demolish	Ea.		23		23	Cost includes material and labor to
	Install	Ea.	167	26		193	install 18 gauge hollow metal door
	Demolish and Install	Ea.	167	49		216	frame to fit a 4-1/2″ jamb 6′ 8″ high
	Reinstall	Ea.		25.90		25.90	and up to 3′ 6″ opening.
	Clean	Ea.	1	6.40		7.40	
	Paint	Ea.	1.79	7.10		8.89	
	Minimum Charge	Job		207		207	
7′ High							
	Demolish	Ea.		23		23	Cost includes material and labor to
	Install	Ea.	173	27.50		200.50	install 18 gauge hollow metal door
	Demolish and Install	Ea.	173	50.50		223.50	frame to fit a 4-1/2″ jamb 7′ high and
	Reinstall	Ea.		27.63		27.63	up to 3′ 6″ opening.
	Clean	Ea.	1	6.40		7.40	
	Paint	Ea.	1.79	7.10		8.89	
	Minimum Charge	Job		207		207	
8′ High							
	Demolish	Ea.		23		23	Cost includes material and labor to
	Install	Ea.	212	34.50		246.50	install 18 gauge hollow metal door
	Demolish and Install	Ea.	212	57.50		269.50	frame to fit a 4-1/2″ jamb 8′ high and
	Reinstall	Ea.		34.53		34.53	up to 3′ 6″ opening.
	Clean	Ea.	1.41	7.65		9.06	
	Paint	Ea.	2	7.90		9.90	
	Minimum Charge	Job		207		207	
9′ High							
	Demolish	Ea.		23		23	Cost includes material and labor to
	Install	Ea.	277	41.50		318.50	install 18 gauge hollow metal door
	Demolish and Install	Ea.	277	64.50		341.50	frame to fit a 4-1/2″ jamb 9′ high and
	Reinstall	Ea.		41.44		41.44	up to 3′ 6″ opening.
	Clean	Ea.	1.41	7.65		9.06	
	Paint	Ea.	2	7.90		9.90	
	Minimum Charge	Job		207		207	
Hardware							
Doorknob w / Lock							
	Demolish	Ea.		16.45		16.45	Includes material and labor to install
	Install	Ea.	154	34.50		188.50	keyed entry lock set, bored type
	Demolish and Install	Ea.	154	50.95		204.95	including knob trim, strike and strike
	Reinstall	Ea.		27.63		27.63	box for standard commercial
	Clean	Ea.	.47	9.60		10.07	application.
	Minimum Charge	Job		207		207	

Exterior Doors and Windows

Commercial Metal Door		Unit	Material	Labor	Equip.	Total	Specification
Lever Handle							Includes material and labor to install
	Demolish	Ea.		16.45		16.45	passage lockset, keyless bored type
	Install	Ea.	130	41.50		171.50	with lever handle, non-locking
	Demolish and Install	Ea.	130	57.95		187.95	standard commercial latchset.
	Reinstall	Ea.		33.15		33.15	
	Clean	Ea.	.47	9.60		10.07	
	Minimum Charge	Job		207		207	
Deadbolt							Includes material and labor to install a
	Demolish	Ea.		14.40		14.40	deadbolt.
	Install	Ea.	70	29.50		99.50	
	Demolish and Install	Ea.	70	43.90		113.90	
	Reinstall	Ea.		23.68		23.68	
	Clean	Ea.	.47	9.60		10.07	
	Minimum Charge	Job		207		207	
Panic Device							Includes material and labor to install
	Demolish	Ea.		34		34	touch bar, low profile, exit only.
	Install	Ea.	425	69		494	
	Demolish and Install	Ea.	425	103		528	
	Reinstall	Ea.		55.25		55.25	
	Clean	Ea.	.24	17		17.24	
	Minimum Charge	Job		207		207	
Closer							Includes material and labor to install
	Demolish	Ea.		8.65		8.65	pneumatic heavy duty model for
	Install	Ea.	272	69		341	exterior type doors.
	Demolish and Install	Ea.	272	77.65		349.65	
	Reinstall	Ea.		55.25		55.25	
	Clean	Ea.	.24	12.75		12.99	
	Minimum Charge	Job		207		207	
Peep-Hole							Includes material and labor to install
	Demolish	Ea.		7.55		7.55	peep-hole for door.
	Install	Ea.	17.40	12.95		30.35	
	Demolish and Install	Ea.	17.40	20.50		37.90	
	Reinstall	Ea.		10.36		10.36	
	Clean	Ea.	.03	3.46		3.49	
	Minimum Charge	Job		207		207	
Exit Sign							Includes material and labor to install a
	Demolish	Ea.		23		23	wall mounted interior electric exit sign.
	Install	Ea.	113	56.50		169.50	
	Demolish and Install	Ea.	113	79.50		192.50	
	Reinstall	Ea.		45.20		45.20	
	Clean	Ea.	.03	7.05		7.08	
	Minimum Charge	Job		207		207	
Kickplate							Includes material and labor to install
	Demolish	Ea.		12.80		12.80	stainless steel kickplate, 10" x 36".
	Install	Ea.	53.50	27.50		81	
	Demolish and Install	Ea.	53.50	40.30		93.80	
	Reinstall	Ea.		22.10		22.10	
	Clean	Ea.	.47	9.60		10.07	
	Minimum Charge	Job		207		207	

Aluminum Window		Unit	Material	Labor	Equip.	Total	Specification
Single Hung Two Light							
2' x 2'							
	Demolish	Ea.		21.50		21.50	Cost includes material and labor to
	Install	Ea.	189	92.50		281.50	install 2' x 2' single hung, two light,
	Demolish and Install	Ea.	189	114		303	double glazed aluminum window
	Reinstall	Ea.		74.12		74.12	including screen.
	Clean	Ea.	.06	8.05		8.11	
	Minimum Charge	Job		255		255	

Exterior Doors and Windows

Aluminum Window		Unit	Material	Labor	Equip.	Total	Specification
2' x 2' 6"							
	Demolish	Ea.		21.50		21.50	Cost includes material and labor to
	Install	Ea.	78.50	92.50		171	install 2' x 2' 6" single hung, two
	Demolish and Install	Ea.	78.50	114		192.50	light, double glazed aluminum
	Reinstall	Ea.		74.12		74.12	window including screen.
	Clean	Ea.	.06	8.05		8.11	
	Minimum Charge	Job		255		255	
3' x 1' 6"							
	Demolish	Ea.		21.50		21.50	Cost includes material and labor to
	Install	Ea.	74.50	102		176.50	install 3' x 1' 6" single hung, two
	Demolish and Install	Ea.	74.50	123.50		198	light, double glazed aluminum
	Reinstall	Ea.		81.54		81.54	window including screen.
	Clean	Ea.	.03	7.05		7.08	
	Minimum Charge	Job		255		255	
3' x 2'							
	Demolish	Ea.		21.50		21.50	Cost includes material and labor to
	Install	Ea.	89	102		191	install 3' x 2' single hung, two light,
	Demolish and Install	Ea.	89	123.50		212.50	double glazed aluminum window
	Reinstall	Ea.		81.54		81.54	including screen.
	Clean	Ea.	.03	7.05		7.08	
	Minimum Charge	Job		255		255	
3' x 2' 6"							
	Demolish	Ea.		21.50		21.50	Cost includes material and labor to
	Install	Ea.	95	102		197	install 3' x 2' 6" single hung, two
	Demolish and Install	Ea.	95	123.50		218.50	light, double glazed aluminum
	Reinstall	Ea.		81.54		81.54	window including screen.
	Clean	Ea.	.06	8.05		8.11	
	Minimum Charge	Job		255		255	
3' x 3'							
	Demolish	Ea.		21.50		21.50	Cost includes material and labor to
	Install	Ea.	105	102		207	install 3' x 3' single hung, two light,
	Demolish and Install	Ea.	105	123.50		228.50	double glazed aluminum window
	Reinstall	Ea.		81.54		81.54	including screen.
	Clean	Ea.	.06	8.05		8.11	
	Minimum Charge	Job		255		255	
3' x 3' 6"							
	Demolish	Ea.		21.50		21.50	Cost includes material and labor to
	Install	Ea.	264	102		366	install 3' x 3' 6" single hung, two
	Demolish and Install	Ea.	264	123.50		387.50	light, double glazed aluminum
	Reinstall	Ea.		81.54		81.54	window including screen.
	Clean	Ea.	.08	9.35		9.43	
	Minimum Charge	Job		255		255	
3' x 4'							
	Demolish	Ea.		21.50		21.50	Cost includes material and labor to
	Install	Ea.	276	102		378	install 3' x 4' single hung, two light,
	Demolish and Install	Ea.	276	123.50		399.50	double glazed aluminum window
	Reinstall	Ea.		81.54		81.54	including screen.
	Clean	Ea.	.08	9.35		9.43	
	Minimum Charge	Job		255		255	
3' x 5'							
	Demolish	Ea.		31		31	Cost includes material and labor to
	Install	Ea.	133	102		235	install 3' x 5' single hung, two light,
	Demolish and Install	Ea.	133	133		266	double glazed aluminum window
	Reinstall	Ea.		81.54		81.54	including screen.
	Clean	Ea.	.09	11.25		11.34	
	Minimum Charge	Job		255		255	

Aluminum Window		Unit	Material	Labor	Equip.	Total	Specification
3' x 6'							
	Demolish	Ea.		31		31	Cost includes material and labor to
	Install	Ea.	375	113		488	install 3' x 6' single hung, two light,
	Demolish and Install	Ea.	375	144		519	double glazed aluminum window
	Reinstall	Ea.		90.60		90.60	including screen.
	Clean	Ea.	.11	13.20		13.31	
	Minimum Charge	Job		255		255	
Double Hung Two Light							
2' x 2'							
	Demolish	Ea.		21.50		21.50	Cost includes material and labor to
	Install	Ea.	127	92.50		219.50	install 2' x 2' double hung, two light,
	Demolish and Install	Ea.	127	114		241	double glazed aluminum window
	Reinstall	Ea.		74.12		74.12	including screen.
	Clean	Ea.	.03	7.05		7.08	
	Minimum Charge	Job		255		255	
2' x 2' 6"							
	Demolish	Ea.		21.50		21.50	Cost includes material and labor to
	Install	Ea.	136	92.50		228.50	install 2' x 2' 6" double hung, two
	Demolish and Install	Ea.	136	114		250	light, double glazed aluminum
	Reinstall	Ea.		74.12		74.12	window including screen.
	Clean	Ea.	.03	7.05		7.08	
	Minimum Charge	Job		255		255	
3' x 1' 6"							
	Demolish	Ea.		21.50		21.50	Cost includes material and labor to
	Install	Ea.	297	102		399	install 3' x 1' 6" double hung, two
	Demolish and Install	Ea.	297	123.50		420.50	light, double glazed aluminum
	Reinstall	Ea.		81.54		81.54	window including screen.
	Clean	Ea.	.03	7.05		7.08	
	Minimum Charge	Job		255		255	
3' x 2'							
	Demolish	Ea.		21.50		21.50	Cost includes material and labor to
	Install	Ea.	340	102		442	install 3' x 2' double hung, two light,
	Demolish and Install	Ea.	340	123.50		463.50	double glazed aluminum window
	Reinstall	Ea.		81.54		81.54	including screen.
	Clean	Ea.	.03	7.05		7.08	
	Minimum Charge	Job		255		255	
3' x 2' 6"							
	Demolish	Ea.		21.50		21.50	Cost includes material and labor to
	Install	Ea.	420	102		522	install 3' x 2' 6" double hung, two
	Demolish and Install	Ea.	420	123.50		543.50	light, double glazed aluminum
	Reinstall	Ea.		81.54		81.54	window including screen.
	Clean	Ea.	.06	8.05		8.11	
	Minimum Charge	Job		255		255	
3' x 3'							
	Demolish	Ea.		21.50		21.50	Cost includes material and labor to
	Install	Ea.	470	102		572	install 3' x 3' double hung, two light,
	Demolish and Install	Ea.	470	123.50		593.50	double glazed aluminum window
	Reinstall	Ea.		81.54		81.54	including screen.
	Clean	Ea.	.06	8.05		8.11	
	Minimum Charge	Job		255		255	
3' x 3' 6"							
	Demolish	Ea.		21.50		21.50	Cost includes material and labor to
	Install	Ea.	490	102		592	install 3' x 3' 6" double hung, two
	Demolish and Install	Ea.	490	123.50		613.50	light, double glazed aluminum
	Reinstall	Ea.		81.54		81.54	window including screen.
	Clean	Ea.	.08	9.35		9.43	
	Minimum Charge	Job		255		255	

Exterior Doors and Windows

Aluminum Window		Unit	Material	Labor	Equip.	Total	Specification
3' x 4'							
	Demolish	Ea.		21.50		21.50	Cost includes material and labor to
	Install	Ea.	530	102		632	install 3' x 4' double hung, two light,
	Demolish and Install	Ea.	530	123.50		653.50	double glazed aluminum window
	Reinstall	Ea.		81.54		81.54	including screen.
	Clean	Ea.	.08	9.35		9.43	
	Minimum Charge	Job		255		255	
3' x 5'							
	Demolish	Ea.		31		31	Cost includes material and labor to
	Install	Ea.	585	102		687	install 3' x 5' double hung, two light,
	Demolish and Install	Ea.	585	133		718	double glazed aluminum window
	Reinstall	Ea.		81.54		81.54	including screen.
	Clean	Ea.	.09	11.25		11.34	
	Minimum Charge	Job		255		255	
3' x 6'							
	Demolish	Ea.		31		31	Cost includes material and labor to
	Install	Ea.	615	113		728	install 3' x 6' double hung, two light,
	Demolish and Install	Ea.	615	144		759	double glazed aluminum window
	Reinstall	Ea.		90.60		90.60	including screen.
	Clean	Ea.	.11	13.20		13.31	
	Minimum Charge	Job		255		255	
Sliding Sash							
1' 6" x 3'							
	Demolish	Ea.		21.50		21.50	Cost includes material and labor to
	Install	Ea.	239	92.50		331.50	install 1' 6" x 3' sliding sash, two
	Demolish and Install	Ea.	239	114		353	light, double glazed aluminum
	Reinstall	Ea.		74.12		74.12	window including screen.
	Clean	Ea.	.03	7.05		7.08	
	Minimum Charge	Job		255		255	
2' x 2'							
	Demolish	Ea.		21.50		21.50	Cost includes material and labor to
	Install	Ea.	64	102		166	install 2' x 2' sliding sash, two light,
	Demolish and Install	Ea.	64	123.50		187.50	double glazed aluminum window
	Reinstall	Ea.		81.54		81.54	including screen.
	Clean	Ea.	.03	7.05		7.08	
	Minimum Charge	Job		255		255	
3' x 2'							
	Demolish	Ea.		21.50		21.50	Cost includes material and labor to
	Install	Ea.	252	102		354	install 3' x 2' sliding sash, two light,
	Demolish and Install	Ea.	252	123.50		375.50	double glazed aluminum window
	Reinstall	Ea.		81.54		81.54	including screen.
	Clean	Ea.	.03	7.05		7.08	
	Minimum Charge	Job		255		255	
3' x 2' 6"							
	Demolish	Ea.		21.50		21.50	Cost includes material and labor to
	Install	Ea.	87	102		189	install 3' x 2' 6" sliding sash, two
	Demolish and Install	Ea.	87	123.50		210.50	light, double glazed aluminum
	Reinstall	Ea.		81.54		81.54	window including screen.
	Clean	Ea.	.06	8.05		8.11	
	Minimum Charge	Job		255		255	
3' x 3'							
	Demolish	Ea.		21.50		21.50	Cost includes material and labor to
	Install	Ea.	305	102		407	install 3' x 3' sliding sash, two light,
	Demolish and Install	Ea.	305	123.50		428.50	double glazed aluminum window
	Reinstall	Ea.		81.54		81.54	including screen.
	Clean	Ea.	.06	8.05		8.11	
	Minimum Charge	Job		255		255	

Exterior Doors and Windows

Aluminum Window		Unit	Material	Labor	Equip.	Total	Specification
3' x 3' 6"							
	Demolish	Ea.		21.50		21.50	Cost includes material and labor to
	Install	Ea.	103	102		205	install 3' x 3' 6" sliding sash, two
	Demolish and Install	Ea.	103	123.50		226.50	light, double glazed aluminum
	Reinstall	Ea.		81.54		81.54	window including screen.
	Clean	Ea.	.08	9.35		9.43	
	Minimum Charge	Job		255		255	
3' x 4'							
	Demolish	Ea.		21.50		21.50	Cost includes material and labor to
	Install	Ea.	112	113		225	install 3' x 4' sliding sash, two light,
	Demolish and Install	Ea.	112	134.50		246.50	double glazed aluminum window
	Reinstall	Ea.		90.60		90.60	including screen.
	Clean	Ea.	.08	9.35		9.43	
	Minimum Charge	Job		255		255	
3' x 5'							
	Demolish	Ea.		31		31	Cost includes material and labor to
	Install	Ea.	143	113		256	install 3' x 5' sliding sash, two light,
	Demolish and Install	Ea.	143	144		287	double glazed aluminum window
	Reinstall	Ea.		90.60		90.60	including screen.
	Clean	Ea.	.09	11.25		11.34	
	Minimum Charge	Job		255		255	
4' x 5'							
	Demolish	Ea.		31		31	Cost includes material and labor to
	Install	Ea.	145	146		291	install 4' x 5' sliding sash, two light,
	Demolish and Install	Ea.	145	177		322	double glazed aluminum window
	Reinstall	Ea.		116.48		116.48	including screen.
	Clean	Ea.	.15	16.05		16.20	
	Minimum Charge	Job		255		255	
5' x 5'							
	Demolish	Ea.		31		31	Cost includes material and labor to
	Install	Ea.	350	146		496	install 5' x 5' sliding sash, two light,
	Demolish and Install	Ea.	350	177		527	double glazed aluminum window
	Reinstall	Ea.		116.48		116.48	including screen.
	Clean	Ea.	.15	16.05		16.20	
	Minimum Charge	Job		255		255	
Awning Sash							
26" x 26", 2 Light							
	Demolish	Ea.		21.50		21.50	Cost includes material and labor to
	Install	Ea.	299	113		412	install 26" x 26" two light awning,
	Demolish and Install	Ea.	299	134.50		433.50	double glazed aluminum window
	Reinstall	Ea.		90.60		90.60	including screen.
	Clean	Ea.	.06	8.05		8.11	
	Minimum Charge	Job		255		255	
26" x 37", 2 Light							
	Demolish	Ea.		21.50		21.50	Cost includes material and labor to
	Install	Ea.	340	113		453	install 26" x 37" two light awning,
	Demolish and Install	Ea.	340	134.50		474.50	double glazed aluminum window
	Reinstall	Ea.		90.60		90.60	including screen.
	Clean	Ea.	.06	8.05		8.11	
	Minimum Charge	Job		255		255	
38" x 26", 3 Light							
	Demolish	Ea.		21.50		21.50	Cost includes material and labor to
	Install	Ea.	385	113		498	install 38" x 26" three light awning,
	Demolish and Install	Ea.	385	134.50		519.50	double glazed aluminum window
	Reinstall	Ea.		90.60		90.60	including screen.
	Clean	Ea.	.08	9.35		9.43	
	Minimum Charge	Job		255		255	

Exterior Doors and Windows

Aluminum Window		Unit	Material	Labor	Equip.	Total	Specification
38" x 37", 3 Light							
	Demolish	Ea.		21.50		21.50	Cost includes material and labor to
	Install	Ea.	390	127		517	install 38" x 37" three light awning,
	Demolish and Install	Ea.	390	148.50		538.50	double glazed aluminum window
	Reinstall	Ea.		101.92		101.92	including screen.
	Clean	Ea.	.08	9.35		9.43	
	Minimum Charge	Job		255		255	
38" x 53", 3 Light							
	Demolish	Ea.		31		31	Cost includes material and labor to
	Install	Ea.	670	127		797	install 38" x 53" three light awning,
	Demolish and Install	Ea.	670	158		828	double glazed aluminum window
	Reinstall	Ea.		101.92		101.92	including screen.
	Clean	Ea.	.09	11.25		11.34	
	Minimum Charge	Job		255		255	
50" x 37", 4 Light							
	Demolish	Ea.		31		31	Cost includes material and labor to
	Install	Ea.	655	127		782	install 50" x 37" four light awning,
	Demolish and Install	Ea.	655	158		813	double glazed aluminum window
	Reinstall	Ea.		101.92		101.92	including screen.
	Clean	Ea.	.09	11.25		11.34	
	Minimum Charge	Job		255		255	
50" x 53", 4 Light							
	Demolish	Ea.		31		31	Cost includes material and labor to
	Install	Ea.	1100	146		1246	install 50" x 53" four light awning,
	Demolish and Install	Ea.	1100	177		1277	double glazed aluminum window
	Reinstall	Ea.		116.48		116.48	including screen.
	Clean	Ea.	.11	13.20		13.31	
	Minimum Charge	Job		255		255	
63" x 37", 5 Light							
	Demolish	Ea.		31		31	Cost includes material and labor to
	Install	Ea.	845	146		991	install 63" x 37" five light awning,
	Demolish and Install	Ea.	845	177		1022	double glazed aluminum window
	Reinstall	Ea.		116.48		116.48	including screen.
	Clean	Ea.	.11	13.20		13.31	
	Minimum Charge	Job		255		255	
63" x 53", 5 Light							
	Demolish	Ea.		31		31	Cost includes material and labor to
	Install	Ea.	1200	146		1346	install 63" x 53" five light awning,
	Demolish and Install	Ea.	1200	177		1377	double glazed aluminum window
	Reinstall	Ea.		116.48		116.48	including screen.
	Clean	Ea.	.15	16.05		16.20	
	Minimum Charge	Job		255		255	
Mullion Bars							
	Install	Ea.	13.30	41		54.30	Includes labor and material to install
	Minimum Charge	Job		255		255	mullions for sliding aluminum window.
Bay							
4' 8" x 6' 4"							
	Demolish	Ea.		22.50		22.50	Cost includes material and labor to
	Install	Ea.	1600	104		1704	install 4' 8" x 6' 4" angle bay double
	Demolish and Install	Ea.	1600	126.50		1726.50	hung unit, pine frame with aluminum
	Reinstall	Ea.		82.88		82.88	cladding, picture center sash,
	Clean	Ea.	.21	18.75		18.96	hardware, screens.
	Minimum Charge	Job		255		255	

Exterior Doors and Windows

Aluminum Window		Unit	Material	Labor	Equip.	Total	Specification
4' 8" x 7' 2"							Cost includes material and labor to
	Demolish	Ea.		22.50		22.50	install 4' 8" x 7' 2" angle bay double
	Install	Ea.	1650	104		1754	hung unit, pine frame with aluminum
	Demolish and Install	Ea.	1650	126.50		1776.50	cladding, picture center sash,
	Reinstall	Ea.		82.88		82.88	hardware, screens.
	Clean	Ea.	.21	18.75		18.96	
	Minimum Charge	Job		255		255	
4' 8" x 7' 10"							Cost includes material and labor to
	Demolish	Ea.		22.50		22.50	install 4' 8" x 7' 10" angle bay
	Install	Ea.	1675	104		1779	double hung unit, pine frame with
	Demolish and Install	Ea.	1675	126.50		1801.50	aluminum cladding, picture center
	Reinstall	Ea.		82.88		82.88	sash, hardware, screens.
	Clean	Ea.	.21	18.75		18.96	
	Minimum Charge	Job		255		255	
4' 8" x 8' 6"							Cost includes material and labor to
	Demolish	Ea.		26		26	install 4' 8" x 8' 6" angle bay double
	Install	Ea.	1650	118		1768	hung unit, pine frame with aluminum
	Demolish and Install	Ea.	1650	144		1794	cladding, picture center sash,
	Reinstall	Ea.		94.72		94.72	hardware, screens.
	Clean	Ea.	.03	25		25.03	
	Minimum Charge	Job		255		255	
4' 8" x 8' 10"							Cost includes material and labor to
	Demolish	Ea.		26		26	install 4' 8" x 8' 10" angle bay
	Install	Ea.	1675	118		1793	double hung unit, pine frame with
	Demolish and Install	Ea.	1675	144		1819	aluminum cladding, picture center
	Reinstall	Ea.		94.72		94.72	sash, hardware, screens.
	Clean	Ea.	.03	25		25.03	
	Minimum Charge	Job		255		255	
4' 8" x 9' 2"							Cost includes material and labor to
	Demolish	Ea.		26		26	install 4' 8" x 9' 2" angle bay double
	Install	Ea.	1700	207		1907	hung unit, pine frame with aluminum
	Demolish and Install	Ea.	1700	233		1933	cladding, picture center sash,
	Reinstall	Ea.		165.76		165.76	hardware, screens.
	Clean	Ea.	.03	25		25.03	
	Minimum Charge	Job		255		255	
4' 8" x 9' 10"							Cost includes material and labor to
	Demolish	Ea.		26		26	install 4' 8" x 9' 10" angle bay
	Install	Ea.	1800	207		2007	double hung unit, pine frame with
	Demolish and Install	Ea.	1800	233		2033	aluminum cladding, picture center
	Reinstall	Ea.		165.76		165.76	sash, hardware, screens.
	Clean	Ea.	.03	25		25.03	
	Minimum Charge	Job		255		255	
Casing							Cost includes material and labor to
	Demolish	Ea.		9.60		9.60	install 11/16" x 2-1/2" pine ranch
	Install	Opng.	38	32		70	style window casing.
	Demolish and Install	Opng.	38	41.60		79.60	
	Reinstall	Opng.		25.50		25.50	
	Clean	Opng.	.68	3.06		3.74	
	Paint	Ea.	5.25	7.10		12.35	
	Minimum Charge	Job		255		255	
Storm Window							
2' x 3' 6"							Includes material and labor to install
	Demolish	Ea.		12.60		12.60	residential aluminum storm window
	Install	Ea.	82.50	27.50		110	with mill finish, 2' x 3' 5" high.
	Demolish and Install	Ea.	82.50	40.10		122.60	
	Reinstall	Ea.		22.10		22.10	
	Clean	Ea.	.03	7.05		7.08	
	Minimum Charge	Job		255		255	

Exterior Doors and Windows

Aluminum Window		Unit	Material	Labor	Equip.	Total	Specification
2' 6" x 5'							
	Demolish	Ea.		12.60		12.60	Includes material and labor to install
	Install	Ea.	93.50	29.50		123	residential aluminum storm window
	Demolish and Install	Ea.	93.50	42.10		135.60	with mill finish, 2' 6" x 5' high.
	Reinstall	Ea.		23.68		23.68	
	Clean	Ea.	.08	9.35		9.43	
	Minimum Charge	Job		255		255	
4' x 6'							
	Demolish	Ea.		24.50		24.50	Includes material and labor to install
	Install	Ea.	108	33		141	residential aluminum storm window, 4'
	Demolish and Install	Ea.	108	57.50		165.50	x 6' high.
	Reinstall	Ea.		26.52		26.52	
	Clean	Ea.	.14	14.05		14.19	
	Minimum Charge	Job		255		255	
Hardware							
Weatherstripping							
	Install	L.F.	.52	3.45		3.97	Includes labor and material to install
	Minimum Charge	Job		138		138	vinyl V strip weatherstripping for double-hung window.
Trim Set							
	Demolish	Ea.		9.60		9.60	Cost includes material and labor to
	Install	Opng.	38	32		70	install 11/16" x 2-1/2" pine ranch
	Demolish and Install	Opng.	38	41.60		79.60	style window casing.
	Reinstall	Opng.		25.50		25.50	
	Clean	Opng.	.68	3.06		3.74	
	Paint	Ea.	5.25	7.10		12.35	
	Minimum Charge	Job		207		207	

Vinyl Window		Unit	Material	Labor	Equip.	Total	Specification
Double Hung							
2' x 2' 6"							
	Demolish	Ea.		15.45		15.45	Cost includes material and labor to
	Install	Ea.	219	55.50		274.50	install 2' x 2' 6" double hung, two
	Demolish and Install	Ea.	219	70.95		289.95	light, vinyl window with screen.
	Reinstall	Ea.		44.20		44.20	
	Clean	Ea.	.03	7.05		7.08	
	Minimum Charge	Job		138		138	
2' x 3' 6"							
	Demolish	Ea.		15.45		15.45	Cost includes material and labor to
	Install	Ea.	233	59		292	install 2' x 3' 6" double hung, two
	Demolish and Install	Ea.	233	74.45		307.45	light, vinyl window with screen.
	Reinstall	Ea.		47.36		47.36	
	Clean	Ea.	.06	8.05		8.11	
	Minimum Charge	Job		138		138	
2' 6" x 4' 6"							
	Demolish	Ea.		15.45		15.45	Cost includes material and labor to
	Install	Ea.	275	64		339	install 2' 6" x 4' 6" double hung, two
	Demolish and Install	Ea.	275	79.45		354.45	light, vinyl window with screen.
	Reinstall	Ea.		51		51	
	Clean	Ea.	.08	9.35		9.43	
	Minimum Charge	Job		138		138	
3' x 4'							
	Demolish	Ea.		15.45		15.45	Includes material and labor to install
	Install	Ea.	238	83		321	medium size double hung, 3' x 4',
	Demolish and Install	Ea.	238	98.45		336.45	two light, vinyl window with screen.
	Reinstall	Ea.		66.30		66.30	
	Clean	Ea.	.08	9.35		9.43	
	Minimum Charge	Job		138		138	

Exterior Doors and Windows

Vinyl Window		Unit	Material	Labor	Equip.	Total	Specification
3' x 4' 6"							
	Demolish	Ea.		18.90		18.90	Cost includes material and labor to
	Install	Ea.	305	92		397	install 3' x 4' 6" double hung, two
	Demolish and Install	Ea.	305	110.90		415.90	light, vinyl window with screen.
	Reinstall	Ea.		73.67		73.67	
	Clean	Ea.	.09	11.25		11.34	
	Minimum Charge	Job		138		138	
4' x 4' 6"							
	Demolish	Ea.		18.90		18.90	Cost includes material and labor to
	Install	Ea.	320	104		424	install 4' x 4' 6" double hung, two
	Demolish and Install	Ea.	320	122.90		442.90	light, vinyl window with screen.
	Reinstall	Ea.		82.88		82.88	
	Clean	Ea.	.11	13.20		13.31	
	Minimum Charge	Job		138		138	
4' x 6'							
	Demolish	Ea.		18.90		18.90	Includes material and labor to install
	Install	Ea.	375	118		493	large double hung, 4' x 6', two light,
	Demolish and Install	Ea.	375	136.90		511.90	vinyl window with screen.
	Reinstall	Ea.		94.72		94.72	
	Clean	Ea.	.15	16.05		16.20	
	Minimum Charge	Job		138		138	
Trim Set							
	Demolish	Ea.		9.60		9.60	Cost includes material and labor to
	Install	Opng.	38	32		70	install 11/16" x 2-1/2" pine ranch
	Demolish and Install	Opng.	38	41.60		79.60	style window casing.
	Reinstall	Opng.		25.50		25.50	
	Clean	Opng.	.68	3.06		3.74	
	Paint	Ea.	5.25	7.10		12.35	
	Minimum Charge	Job		255		255	

Wood Window		Unit	Material	Labor	Equip.	Total	Specification
2' 2" x 3' 4"							
	Demolish	Ea.		15.45		15.45	Cost includes material and labor to
	Install	Ea.	231	55.50		286.50	install 2' 2" x 3' 4" double hung, two
	Demolish and Install	Ea.	231	70.95		301.95	light, double glazed wood window
	Reinstall	Ea.		44.20		44.20	with screen.
	Clean	Ea.	.06	8.05		8.11	
	Paint	Ea.	3.29	14.80		18.09	
	Minimum Charge	Job		207		207	
2' 2" x 4' 4"							
	Demolish	Ea.		15.45		15.45	Cost includes material and labor to
	Install	Ea.	252	59		311	install 2' 2" x 4' 4" double hung, two
	Demolish and Install	Ea.	252	74.45		326.45	light, double glazed wood window
	Reinstall	Ea.		47.36		47.36	with screen.
	Clean	Ea.	.06	8.05		8.11	
	Paint	Ea.	3.29	14.80		18.09	
	Minimum Charge	Job		207		207	
2' 6" x 3' 4"							
	Demolish	Ea.		15.45		15.45	Cost includes material and labor to
	Install	Ea.	241	64		305	install 2' 6" x 3' 4" double hung, two
	Demolish and Install	Ea.	241	79.45		320.45	light, double glazed wood window
	Reinstall	Ea.		51		51	with screen.
	Clean	Ea.	.08	9.35		9.43	
	Paint	Ea.	4.21	17.75		21.96	
	Minimum Charge	Job		207		207	

Exterior Doors and Windows

Wood Window		Unit	Material	Labor	Equip.	Total	Specification
2' 6" x 4'							
	Demolish	Ea.		15.45		15.45	Cost includes material and labor to
	Install	Ea.	252	69		321	install 2' 6" x 4' double hung, two
	Demolish and Install	Ea.	252	84.45		336.45	light, double glazed wood window
	Reinstall	Ea.		55.25		55.25	with screen.
	Clean	Ea.	.08	9.35		9.43	
	Paint	Ea.	4.21	17.75		21.96	
	Minimum Charge	Job		207		207	
2' 6" x 4' 8"							
	Demolish	Ea.		15.45		15.45	Cost includes material and labor to
	Install	Ea.	275	69		344	install 2' 6" x 4' 8" double hung, two
	Demolish and Install	Ea.	275	84.45		359.45	light, double glazed wood window
	Reinstall	Ea.		55.25		55.25	with screen.
	Clean	Ea.	.08	9.35		9.43	
	Paint	Ea.	4.21	17.75		21.96	
	Minimum Charge	Job		207		207	
2' 10" x 3' 4"							
	Demolish	Ea.		15.45		15.45	Cost includes material and labor to
	Install	Ea.	246	83		329	install 2' 10" x 3' 4" double hung, two
	Demolish and Install	Ea.	246	98.45		344.45	light, double glazed wood window
	Reinstall	Ea.		66.30		66.30	with screen.
	Clean	Ea.	.08	9.35		9.43	
	Paint	Ea.	4.21	17.75		21.96	
	Minimum Charge	Job		207		207	
2' 10" x 4'							
	Demolish	Ea.		15.45		15.45	Cost includes material and labor to
	Install	Ea.	272	83		355	install 2' 10" x 4' double hung, two
	Demolish and Install	Ea.	272	98.45		370.45	light, double glazed wood window
	Reinstall	Ea.		66.30		66.30	with screen.
	Clean	Ea.	.08	9.35		9.43	
	Paint	Ea.	4.21	17.75		21.96	
	Minimum Charge	Job		207		207	
3' 7" x 3' 4"							
	Demolish	Ea.		15.45		15.45	Cost includes material and labor to
	Install	Ea.	279	92		371	install 3' 7" x 3' 4" double hung, two
	Demolish and Install	Ea.	279	107.45		386.45	light, double glazed wood window
	Reinstall	Ea.		73.67		73.67	with screen.
	Clean	Ea.	.08	9.35		9.43	
	Paint	Ea.	4.21	17.75		21.96	
	Minimum Charge	Job		207		207	
3' 7" x 5' 4"							
	Demolish	Ea.		18.90		18.90	Cost includes material and labor to
	Install	Ea.	310	92		402	install 3' 7" x 5' 4" double hung, two
	Demolish and Install	Ea.	310	110.90		420.90	light, double glazed wood window
	Reinstall	Ea.		73.67		73.67	with screen.
	Clean	Ea.	.15	16.05		16.20	
	Paint	Ea.	7.05	29.50		36.55	
	Minimum Charge	Job		207		207	
4' 3" x 5' 4"							
	Demolish	Ea.		18.90		18.90	Cost includes material and labor to
	Install	Ea.	560	104		664	install 4' 3" x 5' 4" double hung, two
	Demolish and Install	Ea.	560	122.90		682.90	light, double glazed wood window
	Reinstall	Ea.		82.88		82.88	with screen.
	Clean	Ea.	.15	16.05		16.20	
	Paint	Ea.	4.84	35.50		40.34	
	Minimum Charge	Job		207		207	

Wood Window		Unit	Material	Labor	Equip.	Total	Specification
Casement							
2' x 3' 4"							
	Demolish	Ea.		15.45		15.45	Cost includes material and labor to
	Install	Ea.	288	41.50		329.50	install 2' x 3' 4" casement window
	Demolish and Install	Ea.	288	56.95		344.95	with 3/4" insulated glass, screens,
	Reinstall	Ea.		33.15		33.15	weatherstripping, hardware.
	Clean	Ea.	.06	8.05		8.11	
	Paint	Ea.	3.29	14.80		18.09	
	Minimum Charge	Job		415		415	
2' x 4'							
	Demolish	Ea.		15.45		15.45	Cost includes material and labor to
	Install	Ea.	305	46		351	install 2' x 4' casement window with
	Demolish and Install	Ea.	305	61.45		366.45	3/4" insulated glass, screens,
	Reinstall	Ea.		36.84		36.84	weatherstripping, hardware.
	Clean	Ea.	.06	8.05		8.11	
	Paint	Ea.	3.29	14.80		18.09	
	Minimum Charge	Job		415		415	
2' x 5'							
	Demolish	Ea.		15.45		15.45	Cost includes material and labor to
	Install	Ea.	335	49		384	install 2' x 5' casement window with
	Demolish and Install	Ea.	335	64.45		399.45	3/4" insulated glass, screens,
	Reinstall	Ea.		39		39	weatherstripping, hardware.
	Clean	Ea.	.08	9.35		9.43	
	Paint	Ea.	4.21	17.75		21.96	
	Minimum Charge	Job		415		415	
2' x 6'							
	Demolish	Ea.		15.45		15.45	Cost includes material and labor to
	Install	Ea.	335	52		387	install 2' x 6' casement window with
	Demolish and Install	Ea.	335	67.45		402.45	3/4" insulated glass, screens,
	Reinstall	Ea.		41.44		41.44	weatherstripping, hardware.
	Clean	Ea.	.08	9.35		9.43	
	Paint	Ea.	4.21	17.75		21.96	
	Minimum Charge	Job		415		415	
4' x 3' 4"							
	Demolish	Ea.		18.90		18.90	Cost includes material and labor to
	Install	Ea.	645	55.50		700.50	install 4' x 3' 4" casement windows
	Demolish and Install	Ea.	645	74.40		719.40	with 3/4" insulated glass, screens,
	Reinstall	Ea.		44.20		44.20	weatherstripping, hardware.
	Clean	Ea.	.08	9.35		9.43	
	Paint	Ea.	2.42	17.75		20.17	
	Minimum Charge	Job		415		415	
4' x 4'							
	Demolish	Ea.		18.90		18.90	Cost includes material and labor to
	Install	Ea.	720	55.50		775.50	install 4' x 4' casement windows with
	Demolish and Install	Ea.	720	74.40		794.40	3/4" insulated glass, screens,
	Reinstall	Ea.		44.20		44.20	weatherstripping, hardware.
	Clean	Ea.	.11	13.20		13.31	
	Paint	Ea.	2.86	22		24.86	
	Minimum Charge	Job		415		415	
4' x 5'							
	Demolish	Ea.		18.90		18.90	Cost includes material and labor to
	Install	Ea.	815	59		874	install 4' x 5' casement windows with
	Demolish and Install	Ea.	815	77.90		892.90	3/4" insulated glass, screens,
	Reinstall	Ea.		47.36		47.36	weatherstripping, hardware.
	Clean	Ea.	.15	16.05		16.20	
	Paint	Ea.	3.74	29.50		33.24	
	Minimum Charge	Job		415		415	

Wood Window	Unit	Material	Labor	Equip.	Total	Specification
4' x 6'						
Demolish	Ea.		18.90		18.90	Cost includes material and labor to
Install	Ea.	920	69		989	install 4' x 6' casement windows with
Demolish and Install	Ea.	920	87.90		1007.90	3/4" insulated glass, screens,
Reinstall	Ea.		55.25		55.25	weatherstripping, hardware.
Clean	Ea.	.15	16.05		16.20	
Paint	Ea.	4.40	35.50		39.90	
Minimum Charge	Job		415		415	
Casement Bow						
4' 8" x 8' 1"						
Demolish	Ea.		26		26	Includes material and labor to install
Install	Ea.	1725	155		1880	casement bow window unit with 4
Demolish and Install	Ea.	1725	181		1906	lights, pine frame, 1/2" insulated
Reinstall	Ea.		124.32		124.32	glass, weatherstripping, hardware,
Clean	Ea.	.21	18.75		18.96	screens.
Paint	Ea.	8.15	71		79.15	
Minimum Charge	Job		415		415	
4' 8" x 10'						
Demolish	Ea.		26		26	Includes material and labor to install
Install	Ea.	2125	207		2332	casement bow window unit with 5
Demolish and Install	Ea.	2125	233		2358	lights, pine frame, 1/2" insulated
Reinstall	Ea.		165.76		165.76	glass, weatherstripping, hardware,
Clean	Ea.	.03	25		25.03	screens.
Paint	Ea.	10.10	89		99.10	
Minimum Charge	Job		415		415	
5' 4" x 8' 1"						
Demolish	Ea.		26		26	Includes material and labor to install
Install	Ea.	1850	155		2005	casement bow window unit with 4
Demolish and Install	Ea.	1850	181		2031	lights, pine frame, 1/2" insulated
Reinstall	Ea.		124.32		124.32	glass, weatherstripping, hardware,
Clean	Ea.	.03	25		25.03	screens.
Paint	Ea.	9.25	71		80.25	
Minimum Charge	Job		415		415	
5' 4" x 10'						
Demolish	Ea.		26		26	Includes material and labor to install
Install	Ea.	2100	207		2307	casement bow window unit with 5
Demolish and Install	Ea.	2100	233		2333	lights, pine frame, 1/2" insulated
Reinstall	Ea.		165.76		165.76	glass, weatherstripping, hardware,
Clean	Ea.	.03	25		25.03	screens.
Paint	Ea.	11.65	89		100.65	
Minimum Charge	Job		415		415	
6' x 8' 1"						
Demolish	Ea.		26		26	Includes material and labor to install
Install	Ea.	2125	207		2332	casement bow window unit with 5
Demolish and Install	Ea.	2125	233		2358	lights, pine frame, 1/2" insulated
Reinstall	Ea.		165.76		165.76	glass, weatherstripping, hardware,
Clean	Ea.	.03	25		25.03	screens.
Paint	Ea.	10.55	89		99.55	
Minimum Charge	Job		415		415	
6' x 10'						
Demolish	Ea.		26		26	Includes material and labor to install
Install	Ea.	2200	207		2407	casement bow window unit with 5
Demolish and Install	Ea.	2200	233		2433	lights, pine frame, 1/2" insulated
Reinstall	Ea.		165.76		165.76	glass, weatherstripping, hardware,
Clean	Ea.	.03	25		25.03	screens.
Paint	Ea.	13.20	118		131.20	
Minimum Charge	Job		415		415	

Exterior Doors and Windows

Wood Window		Unit	Material	Labor	Equip.	Total	Specification
Casing							
	Demolish	Ea.		9.60		9.60	Cost includes material and labor to
	Install	Opng.	38	32		70	install 11/16" x 2-1/2" pine ranch
	Demolish and Install	Opng.	38	41.60		79.60	style window casing.
	Reinstall	Opng.		25.50		25.50	
	Clean	Opng.	.68	3.06		3.74	
	Paint	Ea.	5.25	7.10		12.35	
	Minimum Charge	Job		255		255	
Trim Set							
	Demolish	Ea.		7.30		7.30	Cost includes material and labor to
	Install	Opng.	38	32		70	install 11/16" x 2-1/2" pine ranch
	Demolish and Install	Opng.	38	39.30		77.30	style window casing.
	Reinstall	Opng.		25.50		25.50	
	Clean	Opng.	.68	3.06		3.74	
	Paint	Ea.	5.25	7.10		12.35	
	Minimum Charge	Job		207		207	
Wood Picture Window							
3' 6" x 4'							
	Demolish	Ea.		18.90		18.90	Includes material and labor to install a
	Install	Ea.	450	69		519	wood framed picture window
	Demolish and Install	Ea.	450	87.90		537.90	including exterior trim.
	Clean	Ea.	.15	16.05		16.20	
	Paint	Ea.	3.47	27.50		30.97	
	Minimum Charge	Job		415		415	
4' x 4' 6"							
	Demolish	Ea.		18.90		18.90	Includes material and labor to install a
	Install	Ea.	585	75.50		660.50	wood framed picture window
	Demolish and Install	Ea.	585	94.40		679.40	including exterior trim.
	Clean	Ea.	.15	16.05		16.20	
	Paint	Ea.	3.47	27.50		30.97	
	Minimum Charge	Job		415		415	
5' x 4'							
	Demolish	Ea.		18.90		18.90	Includes material and labor to install a
	Install	Ea.	665	75.50		740.50	wood framed picture window
	Demolish and Install	Ea.	665	94.40		759.40	including exterior trim.
	Clean	Ea.	.15	16.05		16.20	
	Paint	Ea.	7.45	44.50		51.95	
	Minimum Charge	Job		415		415	
6' x 4' 6"							
	Demolish	Ea.		18.90		18.90	Includes material and labor to install a
	Install	Ea.	700	83		783	wood framed picture window
	Demolish and Install	Ea.	700	101.90		801.90	including exterior trim.
	Clean	Ea.	.15	16.05		16.20	
	Paint	Ea.	7.45	44.50		51.95	
	Minimum Charge	Job		415		415	

Window Screens		Unit	Material	Labor	Equip.	Total	Specification
Small							
	Demolish	Ea.		3.55		3.55	Includes material and labor to install
	Install	Ea.	19.70	12.55		32.25	small window screen, 4 S.F.
	Demolish and Install	Ea.	19.70	16.10		35.80	
	Reinstall	Ea.		10.05		10.05	
	Clean	Ea.	.47	6.40		6.87	
	Minimum Charge	Job		104		104	

Exterior Doors and Windows

Window Screens		Unit	Material	Labor	Equip.	Total	Specification
Standard Size							
	Demolish	Ea.		3.55		3.55	Includes material and labor to install
	Install	Ea.	48	12.55		60.55	medium window screen, 12 S.F.
	Demolish and Install	Ea.	48	16.10		64.10	
	Reinstall	Ea.		10.05		10.05	
	Clean	Ea.	.47	6.40		6.87	
	Minimum Charge	Job		104		104	
Large							
	Demolish	Ea.		3.55		3.55	Includes material and labor to install
	Install	Ea.	64	12.55		76.55	large window screen, 16 S.F.
	Demolish and Install	Ea.	64	16.10		80.10	
	Reinstall	Ea.		10.05		10.05	
	Clean	Ea.	.47	6.40		6.87	
	Minimum Charge	Job		104		104	

Window Glass		Unit	Material	Labor	Equip.	Total	Specification
Plate, Clear, 1/4"							
	Demolish	S.F.		1.70		1.70	Includes material and labor to install
	Install	S.F.	9.10	6.70		15.80	clear glass.
	Demolish and Install	S.F.	9.10	8.40		17.50	
	Reinstall	S.F.		5.36		5.36	
	Clean	S.F.	.04	.18		.22	
	Minimum Charge	Job		201		201	
Insulated							
	Demolish	S.F.		1.70		1.70	Includes material and labor to install
	Install	S.F.	14.80	11.50		26.30	insulated glass.
	Demolish and Install	S.F.	14.80	13.20		28	
	Reinstall	S.F.		9.19		9.19	
	Clean	S.F.	.04	.18		.22	
	Minimum Charge	Job		201		201	
Tinted							
	Demolish	S.F.		1.70		1.70	Includes material and labor to install
	Install	S.F.	8.20	6.20		14.40	tinted glass.
	Demolish and Install	S.F.	8.20	7.90		16.10	
	Reinstall	S.F.		4.95		4.95	
	Clean	S.F.	.04	.18		.22	
	Minimum Charge	Job		201		201	
Obscure / Florentine							
	Demolish	S.F.		1.70		1.70	Includes material and labor to install
	Install	S.F.	12.30	5.75		18.05	obscure glass.
	Demolish and Install	S.F.	12.30	7.45		19.75	
	Reinstall	S.F.		4.59		4.59	
	Clean	S.F.	.04	.18		.22	
	Minimum Charge	Job		201		201	
Laminated Safety							
	Demolish	S.F.		1.70		1.70	Includes material and labor to install
	Install	S.F.	12.95	8.95		21.90	clear laminated glass.
	Demolish and Install	S.F.	12.95	10.65		23.60	
	Reinstall	S.F.		7.15		7.15	
	Clean	S.F.	.04	.18		.22	
	Minimum Charge	Job		201		201	

Exterior Doors and Windows

Window Glass		Unit	Material	Labor	Equip.	Total	Specification
Wired							
	Demolish	S.F.		1.70		1.70	Includes material and labor to install
	Install	S.F.	23	5.95		28.95	rough obscure wire glass.
	Demolish and Install	S.F.	23	7.65		30.65	
	Reinstall	S.F.		4.76		4.76	
	Clean	S.F.	.04	.18		.22	
	Minimum Charge	Job		201		201	
Tempered							
	Demolish	S.F.		1.70		1.70	Includes material and labor to install
	Install	S.F.	9.10	6.70		15.80	clear glass.
	Demolish and Install	S.F.	9.10	8.40		17.50	
	Reinstall	S.F.		5.36		5.36	
	Clean	S.F.	.04	.18		.22	
	Minimum Charge	Job		201		201	
Stained							
	Demolish	S.F.		1.70		1.70	Includes material and labor to install
	Install	S.F.	67	6.70		73.70	stained glass.
	Demolish and Install	S.F.	67	8.40		75.40	
	Reinstall	S.F.		5.36		5.36	
	Clean	S.F.	.04	.18		.22	
	Minimum Charge	Job		201		201	
Etched							
	Demolish	S.F.		1.70		1.70	Includes material and labor to install
	Install	S.F.	55	6.70		61.70	etched glass.
	Demolish and Install	S.F.	55	8.40		63.40	
	Reinstall	S.F.		5.36		5.36	
	Clean	S.F.	.04	.18		.22	
	Minimum Charge	Job		201		201	
Wall Mirror							
	Demolish	S.F.		1.70		1.70	Includes material and labor to install
	Install	S.F.	10.45	6.45		16.90	distortion-free float glass mirror, 1/4"
	Demolish and Install	S.F.	10.45	8.15		18.60	thick, cut and polished edges.
	Reinstall	S.F.		5.15		5.15	
	Clean	S.F.	.04	.18		.22	
	Minimum Charge	Job		201		201	
Bullet Resistant							
	Demolish	S.F.		1.70		1.70	Includes material and labor to install
	Install	S.F.	124	80.50		204.50	bullet resistant clear laminated glass.
	Demolish and Install	S.F.	124	82.20		206.20	
	Reinstall	S.F.		64.32		64.32	
	Clean	S.F.	.04	.18		.22	
	Minimum Charge	Job		201		201	

Storefront System		Unit	Material	Labor	Equip.	Total	Specification
Clear Glass							
Stub Wall to 8'							
	Demolish	S.F.		2.66		2.66	Includes material and labor to install
	Install	S.F.	24	11.10		35.10	commercial grade 4-1/2" section,
	Demolish and Install	S.F.	24	13.76		37.76	anodized aluminum with clear glass in
	Reinstall	S.F.		8.88		8.88	upper section and safety glass in
	Clean	S.F.	.01	.37		.38	lower section.
	Minimum Charge	Job		255		255	

Exterior Doors and Windows

Storefront System		Unit	Material	Labor	Equip.	Total	Specification
Floor to 10'							
	Demolish	S.F.		2.66		2.66	Includes material and labor to install
	Install	S.F.	25	11.10		36.10	commercial grade 4-1/2" section,
	Demolish and Install	S.F.	25	13.76		38.76	anodized aluminum with clear glass in
	Reinstall	S.F.		8.88		8.88	upper section and safety glass in
	Clean	S.F.	.01	.37		.38	lower section.
	Minimum Charge	Job		255		255	
Polished Plate Glass							
Stub Wall to 9'							
	Demolish	S.F.		2.66		2.66	Cost includes material and labor to
	Install	S.F.	15.95	11.10		27.05	install 4' x 9' polished plate glass
	Demolish and Install	S.F.	15.95	13.76		29.71	window built on 8" stub wall.
	Reinstall	S.F.		8.88		8.88	
	Clean	S.F.	.01	.37		.38	
	Minimum Charge	Job		255		255	
Stub Wall to 13'							
	Demolish	S.F.		2.66		2.66	Cost includes material and labor to
	Install	S.F.	17.25	11.10		28.35	install 4' x 13' polished plate glass
	Demolish and Install	S.F.	17.25	13.76		31.01	window built on 8" stub wall.
	Reinstall	S.F.		8.88		8.88	
	Clean	S.F.	.01	.37		.38	
	Minimum Charge	Job		255		255	
Floor to 9'							
	Demolish	S.F.		2.66		2.66	Cost includes material and labor to
	Install	S.F.	17.80	11.10		28.90	install 4' x 9' polished plate glass
	Demolish and Install	S.F.	17.80	13.76		31.56	window built on floor.
	Reinstall	S.F.		8.88		8.88	
	Clean	S.F.	.01	.37		.38	
	Minimum Charge	Job		255		255	
Floor to 13'							
	Demolish	S.F.		2.66		2.66	Cost includes material and labor to
	Install	S.F.	19.15	11.10		30.25	install 4' x 13' polished plate glass
	Demolish and Install	S.F.	19.15	13.76		32.91	window built on floor.
	Reinstall	S.F.		8.88		8.88	
	Clean	S.F.	.01	.37		.38	
	Minimum Charge	Job		255		255	
Clear Plate Glass							
Floor to 9'							
	Demolish	S.F.		2.66		2.66	Cost includes material and labor to
	Install	S.F.	25.50	11.10		36.60	install 4' x 9' clear plate glass window
	Demolish and Install	S.F.	25.50	13.76		39.26	built on floor.
	Reinstall	S.F.		8.88		8.88	
	Clean	S.F.	.01	.37		.38	
	Minimum Charge	Job		255		255	
Floor to 11'							
	Demolish	S.F.		2.66		2.66	Cost includes material and labor to
	Install	S.F.	25	11.10		36.10	install 4' x 11' clear plate glass
	Demolish and Install	S.F.	25	13.76		38.76	window built on floor.
	Reinstall	S.F.		8.88		8.88	
	Clean	S.F.	.01	.37		.38	
	Minimum Charge	Job		255		255	
Floor to 13'							
	Demolish	S.F.		2.66		2.66	Cost includes material and labor to
	Install	S.F.	25	11.10		36.10	install 4' x 13' clear plate glass
	Demolish and Install	S.F.	25	13.76		38.76	window built on floor.
	Reinstall	S.F.		8.88		8.88	
	Clean	S.F.	.01	.37		.38	
	Minimum Charge	Job		255		255	

Exterior Doors and Windows

Storefront System		Unit	Material	Labor	Equip.	Total	Specification
Entrance							
Narrow Stile 3' x 7"							
	Demolish	Ea.		23		23	Cost includes material and labor to
	Install	Ea.	855	276		1131	install 3' x 7' narrow stile door, center
	Demolish and Install	Ea.	855	299		1154	pivot concealed closer.
	Reinstall	Ea.		221.01		221.01	
	Clean	Ea.	6	38.50		44.50	
	Minimum Charge	Job		255		255	
Tempered Glass							
	Demolish	Ea.		23		23	Cost includes material and labor to
	Install	Ea.	3350	550		3900	install 3' x 7' tempered glass door,
	Demolish and Install	Ea.	3350	573		3923	center pivot concealed closer,.
	Reinstall	Ea.		440.74		440.74	
	Clean	Ea.	6	38.50		44.50	
	Minimum Charge	Job		255		255	
Heavy Section							
	Demolish	Ea.		23		23	Includes material and labor to install
	Install	Ea.	1275	510		1785	wide stile door with 3' 6" x 7'
	Demolish and Install	Ea.	1275	533		1808	opening.
	Reinstall	Ea.		407.68		407.68	
	Clean	Ea.	1.20	12.75		13.95	
	Minimum Charge	Job		805		805	

Curtain Wall System		Unit	Material	Labor	Equip.	Total	Specification
Regular Weight							
Bronze Anodized							
	Demolish	S.F.		2.66		2.66	Includes material and labor to install
	Install	S.F.	39.50	11.10		50.60	structural curtain wall system with
	Demolish and Install	S.F.	39.50	13.76		53.26	bronze anodized frame of heavy
	Clean	S.F.	.01	.37		.38	weight, float glass.
	Minimum Charge	Job		207		207	
Black Anodized							
	Demolish	S.F.		2.66		2.66	Includes material and labor to install
	Install	S.F.	43	11.10		54.10	structural curtain wall system with
	Demolish and Install	S.F.	43	13.76		56.76	black anodized frame of regular
	Clean	S.F.	.01	.37		.38	weight, float glass.
	Minimum Charge	Job		207		207	
Heavy Weight							
Bronze Anodized							
	Demolish	S.F.		2.66		2.66	Includes material and labor to install
	Install	S.F.	39.50	11.10		50.60	structural curtain wall system with
	Demolish and Install	S.F.	39.50	13.76		53.26	bronze anodized frame of heavy
	Clean	S.F.	.01	.37		.38	weight, float glass.
	Minimum Charge	Job		207		207	
Black Anodized							
	Demolish	S.F.		2.66		2.66	Includes material and labor to install
	Install	S.F.	40.50	11.10		51.60	structural curtain wall system with
	Demolish and Install	S.F.	40.50	13.76		54.26	black anodized frame of heavy
	Clean	S.F.	.01	.37		.38	weight, float glass.
	Minimum Charge	Job		207		207	
Glass							
1" Insulated							
	Install	S.F.	17.55	10.70		28.25	Cost includes labor and material to
	Minimum Charge	Job		201		201	install 1" insulated glass.

Skylight		Unit	Material	Labor	Equip.	Total	Specification
Dome							
22″ x 22″							
	Demolish	Ea.		78.50		78.50	Cost includes material and labor to
	Install	Ea.	220	127		347	install 22″ x 22″ fixed dome skylight.
	Demolish and Install	Ea.	220	205.50		425.50	
	Reinstall	Ea.		101.93		101.93	
	Clean	Ea.	.54	10.95		11.49	
	Minimum Charge	Job		765		765	
22″ x 46″							
	Demolish	Ea.		78.50		78.50	Cost includes material and labor to
	Install	Ea.	252	153		405	install 22″ x 46″ fixed dome skylight.
	Demolish and Install	Ea.	252	231.50		483.50	
	Reinstall	Ea.		122.32		122.32	
	Clean	Ea.		17		17	
	Minimum Charge	Job		765		765	
30″ x 30″							
	Demolish	Ea.		78.50		78.50	Cost includes material and labor to
	Install	Ea.	253	127		380	install 30″ x 30″ fixed dome skylight.
	Demolish and Install	Ea.	253	205.50		458.50	
	Reinstall	Ea.		101.93		101.93	
	Clean	Ea.		17		17	
	Minimum Charge	Job		765		765	
30″ x 46″							
	Demolish	Ea.		78.50		78.50	Cost includes material and labor to
	Install	Ea.	320	153		473	install 30″ x 46″ fixed dome skylight.
	Demolish and Install	Ea.	320	231.50		551.50	
	Reinstall	Ea.		122.32		122.32	
	Clean	Ea.		17		17	
	Minimum Charge	Job		765		765	
Fixed							
22″ x 27″							
	Demolish	Ea.		78.50		78.50	Includes material and labor to install
	Install	Ea.	234	127		361	double glazed skylight, 22″ x 27″,
	Demolish and Install	Ea.	234	205.50		439.50	fixed.
	Reinstall	Ea.		101.93		101.93	
	Clean	Ea.	.54	10.95		11.49	
	Minimum Charge	Job		765		765	
22″ x 46″							
	Demolish	Ea.		78.50		78.50	Includes material and labor to install
	Install	Ea.	296	153		449	double glazed skylight, 22″ x 46″,
	Demolish and Install	Ea.	296	231.50		527.50	fixed.
	Reinstall	Ea.		122.32		122.32	
	Clean	Ea.		17		17	
	Minimum Charge	Job		765		765	
44″ x 46″							
	Demolish	Ea.		78.50		78.50	Includes material and labor to install
	Install	Ea.	440	153		593	double glazed skylight, 44″ x 46″,
	Demolish and Install	Ea.	440	231.50		671.50	fixed.
	Reinstall	Ea.		122.32		122.32	
	Clean	Ea.		19.15		19.15	
	Minimum Charge	Job		765		765	
Operable							
22″ x 27″							
	Demolish	Ea.		78.50		78.50	Includes material and labor to install
	Install	Ea.	340	127		467	double glazed skylight, 22″ x 27″,
	Demolish and Install	Ea.	340	205.50		545.50	operable.
	Reinstall	Ea.		101.93		101.93	
	Clean	Ea.	.54	10.95		11.49	
	Minimum Charge	Job		765		765	

Exterior Doors and Windows

Skylight

	Unit	Material	Labor	Equip.	Total	Specification
22" x 46"						
Demolish	Ea.		78.50		78.50	Includes material and labor to install
Install	Ea.	400	153		553	double glazed skylight, 22" x 46",
Demolish and Install	Ea.	400	231.50		631.50	operable.
Reinstall	Ea.		122.32		122.32	
Clean	Ea.		17		17	
Minimum Charge	Job		765		765	
44" x 46"						
Demolish	Ea.		78.50		78.50	Includes material and labor to install
Install	Ea.	885	153		1038	double glazed skylight, 44" x 46",
Demolish and Install	Ea.	885	231.50		1116.50	operable.
Reinstall	Ea.		122.32		122.32	
Clean	Ea.		19.15		19.15	
Minimum Charge	Job		765		765	

Industrial Steel Window

	Unit	Material	Labor	Equip.	Total	Specification
100% Fixed						
Demolish	S.F.		2.18		2.18	Includes material and labor to install
Install	S.F.	31	5.10		36.10	commercial grade steel windows,
Demolish and Install	S.F.	31	7.28		38.28	including glazing.
Reinstall	S.F.		4.08		4.08	
Clean	Ea.	.22	1.17		1.39	
Paint	S.F.	.19	.79		.98	
Minimum Charge	Job		255		255	
50% Vented						
Demolish	S.F.		2.18		2.18	Includes material and labor to install
Install	S.F.	58	5.10		63.10	commercial grade steel windows,
Demolish and Install	S.F.	58	7.28		65.28	including glazing.
Reinstall	S.F.		4.08		4.08	
Clean	Ea.	.22	1.17		1.39	
Paint	S.F.	.19	.79		.98	
Minimum Charge	Job		255		255	

Brick Veneer

Concrete Masonry Units

Masonry Wall	Unit	Material	Labor	Equip.	Total	Specification
Unreinforced CMU						
4″ x 8″ x 16″						
Demolish	S.F.		1.89		1.89	Includes material and labor to install
Install	S.F.	1.74	4.09		5.83	normal weight 4″ x 8″ x 16″ block.
Demolish and Install	S.F.	1.74	5.98		7.72	
Clean	S.F.	.08	.47		.55	
Paint	S.F.	.14	.81		.95	
Minimum Charge	Job		204		204	
6″ x 8″ x 16″						
Demolish	S.F.		2		2	Includes material and labor to install
Install	S.F.	2.41	4.27		6.68	normal weight 6″ x 8″ x 16″ block.
Demolish and Install	S.F.	2.41	6.27		8.68	
Clean	S.F.	.08	.47		.55	
Paint	S.F.	.14	.81		.95	
Minimum Charge	Job		204		204	
8″ x 8″ x 16″						
Demolish	S.F.		2.27		2.27	Includes material and labor to install
Install	S.F.	2.74	4.70		7.44	normal weight 8″ x 8″ x 16″ block.
Demolish and Install	S.F.	2.74	6.97		9.71	
Clean	S.F.	.08	.47		.55	
Paint	S.F.	.14	.81		.95	
Minimum Charge	Job		204		204	
12″ x 8″ x 16″						
Demolish	S.F.		2.27		2.27	Includes material and labor to install
Install	S.F.	3.92	7.10		11.02	normal weight 12″ x 8″ x 16″ block.
Demolish and Install	S.F.	3.92	9.37		13.29	
Clean	S.F.	.08	.47		.55	
Paint	S.F.	.14	.81		.95	
Minimum Charge	Job		204		204	
Reinforced CMU						
4″ x 8″ x 16″						
Demolish	S.F.		1.89	1	2.89	Includes material and labor to install
Install	S.F.	1.89	4.18		6.07	normal weight 4″ x 8″ x 16″ block,
Demolish and Install	S.F.	1.89	6.07	1	8.96	mortar and 1/2″ re-bar installed
Clean	S.F.	.08	.47		.55	vertically every 24″ O.C.
Paint	S.F.	.14	.81		.95	
Minimum Charge	Job		370		370	
6″ x 8″ x 16″						
Demolish	S.F.		1.99	.47	2.46	Includes material and labor to install
Install	S.F.	2.57	4.37		6.94	normal weight 6″ x 8″ x 16″ block,
Demolish and Install	S.F.	2.57	6.36	.47	9.40	mortar and 1/2″ re-bar installed
Clean	S.F.	.08	.47		.55	vertically every 24″ O.C.
Paint	S.F.	.14	.81		.95	
Minimum Charge	Job		370		370	

Masonry

Masonry Wall		Unit	Material	Labor	Equip.	Total	Specification
8" x 8" x 16"							
	Demolish	S.F.		2.10	.50	2.60	Includes material and labor to install
	Install	S.F.	2.92	4.76		7.68	normal weight 8" x 8" x 16" block,
	Demolish and Install	S.F.	2.92	6.86	.50	10.28	mortar and 1/2" re-bar installed
	Clean	S.F.	.08	.47		.55	vertically every 24" O.C.
	Paint	S.F.	.14	.81		.95	
	Minimum Charge	Job		370		370	
12" x 8" x 16"							
	Demolish	S.F.		2.17	.51	2.68	Includes material and labor to install
	Install	S.F.	4.08	7.35		11.43	normal weight 12" x 8" x 16" block,
	Demolish and Install	S.F.	4.08	9.52	.51	14.11	mortar and 1/2" re-bar installed
	Clean	S.F.	.08	.47		.55	vertically every 24" O.C.
	Paint	S.F.	.14	.81		.95	
	Minimum Charge	Job		370		370	
Structural Brick							
4" Single Row							
	Demolish	S.F.		2.72		2.72	Cost includes material and labor to
	Install	S.F.	4.53	8.75		13.28	install 4" red brick wall, running bond
	Demolish and Install	S.F.	4.53	11.47		16	with 3/8" concave joints, mortar and
	Clean	S.F.	.08	.40		.48	ties.
	Paint	S.F.	.14	.81		.95	
	Minimum Charge	Job		370		370	
8" Double Row							
	Demolish	S.F.		2.72		2.72	Cost includes material and labor to
	Install	S.F.	6.80	13.90		20.70	install 8" red brick wall, running bond,
	Demolish and Install	S.F.	6.80	16.62		23.42	with 3/8" concave joints, mortar and
	Clean	S.F.	.08	.40		.48	wall ties.
	Paint	S.F.	.14	.81		.95	
	Minimum Charge	Job		370		370	
12" Triple Row							
	Demolish	S.F.		3.78		3.78	Cost includes material and labor to
	Install	S.F.	10.30	19.80		30.10	install 12" red brick wall, running
	Demolish and Install	S.F.	10.30	23.58		33.88	bond, with 3/8" concave joints,
	Clean	S.F.	.08	.40		.48	mortar and wall ties.
	Paint	S.F.	.14	.81		.95	
	Minimum Charge	Job		370		370	
Brick Veneer							
4" Red Common							
	Demolish	S.F.		2.72		2.72	Cost includes material and labor to
	Install	S.F.	3.20	8.15		11.35	install 4" common red face brick,
	Demolish and Install	S.F.	3.20	10.87		14.07	running bond with 3/8" concave
	Clean	S.F.	.08	.40		.48	joints, mortar and wall ties.
	Paint	S.F.	.14	.81		.95	
	Minimum Charge	Job		204		204	
4" Used							
	Demolish	S.F.		2.72		2.72	Cost includes material and labor to
	Install	S.F.	4.53	8.75		13.28	install 4" red brick wall, running bond
	Demolish and Install	S.F.	4.53	11.47		16	with 3/8" concave joints, mortar and
	Clean	S.F.	.08	.40		.48	ties.
	Paint	S.F.	.14	.81		.95	
	Minimum Charge	Job		204		204	

Masonry Wall		Unit	Material	Labor	Equip.	Total	Specification
6" Jumbo							
	Demolish	S.F.		2.72		2.72	Cost includes material and labor to
	Install	S.F.	5.40	4.32		9.72	install 6" red jumbo brick veneer,
	Demolish and Install	S.F.	5.40	7.04		12.44	running bond with 3/8" concave
	Clean	S.F.	.08	.40		.48	joints, mortar and ties.
	Paint	S.F.	.14	.81		.95	
	Minimum Charge	Job		204		204	
Norman (11-1/2")							
	Demolish	S.F.		2.72		2.72	Cost includes material and labor to
	Install	S.F.	6.35	5.85		12.20	install 4" norman red brick wall,
	Demolish and Install	S.F.	6.35	8.57		14.92	running bond with 3/8" concave
	Clean	S.F.	.08	.40		.48	joints, mortar and ties.
	Paint	S.F.	.14	.81		.95	
	Minimum Charge	Job		204		204	
Glazed							
	Demolish	S.F.		2.72		2.72	Includes material, labor and
	Install	S.F.	18	8.95		26.95	equipment to install glazed brick.
	Demolish and Install	S.F.	18	11.67		29.67	
	Clean	S.F.	.08	.40		.48	
	Paint	S.F.	.14	.81		.95	
	Minimum Charge	Job		204		204	
Slumpstone							
6" x 4"							
	Demolish	S.F.		1.89		1.89	Cost includes material and labor to
	Install	S.F.	5.35	4.60		9.95	install 6" x 4" x 16" concrete slump
	Demolish and Install	S.F.	5.35	6.49		11.84	block.
	Clean	S.F.	.08	.47		.55	
	Paint	S.F.	.14	.81		.95	
	Minimum Charge	Job		204		204	
6" x 6"							
	Demolish	S.F.		2		2	Cost includes material and labor to
	Install	S.F.	4.96	4.75		9.71	install 6" x 6" x 16" concrete slump
	Demolish and Install	S.F.	4.96	6.75		11.71	block.
	Clean	S.F.	.08	.47		.55	
	Paint	S.F.	.14	.81		.95	
	Minimum Charge	Job		204		204	
8" x 6"							
	Demolish	S.F.		2		2	Cost includes material and labor to
	Install	S.F.	7.30	4.91		12.21	install 8" x 6" x 16" concrete slump
	Demolish and Install	S.F.	7.30	6.91		14.21	block.
	Clean	S.F.	.08	.47		.55	
	Paint	S.F.	.14	.81		.95	
	Minimum Charge	Job		204		204	
12" x 4"							
	Demolish	S.F.		1.89		1.89	Cost includes material and labor to
	Install	S.F.	11.30	5.65		16.95	install 12" x 4" x 16" concrete slump
	Demolish and Install	S.F.	11.30	7.54		18.84	block.
	Clean	S.F.	.08	.47		.55	
	Paint	S.F.	.14	.81		.95	
	Minimum Charge	Job		204		204	
12" x 6"							
	Demolish	S.F.		2		2	Cost includes material and labor to
	Install	S.F.	11.75	6.15		17.90	install 12" x 6" x 16" concrete slump
	Demolish and Install	S.F.	11.75	8.15		19.90	block.
	Clean	S.F.	.08	.47		.55	
	Paint	S.F.	.14	.81		.95	
	Minimum Charge	Job		204		204	

Masonry

Masonry Wall	Unit	Material	Labor	Equip.	Total	Specification
Stucco						
Three Coat						
Demolish	S.Y.		2.35		2.35	Includes material and labor to install
Install	S.Y.	3.89	8.85	.72	13.46	stucco on exterior masonry walls.
Demolish and Install	S.Y.	3.89	11.20	.72	15.81	
Clean	S.Y.		4.26		4.26	
Paint	S.F.	.28	.58		.86	
Minimum Charge	Job		185		185	
Three Coat w / Wire Mesh						
Demolish	S.Y.		4.26		4.26	Includes material and labor to install
Install	S.Y.	6.40	33.50	2.29	42.19	stucco on wire mesh over wood
Demolish and Install	S.Y.	6.40	37.76	2.29	46.45	framing.
Clean	S.Y.		4.26		4.26	
Paint	S.F.	.28	.58		.86	
Minimum Charge	Job		185		185	
Fill Cracks						
Install	S.F.	.43	2.96		3.39	Includes labor and material to fill-in
Minimum Charge	Job		185		185	hairline cracks up to 1/8" with filler, including sand and fill per S.F.
Furring						
1" x 2"						
Demolish	L.F.		.14		.14	Cost includes material and labor to
Install	L.F.	.28	.84		1.12	install 1" x 2" furring on masonry wall.
Demolish and Install	L.F.	.28	.98		1.26	
Minimum Charge	Job		207		207	
2" x 2"						
Demolish	L.F.		.15		.15	Cost includes material and labor to
Install	L.F.	.23	.92		1.15	install 2" x 2" furring on masonry wall.
Demolish and Install	L.F.	.23	1.07		1.30	
Minimum Charge	Job		207		207	
2" x 4"						
Demolish	L.F.		.16		.16	Cost includes material and labor to
Install	L.F.	.36	1.05		1.41	install 2" x 4" furring on masonry wall.
Demolish and Install	L.F.	.36	1.21		1.57	
Reinstall	L.F.		.84		.84	
Minimum Charge	Job		207		207	
Maintenance / Cleaning						
Repoint						
Install	S.F.	.58	5.10		5.68	Includes labor and material to cut and
Minimum Charge	Hr.		51		51	repoint brick, hard mortar, running bond.
Acid Etch						
Install	S.F.	.04	.73		.77	Includes labor and material to acid
Minimum Charge	Job		153	36.50	189.50	wash smooth brick.
Pressure Wash						
Clean	S.F.		.82	.18	1	Includes labor and material to high
Minimum Charge	Job		153	36.50	189.50	pressure water wash masonry, average.
Waterproof						
Install	S.F.	.50	.75		1.25	Includes labor and material to install
Minimum Charge	Job		188		188	masory waterproofing.

Masonry

Chimney

Chimney		Unit	Material	Labor	Equip.	Total	Specification
Demo & Haul Exterior							
	Demolish	C.F.		5.55		5.55	Includes minimum labor and
	Minimum Charge	Job		170		170	equipment to remove masonry and haul debris to truck or dumpster.
Demo & Haul Interior							
	Demolish	C.F.		7.65		7.65	Includes minimum labor and
	Minimum Charge	Job		170		170	equipment to remove masonry and haul debris to truck or dumpster.
Install New (w / flue)							
Brick							
	Install	V.L.F.	37.50	46		83.50	Includes material and labor to install
	Minimum Charge	Job		204		204	brick chimney with flue from ground level up. Foundation not included.
Natural Stone							
	Install	L.F.	55.50	73.50		129	Includes labor and material to install
	Minimum Charge	Job		204		204	natural stone chimney.
Install From Roof Up							
Brick							
	Install	V.L.F.	37.50	46		83.50	Includes material and labor to install
	Minimum Charge	Job		204		204	brick chimney with flue from ground level up. Foundation not included.
Natural Stone							
	Install	L.F.	55.50	61.50		117	Includes labor and material to install
	Minimum Charge	Job		204		204	natural stone chimney.
Install Base Pad							
	Install	Ea.	273	227	1.26	501.26	Includes labor and material to replace
	Minimum Charge	Job		970	30	1000	spread footing, 5' square x 16" deep.
Metal Cap							
	Install	Ea.	51	25.50		76.50	Includes labor and materials to install
	Minimum Charge	Job		207		207	bird and squirrel screens in a chimney flue.

Fireplace

Fireplace		Unit	Material	Labor	Equip.	Total	Specification
Common Brick							
30"							
	Demolish	Ea.		1225		1225	Includes material and labor to install a
	Install	Ea.	1925	3675		5600	complete unit which includes common
	Demolish and Install	Ea.	1925	4900		6825	brick, foundation, damper, flue lining
	Minimum Charge	Job		204		204	stack to 15' high and a 30" fire box.
36"							
	Demolish	Ea.		1225		1225	Includes material and labor to install a
	Install	Ea.	2025	4100		6125	complete unit which includes common
	Demolish and Install	Ea.	2025	5325		7350	brick, foundation, damper, flue lining
	Minimum Charge	Job		204		204	stack to 15' high and a 36" fire box.
42"							
	Demolish	Ea.		1225		1225	Includes material and labor to install a
	Install	Ea.	2225	4600		6825	complete unit which includes common
	Demolish and Install	Ea.	2225	5825		8050	brick, foundation, damper, flue lining
	Minimum Charge	Job		204		204	stack to 15' high and a 42" fire box.

Masonry

Fireplace	Unit	Material	Labor	Equip.	Total	Specification
48"						
Demolish	Ea.		1225		1225	Includes material and labor to install
Install	Ea.	2350	5250		7600	a complete unit which includes common
Demolish and Install	Ea.	2350	6475		8825	brick, foundation, damper, flue lining
Minimum Charge	Job		204		204	stack to 15' high and a 48" fire box.
Raised Hearth						
Brick Hearth						
Demolish	S.F.		5.30		5.30	Includes material and labor to install a
Install	S.F.	18.05	30.50		48.55	brick fireplace hearth based on 30" x
Demolish and Install	S.F.	18.05	35.80		53.85	29" opening.
Clean	S.F.	.08	.40		.48	
Minimum Charge	Job		204		204	
Marble Hearth / Facing						
Demolish	Ea.		34		34	Includes material and labor to install
Install	Ea.	730	124		854	marble fireplace hearth.
Demolish and Install	Ea.	730	158		888	
Reinstall	Ea.		99.14		99.14	
Clean	Ea.	37	6.15		43.15	
Minimum Charge	Job		204		204	
Breast (face) Brick						
Demolish	S.F.		5.30		5.30	Includes material and labor to install
Install	S.F.	4.61	8.55		13.16	standard red brick, running bond.
Demolish and Install	S.F.	4.61	13.85		18.46	
Clean	S.F.		.82	.18	1	
Minimum Charge	Hr.		51		51	
Fire Box						
Demolish	Ea.		272		272	Includes material and labor to install
Install	Ea.	194	370		564	fireplace box only (110 brick).
Demolish and Install	Ea.	194	642		836	
Clean	Ea.	.18	14.05		14.23	
Minimum Charge	Hr.		51		51	
Natural Stone						
Demolish	S.F.		5.30		5.30	Includes material and labor to install
Install	S.F.	15.40	15.65		31.05	high priced stone, split or rock face.
Demolish and Install	S.F.	15.40	20.95		36.35	
Clean	S.F.	.09	.92		1.01	
Minimum Charge	Job		370		370	
Slumpstone Veneer						
Demolish	S.F.		2		2	Cost includes material and labor to
Install	S.F.	7.30	4.91		12.21	install 8" x 6" x 16" concrete slump
Demolish and Install	S.F.	7.30	6.91		14.21	block.
Clean	S.F.	.08	.47		.55	
Paint	S.F.	.14	.81		.95	
Minimum Charge	Job		204		204	
Prefabricated						
Firebox						
Demolish	Ea.		48.50		48.50	Includes material and labor to install
Install	Ea.	2125	375		2500	up to 43" radiant heat, zero
Demolish and Install	Ea.	2125	423.50		2548.50	clearance, prefabricated fireplace.
Reinstall	Ea.		301.38		301.38	Flues, doors or blowers not included.
Clean	Ea.	2.39	19.15		21.54	
Minimum Charge	Job		207		207	

Masonry

Fireplace

		Unit	Material	Labor	Equip.	Total	Specification
Flue							
	Demolish	V.L.F.		5.65		5.65	Includes material and labor to install
	Install	V.L.F.	17.40	15.85		33.25	prefabricated chimney vent, 8"
	Demolish and Install	V.L.F.	17.40	21.50		38.90	exposed metal flue.
	Reinstall	V.L.F.		12.68		12.68	
	Clean	L.F.	.96	3.83		4.79	
	Minimum Charge	Job		410		410	
Blower							
	Demolish	Ea.		4.54		4.54	Includes material and labor to install
	Install	Ea.	155	28.50		183.50	blower for metal fireplace flue.
	Demolish and Install	Ea.	155	33.04		188.04	
	Reinstall	Ea.		22.90		22.90	
	Clean	Ea.	4.77	38.50		43.27	
	Minimum Charge	Job		410		410	
Accessories							
Wood Mantle							
	Demolish	L.F.		5.65		5.65	Includes material and labor to install
	Install	L.F.	12	11.85		23.85	wood fireplace mantel.
	Demolish and Install	L.F.	12	17.50		29.50	
	Reinstall	L.F.		11.84		11.84	
	Clean	Ea.	.03	.86		.89	
	Paint	L.F.	.11	9.65		9.76	
	Minimum Charge	Job		207		207	
Colonial Style							
	Demolish	Ea.		51		51	Includes material and labor to install
	Install	Opng.	1375	207		1582	wood fireplace mantel.
	Demolish and Install	Opng.	1375	258		1633	
	Reinstall	Opng.		207.20		207.20	
	Clean	Ea.		.62		.62	
	Paint	Ea.	19.30	133		152.30	
	Minimum Charge	Job		207		207	
Modern Design							
	Demolish	Ea.		51		51	Includes material and labor to install
	Install	Opng.	450	83		533	wood fireplace mantel.
	Demolish and Install	Opng.	450	134		584	
	Reinstall	Opng.		82.88		82.88	
	Clean	Ea.		.62		.62	
	Paint	Ea.	19.30	133		152.30	
	Minimum Charge	Job		207		207	
Glass Door Unit							
	Demolish	Ea.		7.10		7.10	Includes material and labor to install a
	Install	Ea.	335	8.50		343.50	fireplace glass door unit.
	Demolish and Install	Ea.	335	15.60		350.60	
	Reinstall	Ea.		8.48		8.48	
	Clean	Ea.	.57	11.80		12.37	
	Minimum Charge	Job		207		207	
Fire Screen							
	Demolish	Ea.		3.55		3.55	Includes material and labor to install a
	Install	Ea.	133	4.24		137.24	fireplace fire screen.
	Demolish and Install	Ea.	133	7.79		140.79	
	Reinstall	Ea.		4.24		4.24	
	Clean	Ea.	.29	10.20		10.49	
	Minimum Charge	Job		207		207	

Siding

| Shingles | Board & Batten | Texture 1-11 |

Exterior Siding		Unit	Material	Labor	Equip.	Total	Specification
Trim							
1″ x 2″							
	Demolish	L.F.		.28		.28	Cost includes material and labor to
	Install	L.F.	.28	1.26		1.54	install 1″ x 2″ pine trim.
	Demolish and Install	L.F.	.28	1.54		1.82	
	Clean	L.F.	.01	.20		.21	
	Paint	L.F.	.02	.56		.58	
	Minimum Charge	Job		207		207	
1″ x 3″							
	Demolish	L.F.		.28		.28	Cost includes material and labor to
	Install	L.F.	.28	1.43		1.71	install 1″ x 3″ pine trim.
	Demolish and Install	L.F.	.28	1.71		1.99	
	Clean	L.F.	.01	.20		.21	
	Paint	L.F.	.02	.56		.58	
	Minimum Charge	Job		207		207	
1″ x 4″							
	Demolish	L.F.		.28		.28	Cost includes material and labor to
	Install	L.F.	.45	1.66		2.11	install 1″ x 4″ pine trim.
	Demolish and Install	L.F.	.45	1.94		2.39	
	Clean	L.F.	.01	.20		.21	
	Paint	L.F.	.02	.56		.58	
	Minimum Charge	Job		207		207	
1″ x 6″							
	Demolish	L.F.		.28		.28	Cost includes material and labor to
	Install	L.F.	.79	1.66		2.45	install 1″ x 6″ pine trim.
	Demolish and Install	L.F.	.79	1.94		2.73	
	Clean	L.F.	.02	.20		.22	
	Paint	L.F.	.08	.56		.64	
	Minimum Charge	Job		207		207	
1″ x 8″							
	Demolish	L.F.		.31		.31	Cost includes material and labor to
	Install	L.F.	1.10	2.07		3.17	install 1″ x 8″ pine trim.
	Demolish and Install	L.F.	1.10	2.38		3.48	
	Clean	L.F.	.03	.22		.25	
	Paint	L.F.	.08	.56		.64	
	Minimum Charge	Job		207		207	
Aluminum							
8″ Non-Insulated							
	Demolish	S.F.		.77		.77	Includes material and labor to install
	Install	S.F.	2.43	1.65		4.08	horizontal, colored clapboard, 8″ to
	Demolish and Install	S.F.	2.43	2.42		4.85	10″ wide, plain.
	Reinstall	S.F.		1.65		1.65	
	Clean	S.F.		.31		.31	
	Minimum Charge	Job		207		207	

Siding

Exterior Siding	Unit	Material	Labor	Equip.	Total	Specification
8" Insulated						
Demolish	S.F.		.77		.77	Includes material and labor to install
Install	S.F.	2.60	1.65		4.25	horizontal, colored insulated
Demolish and Install	S.F.	2.60	2.42		5.02	clapboard, 8" wide, plain.
Reinstall	S.F.		1.65		1.65	
Clean	S.F.		.31		.31	
Minimum Charge	Job		207		207	
12" Non-Insulated						
Demolish	S.F.		.77		.77	Includes material and labor to install
Install	S.F.	2.43	1.42		3.85	horizontal, colored clapboard, plain.
Demolish and Install	S.F.	2.43	2.19		4.62	
Reinstall	S.F.		1.42		1.42	
Clean	S.F.		.31		.31	
Minimum Charge	Job		207		207	
12" Insulated						
Demolish	S.F.		.77		.77	Includes material and labor to install
Install	S.F.	2.60	1.42		4.02	horizontal, colored insulated
Demolish and Install	S.F.	2.60	2.19		4.79	clapboard, plain.
Reinstall	S.F.		1.42		1.42	
Clean	S.F.		.31		.31	
Minimum Charge	Job		207		207	
Clapboard 8" to 10"						
Demolish	S.F.		.77		.77	Includes material and labor to install
Install	S.F.	2.43	1.65		4.08	horizontal, colored clapboard, 8" to
Demolish and Install	S.F.	2.43	2.42		4.85	10" wide, plain.
Reinstall	S.F.		1.65		1.65	
Clean	S.F.		.31		.31	
Minimum Charge	Job		207		207	
Corner Strips						
Demolish	L.F.		.40		.40	Includes material and labor to install
Install	V.L.F.	3.58	1.65		5.23	corners for horizontal lapped
Demolish and Install	V.L.F.	3.58	2.05		5.63	aluminum siding.
Reinstall	V.L.F.		1.65		1.65	
Clean	L.F.		.20		.20	
Minimum Charge	Job		207		207	
Vinyl						
Non-Insulated						
Demolish	S.F.		.60		.60	Cost includes material and labor to
Install	S.F.	1.30	1.51		2.81	install 10" non-insulated solid vinyl
Demolish and Install	S.F.	1.30	2.11		3.41	siding.
Reinstall	S.F.		1.21		1.21	
Clean	S.F.		.31		.31	
Minimum Charge	Job		207		207	
Insulated						
Demolish	S.F.		.60		.60	Cost includes material and labor to
Install	S.F.	3	2.07		5.07	install insulated solid vinyl siding
Demolish and Install	S.F.	3	2.67		5.67	panels.
Reinstall	S.F.		1.66		1.66	
Clean	S.F.		.31		.31	
Minimum Charge	Job		207		207	
Corner Strips						
Demolish	L.F.		.38		.38	Cost includes material and labor to
Install	L.F.	1.74	1.18		2.92	install corner posts for vinyl siding
Demolish and Install	L.F.	1.74	1.56		3.30	panels.
Reinstall	L.F.		.95		.95	
Clean	L.F.		.20		.20	
Minimum Charge	Job		207		207	

Siding

Exterior Siding	Unit	Material	Labor	Equip.	Total	Specification
Fiber Cement Siding						
4' x 8' Panel						
Demolish	S.F.		.62		.62	Cost includes material and labor to
Install	S.F.	1.04	.91		1.95	install 4' x 8' fiber cement 7/16"
Demolish and Install	S.F.	1.04	1.53		2.57	thick.
Clean	S.F.		.31		.31	
Paint	S.F.	.30	1.20		1.50	
Minimum Charge	Job		207		207	
Lap						
Demolish	S.F.		.61		.61	Cost includes material and labor to
Install	S.F.	.96	1.64		2.60	install 8" or 12" fiber cement lap
Demolish and Install	S.F.	.96	2.25		3.21	siding 7/16" thick with wood grain
Clean	S.F.		.31		.31	finish.
Paint	S.F.	.30	1.20		1.50	
Minimum Charge	Job		207		207	
Plywood Panel						
Douglas Fir (T-1-11)						
Demolish	S.F.		.47		.47	Includes material and labor to install
Install	S.F.	1.17	1.26		2.43	Douglas fir 4' x 8' plywood exterior
Demolish and Install	S.F.	1.17	1.73		2.90	siding plain or patterns.
Reinstall	S.F.		1.26		1.26	
Clean	S.F.		.31		.31	
Paint	S.F.	.30	1.20		1.50	
Minimum Charge	Job		207		207	
Redwood						
Demolish	S.F.		.47		.47	Includes material and labor to install
Install	S.F.	2.11	1.26		3.37	redwood 4' x 8' plywood exterior
Demolish and Install	S.F.	2.11	1.73		3.84	siding plain or patterns.
Reinstall	S.F.		1.26		1.26	
Clean	S.F.		.31		.31	
Paint	S.F.	.30	1.20		1.50	
Minimum Charge	Job		207		207	
Cedar						
Demolish	S.F.		.47		.47	Cost includes material and labor to
Install	S.F.	2.67	1.26		3.93	install 4' x 8' cedar plywood exterior
Demolish and Install	S.F.	2.67	1.73		4.40	siding plain or patterns.
Reinstall	S.F.		1.26		1.26	
Clean	S.F.		.31		.31	
Paint	S.F.	.30	1.20		1.50	
Minimum Charge	Job		207		207	
Tongue and Groove						
Fir, Tongue and Groove						
Demolish	S.F.		.85		.85	Includes material and labor to install
Install	S.F.	2.56	1.26		3.82	fir tongue and groove exterior siding
Demolish and Install	S.F.	2.56	2.11		4.67	1" x 8".
Reinstall	S.F.		1		1	
Clean	S.F.		.31		.31	
Paint	S.F.	.30	1.20		1.50	
Minimum Charge	Job		207		207	
Pine, Tongue and Groove						
Demolish	S.F.		.85		.85	Includes labor and material to install
Install	S.F.	2.29	1.26		3.55	Pine tongue and groove exterior
Demolish and Install	S.F.	2.29	2.11		4.40	siding 1" x 8".
Reinstall	S.F.		1.26		1.26	
Clean	S.F.		.31		.31	
Paint	S.F.	.30	1.20		1.50	
Minimum Charge	Job		207		207	

Siding

Exterior Siding	Unit	Material	Labor	Equip.	Total	Specification
Cedar, Tongue and Groove						
Demolish	S.F.		.85		.85	Includes labor and material to install
Install	S.F.	4.27	1.88		6.15	cedar tongue and groove exterior
Demolish and Install	S.F.	4.27	2.73		7	siding 1" x 8".
Reinstall	S.F.		1.51		1.51	
Clean	S.F.		.31		.31	
Paint	S.F.	.30	1.20		1.50	
Minimum Charge	Job		207		207	
Redwood, Tongue and Groove						
Demolish	S.F.		.85		.85	Includes labor and material to install
Install	S.F.	2.79	1.88		4.67	redwood tongue and groove exterior
Demolish and Install	S.F.	2.79	2.73		5.52	siding 1" x 4".
Reinstall	S.F.		1.88		1.88	
Clean	S.F.		.31		.31	
Paint	S.F.	.30	1.20		1.50	
Minimum Charge	Job		207		207	
Board and Batten						
Fir						
Demolish	S.F.		.85		.85	Cost includes material and labor to
Install	S.F.	6.15	1.26		7.41	install 1" x 8" fir boards with 1" x 3"
Demolish and Install	S.F.	6.15	2.11		8.26	battens.
Reinstall	S.F.		1		1	
Clean	S.F.		.31		.31	
Paint	S.F.	.30	1.20		1.50	
Minimum Charge	Job		207		207	
Pine						
Demolish	S.F.		.85		.85	Cost includes material and labor to
Install	S.F.	3.28	1.10		4.38	install 1" x 10" pine boards with 1" x
Demolish and Install	S.F.	3.28	1.95		5.23	3" battens.
Reinstall	S.F.		.88		.88	
Clean	S.F.		.31		.31	
Paint	S.F.	.30	1.20		1.50	
Minimum Charge	Job		207		207	
Cedar						
Demolish	S.F.		.85		.85	Cost includes material and labor to
Install	S.F.	3.09	1.10		4.19	install 1" x 10" cedar boards with 1" x
Demolish and Install	S.F.	3.09	1.95		5.04	3" battens.
Reinstall	S.F.		.88		.88	
Clean	S.F.		.31		.31	
Paint	S.F.	.30	1.20		1.50	
Minimum Charge	Job		207		207	
Redwood						
Demolish	S.F.		.85		.85	Cost includes material and labor to
Install	S.F.	5.80	1.10		6.90	install 1" x 10" redwood boards with
Demolish and Install	S.F.	5.80	1.95		7.75	1" x 3" battens.
Reinstall	S.F.		.88		.88	
Clean	S.F.		.31		.31	
Paint	S.F.	.30	1.20		1.50	
Minimum Charge	Job		207		207	
Wood Shingle						
Demolish	Sq.		78.50		78.50	Includes material and labor to install
Install	Sq.	185	184		369	wood shingles/shakes.
Demolish and Install	Sq.	185	262.50		447.50	
Clean	Sq.		32.50		32.50	
Paint	Sq.	19.80	107		126.80	
Minimum Charge	Job		207		207	

Siding

Exterior Siding	Unit	Material	Labor	Equip.	Total	Specification
Synthetic Stucco System						
Demolish	S.F.		2.84		2.84	Cost includes material and labor to
Install	S.F.	2.92	6.60	.54	10.06	install 2 coats of adhesive mixture,
Demolish and Install	S.F.	2.92	9.44	.54	12.90	glass fiber mesh, 1" insulation board,
Clean	S.F.		.28		.28	and textured finish coat.
Paint	S.F.	.28	.58		.86	
Minimum Charge	Job		885	72	957	

Front-end Loader

Bulldozer

Grading		Unit	Material	Labor	Equip.	Total	Specification
Hand (fine)							
	Install	S.F.		.61		.61	Includes labor and material to install fine grade for slab on grade, hand grade.
	Minimum Charge	Job		153		153	
Machine (fine)							
	Install	S.Y.		.54	.49	1.03	Includes labor and material to install fine grade for roadway, base or leveling course.
	Minimum Charge	Job		365	335	700	

Asphalt Paving		Unit	Material	Labor	Equip.	Total	Specification
Seal Coat							
	Install	S.F.	.12	.11		.23	Includes labor and material to install sealcoat for a small area.
	Minimum Charge	Job		153		153	
Wearing Course							
	Install	S.F.	.18	.33	.26	.77	Cost includes labor and material to install 1" thick wearing course.
	Minimum Charge	Job		153		153	

Masonry Pavers		Unit	Material	Labor	Equip.	Total	Specification
Natural Concrete							
Sand Base							
	Demolish	S.F.		3.40		3.40	Includes material and labor to install concrete pavers on sand base.
	Install	S.F.	2.74	6.80		9.54	
	Demolish and Install	S.F.	2.74	10.20		12.94	
	Reinstall	S.F.		5.43		5.43	
	Clean	S.F.		1.23		1.23	
	Minimum Charge	Job		204		204	
Mortar Base							
	Demolish	S.F.		5.65	2.04	7.69	Includes material and labor to install concrete pavers on mortar base.
	Install	S.F.	3.59	5.65		9.24	
	Demolish and Install	S.F.	3.59	11.30	2.04	16.93	
	Reinstall	S.F.		4.52		4.52	
	Clean	S.F.		1.11		1.11	
	Minimum Charge	Job		204		204	

Site Work

Masonry Pavers	Unit	Material	Labor	Equip.	Total	Specification
Adobe						
Sand Base						
Demolish	S.F.		3.40		3.40	Includes material and labor to install
Install	S.F.	2.37	4.52		6.89	adobe pavers on sand base.
Demolish and Install	S.F.	2.37	7.92		10.29	
Reinstall	S.F.		3.62		3.62	
Clean	S.F.		1.23		1.23	
Minimum Charge	Job		204		204	
Mortar Base						
Demolish	S.F.		5.65	2.04	7.69	Includes material and labor to install
Install	S.F.	3.08	5.65		8.73	adobe pavers on mortar base.
Demolish and Install	S.F.	3.08	11.30	2.04	16.42	
Reinstall	S.F.		4.52		4.52	
Clean	S.F.		1.11		1.11	
Minimum Charge	Job		204		204	
Standard Brick						
Sand Base						
Demolish	S.F.		3.40		3.40	Includes material and labor to install
Install	S.F.	3.33	7.35		10.68	standard brick pavers on sand base.
Demolish and Install	S.F.	3.33	10.75		14.08	
Reinstall	S.F.		5.89		5.89	
Clean	S.F.		1.23		1.23	
Minimum Charge	Job		204		204	
Mortar Base						
Demolish	S.F.		5.65	2.04	7.69	Includes material and labor to install
Install	S.F.	5.50	10.20		15.70	standard brick pavers on mortar base.
Demolish and Install	S.F.	5.50	15.85	2.04	23.39	
Reinstall	S.F.		8.14		8.14	
Clean	S.F.		1.11		1.11	
Minimum Charge	Job		204		204	
Deluxe Brick						
Sand Base						
Demolish	S.F.		3.40		3.40	Includes material and labor to install
Install	S.F.	5.55	5.65		11.20	deluxe brick pavers on sand base.
Demolish and Install	S.F.	5.55	9.05		14.60	
Reinstall	S.F.		4.52		4.52	
Clean	S.F.		1.23		1.23	
Minimum Charge	Job		204		204	
Mortar Base						
Demolish	S.F.		5.65	2.04	7.69	Includes material and labor to install
Install	S.F.	6.25	10.20		16.45	deluxe brick pavers on mortar base.
Demolish and Install	S.F.	6.25	15.85	2.04	24.14	
Reinstall	S.F.		8.14		8.14	
Clean	S.F.		1.11		1.11	
Minimum Charge	Job		204		204	

Fencing	Unit	Material	Labor	Equip.	Total	Specification
Block w / Footing						
4"						
Demolish	S.F.		1.89		1.89	Cost includes material and labor to
Install	S.F.	1.64	4.37		6.01	install 4" non-reinforced concrete
Demolish and Install	S.F.	1.64	6.26		7.90	block.
Clean	S.F.	.22	1.02	.23	1.47	
Paint	S.F.	.32	.68		1	
Minimum Charge	Job		204		204	

Fencing		Unit	Material	Labor	Equip.	Total	Specification
4″ Reinforced							
	Demolish	S.F.		1.89	1	2.89	Cost includes material and labor to
	Install	S.F.	1.79	4.42		6.21	install 4″ reinforced concrete block.
	Demolish and Install	S.F.	1.79	6.31	1	9.10	
	Clean	S.F.	.22	1.02	.23	1.47	
	Paint	S.F.	.32	.68		1	
	Minimum Charge	Job		204		204	
6″							
	Demolish	S.F.		2		2	Cost includes material and labor to
	Install	S.F.	2.31	4.70		7.01	install 6″ non-reinforced concrete
	Demolish and Install	S.F.	2.31	6.70		9.01	block.
	Clean	S.F.	.22	1.02	.23	1.47	
	Paint	S.F.	.32	.68		1	
	Minimum Charge	Job		204		204	
6″ Reinforced							
	Demolish	S.F.		1.99	.47	2.46	Cost includes material and labor to
	Install	S.F.	2.48	4.76		7.24	install 6″ reinforced concrete block.
	Demolish and Install	S.F.	2.48	6.75	.47	9.70	
	Clean	S.F.	.22	1.02	.23	1.47	
	Paint	S.F.	.32	.68		1	
	Minimum Charge	Job		204		204	
Cap for Block Wall							
	Demolish	L.F.		2.13		2.13	Includes labor and equipment to install
	Install	L.F.	19.95	9.80		29.75	precast concrete coping.
	Demolish and Install	L.F.	19.95	11.93		31.88	
	Clean	L.F.	.02	3.19		3.21	
	Paint	S.F.	.32	.68		1	
	Minimum Charge	Job		204		204	
Block Pilaster							
	Demolish	Ea.		146		146	Includes material and labor to install
	Install	Ea.	78	147		225	block pilaster for fence.
	Demolish and Install	Ea.	78	293		371	
	Reinstall	Ea.		147.20		147.20	
	Paint	Ea.	4.25	15.80		20.05	
	Minimum Charge	Job		204		204	
Block w / o Footing							
4″							
	Demolish	S.F.		1.89		1.89	Cost includes material and labor to
	Install	S.F.	1.80	3.35		5.15	install 4″ non-reinforced hollow
	Demolish and Install	S.F.	1.80	5.24		7.04	lightweight block.
	Clean	S.F.	.22	1.02	.23	1.47	
	Paint	S.F.	.32	.68		1	
	Minimum Charge	Job		204		204	
4″ Reinforced							
	Demolish	S.F.		1.89	1	2.89	Cost includes material and labor to
	Install	S.F.	1.93	4.32		6.25	install 4″ reinforced hollow lightweight
	Demolish and Install	S.F.	1.93	6.21	1	9.14	block.
	Clean	S.F.	.22	1.02	.23	1.47	
	Paint	S.F.	.32	.68		1	
	Minimum Charge	Job		204		204	
6″							
	Demolish	S.F.		2		2	Cost includes material and labor to
	Install	S.F.	2.61	3.68		6.29	install 6″ non-reinforced hollow
	Demolish and Install	S.F.	2.61	5.68		8.29	lightweight block.
	Clean	S.F.	.22	1.02	.23	1.47	
	Paint	S.F.	.32	.68		1	
	Minimum Charge	Job		204		204	

Fencing	Unit	Material	Labor	Equip.	Total	Specification
6" Reinforced						
Demolish	S.F.		1.99	.47	2.46	Cost includes material and labor to
Install	S.F.	2.73	4.64		7.37	install 6" reinforced hollow lightweight
Demolish and Install	S.F.	2.73	6.63	.47	9.83	block.
Clean	S.F.	.22	1.02	.23	1.47	
Paint	S.F.	.32	.68		1	
Minimum Charge	Job		204		204	
Cap for Block Wall						
Demolish	L.F.		2.13		2.13	Includes labor and equipment to install
Install	L.F.	19.95	9.80		29.75	precast concrete coping.
Demolish and Install	L.F.	19.95	11.93		31.88	
Clean	L.F.	.02	3.19		3.21	
Paint	S.F.	.32	.68		1	
Minimum Charge	Job		204		204	
Block Pilaster						
Demolish	Ea.		146		146	Includes material and labor to install
Install	Ea.	78	147		225	block pilaster for fence.
Demolish and Install	Ea.	78	293		371	
Reinstall	Ea.		147.20		147.20	
Paint	Ea.	4.25	15.80		20.05	
Minimum Charge	Job		204		204	
Chain Link						
3' High w / o Top Rail						
Demolish	L.F.		2.67	.96	3.63	Includes material and labor to install
Install	L.F.	3.84	1.78	.46	6.08	residential galvanized fence 3' high
Demolish and Install	L.F.	3.84	4.45	1.42	9.71	with 1-3/8" steel post 10' O.C. set
Reinstall	L.F.		1.43	.37	1.80	without concrete.
Clean	L.F.	.14	1.11		1.25	
Minimum Charge	Job		475		475	
4' High w / o Top Rail						
Demolish	L.F.		2.67	.96	3.63	Includes material and labor to install
Install	L.F.	5	2.20	.57	7.77	residential galvanized fence 4' high
Demolish and Install	L.F.	5	4.87	1.53	11.40	with 1-3/8" steel post 10' O.C. set
Reinstall	L.F.		1.76	.45	2.21	without concrete.
Clean	L.F.	.19	1.23		1.42	
Minimum Charge	Job		475		475	
5' High w / o Top Rail						
Demolish	L.F.		2.67	.96	3.63	Includes material and labor to install
Install	L.F.	5.45	2.88	.74	9.07	residential galvanized fence 5' high
Demolish and Install	L.F.	5.45	5.55	1.70	12.70	with 1-3/8" steel post 10' O.C. set
Reinstall	L.F.		2.31	.59	2.90	without concrete.
Clean	L.F.	.24	1.36		1.60	
Minimum Charge	Job		475		475	
3' High w / Top Rail						
Demolish	L.F.		2.83	1.02	3.85	Includes material and labor to install
Install	L.F.	2.34	1.87	.48	4.69	residential galvanized fence 3' high
Demolish and Install	L.F.	2.34	4.70	1.50	8.54	with 1-3/8" steel post 10' O.C. set
Reinstall	L.F.		1.50	.38	1.88	without concrete.
Clean	L.F.	.14	1.13		1.27	
Minimum Charge	Job		475		475	
4' High w / Top Rail						
Demolish	L.F.		2.83	1.02	3.85	Includes material and labor to install
Install	L.F.	5.35	2.34	.60	8.29	residential galvanized fence 4' high
Demolish and Install	L.F.	5.35	5.17	1.62	12.14	with 1-5/8" steel post 10' O.C. set
Reinstall	L.F.		1.87	.48	2.35	without concrete and 1-5/8" top rail
Clean	L.F.	.19	1.25		1.44	with sleeves.
Minimum Charge	Job		475		475	

Fencing		Unit	Material	Labor	Equip.	Total	Specification
5' High w / Top Rail							
	Demolish	L.F.		2.83	1.02	3.85	Includes material and labor to install
	Install	L.F.	3.84	3.12	.80	7.76	residential galvanized fence 5' high
	Demolish and Install	L.F.	3.84	5.95	1.82	11.61	with 1-5/8" steel post 10' O.C. set
	Reinstall	L.F.		2.50	.64	3.14	without concrete and 1-5/8" top rail
	Clean	L.F.	.24	1.39		1.63	with sleeves.
	Minimum Charge	Job		475		475	
6' High w / Top Rail							
	Demolish	L.F.		2.83	1.02	3.85	Includes material and labor to install
	Install	L.F.	7	4.68	1.20	12.88	residential galvanized fence 6' high
	Demolish and Install	L.F.	7	7.51	2.22	16.73	with 2" steel post 10' O.C. set without
	Reinstall	L.F.		3.75	.96	4.71	concrete and 1-3/8" top rail with
	Clean	L.F.	.29	1.57		1.86	sleeves.
	Minimum Charge	Job		475		475	
Barbed Wire							
	Demolish	L.F.		1.58		1.58	Cost includes material and labor to
	Install	L.F.	.46	.61	.19	1.26	install 3 strand galvanized barbed
	Demolish and Install	L.F.	.46	2.19	.19	2.84	wire fence.
	Reinstall	L.F.		.49	.16	.65	
	Minimum Charge	Job		475	365	840	
6' Redwood							
	Demolish	L.F.		10.50		10.50	Cost includes material and labor to
	Install	L.F.	34.50	7.50	1.92	43.92	install 6' high redwood fencing.
	Demolish and Install	L.F.	34.50	18	1.92	54.42	
	Reinstall	L.F.		5.99	1.54	7.53	
	Clean	L.F.	.29	1.43		1.72	
	Paint	L.F.	.81	3.74		4.55	
	Minimum Charge	Job		475		475	
6' Red Cedar							
	Demolish	L.F.		10.50		10.50	Cost includes material and labor to
	Install	L.F.	20.50	7.50	1.92	29.92	install 6' cedar fence.
	Demolish and Install	L.F.	20.50	18	1.92	40.42	
	Reinstall	L.F.		5.99	1.54	7.53	
	Clean	L.F.	.29	1.43		1.72	
	Paint	L.F.	.81	3.74		4.55	
	Minimum Charge	Job		475		475	
6' Shadowbox							
	Demolish	L.F.		10.50		10.50	Cost includes material and labor to
	Install	L.F.	16.60	6.25	1.60	24.45	install 6' pressure treated pine fence.
	Demolish and Install	L.F.	16.60	16.75	1.60	34.95	
	Reinstall	L.F.		4.99	1.28	6.27	
	Clean	L.F.	.29	1.43		1.72	
	Paint	L.F.	.81	3.74		4.55	
	Minimum Charge	Job		475		475	
3' Picket							
	Demolish	L.F.		10.50		10.50	Includes material, labor and
	Install	L.F.	5.90	6.70	1.72	14.32	equipment to install pressure treated
	Demolish and Install	L.F.	5.90	17.20	1.72	24.82	pine picket fence.
	Reinstall	L.F.		5.35	1.37	6.72	
	Clean	L.F.	.14	1.23		1.37	
	Paint	L.F.	.41	2.03		2.44	
	Minimum Charge	Job		475		475	

Fencing	Unit	Material	Labor	Equip.	Total	Specification
Wrought Iron						
Demolish	L.F.		22.50		22.50	Cost includes material and labor to
Install	L.F.	36.50	12.60		49.10	install 5' high wrought iron fence with
Demolish and Install	L.F.	36.50	35.10		71.60	pickets at 4-1/2" O.C.
Reinstall	L.F.		10.09		10.09	
Clean	L.F.		1.23		1.23	
Paint	L.F.	3.99	4.18		8.17	
Minimum Charge	Job		475		475	
Post						
Dirt Based Wood						
Demolish	Ea.		26.50		26.50	Includes material and labor to install
Install	Ea.	25	118		143	wood post set in earth.
Demolish and Install	Ea.	25	144.50		169.50	
Reinstall	Ea.		94.61		94.61	
Clean	Ea.		3.83		3.83	
Paint	Ea.	.89	1.42		2.31	
Minimum Charge	Job		475		475	
Concrete Based Wood						
Demolish	Ea.		38	13.60	51.60	Includes material and labor to install
Install	Ea.	19.35	158		177.35	wood post set in concrete.
Demolish and Install	Ea.	19.35	196	13.60	228.95	
Clean	Ea.		3.83		3.83	
Paint	Ea.	.89	1.42		2.31	
Minimum Charge	Job		475		475	
Block Pilaster						
Demolish	Ea.		146		146	Includes material and labor to install
Install	Ea.	78	147		225	block pilaster for fence.
Demolish and Install	Ea.	78	293		371	
Reinstall	Ea.		147.20		147.20	
Paint	Ea.	4.25	15.80		20.05	
Minimum Charge	Job		204		204	
Gate						
Chain Link						
Demolish	Ea.		35		35	Cost includes material and labor to
Install	Ea.	138	52.50		190.50	install 3' wide chain link pass gate
Demolish and Install	Ea.	138	87.50		225.50	and hardware.
Reinstall	Ea.		42.05		42.05	
Clean	Ea.		4.26		4.26	
Minimum Charge	Job		475		475	
Redwood						
Demolish	Ea.		30		30	Includes material, labor and
Install	Ea.	212	52.50		264.50	equipment to install redwood pass
Demolish and Install	Ea.	212	82.50		294.50	gate and hardware.
Reinstall	Ea.		42.05		42.05	
Clean	Ea.		4.26		4.26	
Paint	Ea.	1.33	7.10		8.43	
Minimum Charge	Job		475		475	
Red Cedar						
Demolish	Ea.		30		30	Cost includes material and labor to
Install	Ea.	97.50	52.50		150	install 3' wide red cedar pass gate
Demolish and Install	Ea.	97.50	82.50		180	and hardware.
Reinstall	Ea.		42.05		42.05	
Clean	Ea.		4.26		4.26	
Paint	Ea.	1.33	7.10		8.43	
Minimum Charge	Job		475		475	

Fencing	Unit	Material	Labor	Equip.	Total	Specification
Wrought Iron						
Demolish	Ea.		22.50		22.50	Includes material, labor and
Install	Ea.	240	118		358	equipment to install wrought iron gate
Demolish and Install	Ea.	240	140.50		380.50	with hardware.
Reinstall	Ea.		94.61		94.61	
Clean	Ea.		4.26		4.26	
Paint	Ea.	8	7.10		15.10	
Minimum Charge	Job		475		475	

Rough Mechanical

Fire-extinguishing System

Space Heater

Hot-air Furnace

Plumbing	Unit	Material	Labor	Equip.	Total	Specification
Components						
3/4″ Supply						
Demolish	L.F.		2.64		2.64	Includes material and labor to install
Install	L.F.	7.25	6.25		13.50	type L copper tubing including
Demolish and Install	L.F.	7.25	8.89		16.14	couplings and hangers at 10′ O.C.
Reinstall	L.F.		6.25		6.25	
Minimum Charge	Job		238		238	
1/2″ Fixture Supply						
Install	Ea.	77.50	158		235.50	Includes labor and materials to install supply pipe only to a plumbing fixture.
2″ Single Vent Stack						
Demolish	Ea.		44		44	Includes material and labor to install
Install	Ea.	28.50	238		266.50	PVC vent stack pipe with couplings at
Demolish and Install	Ea.	28.50	282		310.50	10′ O.C.
Reinstall	Ea.		237.60		237.60	
Minimum Charge	Job		238		238	
4″ Drain						
Demolish	L.F.		3.52		3.52	Includes material and labor to install
Install	L.F.	9.90	7.80		17.70	DVW type PVC pipe with couplings at
Demolish and Install	L.F.	9.90	11.32		21.22	10′ O.C. and 3 strap hangers per 10′
Reinstall	L.F.		7.78		7.78	run.
Minimum Charge	Job		238		238	
1-1/2″ Drain						
Demolish	L.F.		2.64		2.64	Includes material and labor to install
Install	L.F.	3.26	5.05		8.31	DVW type PVC pipe with couplings at
Demolish and Install	L.F.	3.26	7.69		10.95	10′ O.C. and 3 strap hangers per 10′
Reinstall	L.F.		5.06		5.06	run.
Minimum Charge	Job		238		238	
Maintenance						
Flush Out / Unclog						
Clean	Job		238		238	Minimum labor and equipment charge
Minimum Charge	Job		238		238	to install water cooler.
Vent Cap						
Large						
Demolish	Ea.		12		12	Includes labor and material to install a
Install	Ea.	39	21.50		60.50	PVC plumbing pipe vent cap.
Demolish and Install	Ea.	39	33.50		72.50	
Clean	Ea.	.66	6.95		7.61	
Paint	Ea.	.18	8.05		8.23	
Minimum Charge	Job		119		119	

143

Rough Mechanical

Plumbing

Plumbing	Unit	Material	Labor	Equip.	Total	Specification
Medium						
Demolish	Ea.		12		12	Includes labor and material to install a
Install	Ea.	33.50	20.50		54	PVC plumbing pipe vent cap.
Demolish and Install	Ea.	33.50	32.50		66	
Clean	Ea.	.66	6.95		7.61	
Paint	Ea.	.18	8.05		8.23	
Minimum Charge	Job		119		119	
Small						
Demolish	Ea.		12		12	Includes material and labor to install a
Install	Ea.	8.80	19.80		28.60	PVC plumbing pipe vent cap.
Demolish and Install	Ea.	8.80	31.80		40.60	
Clean	Ea.	.66	6.95		7.61	
Paint	Ea.	.18	8.05		8.23	
Minimum Charge	Job		119		119	

Plumbing

Plumbing	Unit	Material	Labor	Equip.	Total	Specification
Sump Pump						
1/4 HP						
Demolish	Ea.		47.50		47.50	Includes material and labor to install a
Install	Ea.	139	79		218	submersible sump pump.
Demolish and Install	Ea.	139	126.50		265.50	
Reinstall	Ea.		63.36		63.36	
Clean	Ea.	1.67	19.15		20.82	
Minimum Charge	Job		238		238	
1/3 HP						
Demolish	Ea.		47.50		47.50	Includes material and labor to install a
Install	Ea.	208	95		303	submersible sump pump.
Demolish and Install	Ea.	208	142.50		350.50	
Reinstall	Ea.		76.03		76.03	
Clean	Ea.	1.67	19.15		20.82	
Minimum Charge	Job		238		238	
1/2 HP						
Demolish	Ea.		47.50		47.50	Includes material and labor to install a
Install	Ea.	228	95		323	submersible sump pump.
Demolish and Install	Ea.	228	142.50		370.50	
Reinstall	Ea.		76.03		76.03	
Clean	Ea.	1.67	19.15		20.82	
Minimum Charge	Job		238		238	
Clean and Service						
Clean	Ea.		29.50		29.50	Includes labor to clean and service a
Minimum Charge	Job		238		238	sump pump.

Water Heater

Water Heater	Unit	Material	Labor	Equip.	Total	Specification
30 Gallon						
Demolish	Ea.		149		149	Includes material and labor to install a
Install	Ea.	635	216		851	30 gallon electric water heater.
Demolish and Install	Ea.	635	365		1000	
Reinstall	Ea.		172.80		172.80	
Clean	Ea.	1.67	19.15		20.82	
Minimum Charge	Job		238		238	

Rough Mechanical

Water Heater		Unit	Material	Labor	Equip.	Total	Specification
40 Gallon							
	Demolish	Ea.		149		149	Includes material and labor to install a
	Install	Ea.	675	238		913	40 gallon electric water heater.
	Demolish and Install	Ea.	675	387		1062	
	Reinstall	Ea.		190.08		190.08	
	Clean	Ea.	1.67	19.15		20.82	
	Minimum Charge	Job		238		238	
52 Gallon							
	Demolish	Ea.		149		149	Includes material and labor to install a
	Install	Ea.	760	238		998	52 gallon electric water heater.
	Demolish and Install	Ea.	760	387		1147	
	Reinstall	Ea.		190.08		190.08	
	Clean	Ea.	1.67	19.15		20.82	
	Minimum Charge	Job		238		238	
82 Gallon							
	Demolish	Ea.		149		149	Includes material and labor to install
	Install	Ea.	1125	297		1422	an 82 gallon electric water heater.
	Demolish and Install	Ea.	1125	446		1571	
	Reinstall	Ea.		237.60		237.60	
	Clean	Ea.	1.67	19.15		20.82	
	Minimum Charge	Job		238		238	
Gas-fired							
30 Gallon Gas-fired							
	Demolish	Ea.		183		183	Includes material and labor to install a
	Install	Ea.	985	238		1223	30 gallon gas water heater.
	Demolish and Install	Ea.	985	421		1406	
	Reinstall	Ea.		190.08		190.08	
	Clean	Ea.	1.67	19.15		20.82	
	Minimum Charge	Job		238		238	
30 Gallon Gas-fired, Flue							
	Install	Ea.	39	68		107	Includes labor and materials to install
	Minimum Charge	Job		238		238	a flue for a water heater (up to 50
							gallon size).
40 Gallon Gas-fired							
	Demolish	Ea.		183		183	Includes material and labor to install a
	Install	Ea.	985	250		1235	40 gallon gas water heater.
	Demolish and Install	Ea.	985	433		1418	
	Reinstall	Ea.		200.08		200.08	
	Clean	Ea.	1.67	19.15		20.82	
	Minimum Charge	Job		238		238	
40 Gallon Gas-fired, Flue							
	Install	Ea.	39	68		107	Includes labor and materials to install
	Minimum Charge	Job		238		238	a flue for a water heater (up to 50
							gallon size).
50 Gallon Gas-fired							
	Demolish	Ea.		183		183	Includes material and labor to install a
	Install	Ea.	1025	264		1289	50 gallon gas water heater.
	Demolish and Install	Ea.	1025	447		1472	
	Reinstall	Ea.		211.20		211.20	
	Clean	Ea.	1.67	19.15		20.82	
	Minimum Charge	Job		238		238	
50 Gallon Gas-fired, Flue							
	Install	Ea.	39	68		107	Includes labor and materials to install
	Minimum Charge	Job		238		238	a flue for a water heater (up to 50
							gallon size).

Rough Mechanical

Water Heater	Unit	Material	Labor	Equip.	Total	Specification
Solar Hot Water System						
Water Heater						
Demolish	Ea.		119		119	Includes material and labor to install a
Install	Ea.	1150	315		1465	solar hot water heat exchanger
Demolish and Install	Ea.	1150	434		1584	storage tank, 100 gallon.
Reinstall	Ea.		253.44		253.44	
Minimum Charge	Job		242		242	
Solar Panel						
Demolish	S.F.		1.74		1.74	Includes material and labor to install
Install	S.F.	34	3.13		37.13	solar panel.
Demolish and Install	S.F.	34	4.87		38.87	
Reinstall	S.F.		2.50		2.50	
Minimum Charge	Job		242		242	
Repair Plumbing						
Install	Job		242		242	Includes 4 hour minimum labor charge
Minimum Charge	Job		242		242	for a steamfitter or pipefitter.
Insulating Wrap						
Demolish	Ea.		5.50		5.50	Includes material and labor to install
Install	Ea.	19.65	14.85		34.50	insulating wrap around a 100 gallon
Demolish and Install	Ea.	19.65	20.35		40	solar hot water heat exchanger
Reinstall	Ea.		11.88		11.88	storage tank.
Minimum Charge	Job		238		238	
Water Softener						
Demolish	Ea.		88		88	Includes material and labor to install a
Install	Ea.	1450	214		1664	14 GPM water softener.
Demolish and Install	Ea.	1450	302		1752	
Reinstall	Ea.		171.14		171.14	
Clean	Ea.	1.67	19.15		20.82	
Minimum Charge	Ea.		238		238	

Ductwork	Unit	Material	Labor	Equip.	Total	Specification
Galvanized, Square or Rectangular						
6"						
Demolish	L.F.		2.12		2.12	Includes material and labor to install
Install	L.F.	1.78	10.20		11.98	rectangular ductwork with a greatest
Demolish and Install	L.F.	1.78	12.32		14.10	dimension of 6".
Reinstall	L.F.		8.14		8.14	
Clean	L.F.		2.44		2.44	
Minimum Charge	Job		229		229	
8"						
Demolish	L.F.		2.12		2.12	Includes material and labor to install
Install	L.F.	2.37	13.10		15.47	rectangular ductwork with a greatest
Demolish and Install	L.F.	2.37	15.22		17.59	dimension of 8".
Reinstall	L.F.		10.47		10.47	
Clean	L.F.		3.26		3.26	
Minimum Charge	Job		229		229	
10"						
Demolish	L.F.		2.12		2.12	Includes material and labor to install
Install	L.F.	2.96	16.95		19.91	rectangular ductwork with a greatest
Demolish and Install	L.F.	2.96	19.07		22.03	dimension of 10".
Reinstall	L.F.		13.57		13.57	
Clean	L.F.		4.07		4.07	
Minimum Charge	Job		229		229	

Ductwork		Unit	Material	Labor	Equip.	Total	Specification
Galvanized, Spiral							
4"							
	Demolish	L.F.		2.54		2.54	Cost includes material and labor to
	Install	L.F.	2.16	2.29		4.45	install 4" diameter spiral pre-formed
	Demolish and Install	L.F.	2.16	4.83		6.99	steel galvanized ductwork.
	Reinstall	L.F.		1.83		1.83	
	Clean	L.F.		1.28		1.28	
	Minimum Charge	Job		229		229	
6"							
	Demolish	L.F.		2.54		2.54	Cost includes material and labor to
	Install	L.F.	2.16	2.94		5.10	install 6" diameter spiral pre-formed
	Demolish and Install	L.F.	2.16	5.48		7.64	steel galvanized ductwork.
	Reinstall	L.F.		2.35		2.35	
	Clean	L.F.		1.92		1.92	
	Minimum Charge	Job		229		229	
8"							
	Demolish	L.F.		2.54		2.54	Cost includes material and labor to
	Install	L.F.	2.87	4.12		6.99	install 8" diameter spiral pre-formed
	Demolish and Install	L.F.	2.87	6.66		9.53	steel galvanized ductwork.
	Reinstall	L.F.		3.30		3.30	
	Clean	L.F.		2.56		2.56	
	Minimum Charge	Job		229		229	
10"							
	Demolish	L.F.		3.18		3.18	Cost includes material and labor to
	Install	L.F.	3.59	5.15		8.74	install 10" diameter spiral pre-formed
	Demolish and Install	L.F.	3.59	8.33		11.92	steel galvanized ductwork.
	Reinstall	L.F.		4.12		4.12	
	Clean	L.F.		3.20		3.20	
	Minimum Charge	Job		229		229	
12"							
	Demolish	L.F.		4.24		4.24	Cost includes material and labor to
	Install	L.F.	4.29	6.85		11.14	install 12" diameter spiral pre-formed
	Demolish and Install	L.F.	4.29	11.09		15.38	steel galvanized ductwork.
	Reinstall	L.F.		5.49		5.49	
	Clean	L.F.		3.84		3.84	
	Minimum Charge	Job		229		229	
16"							
	Demolish	L.F.		8.50		8.50	Cost includes material and labor to
	Install	L.F.	6.65	13.75		20.40	install 16" diameter spiral pre-formed
	Demolish and Install	L.F.	6.65	22.25		28.90	steel galvanized ductwork.
	Reinstall	L.F.		10.99		10.99	
	Clean	L.F.		5.10		5.10	
	Minimum Charge	Job		229		229	
Flexible Fiberglass							
6" Non-insulated							
	Demolish	L.F.		1.96		1.96	Cost includes material and labor to
	Install	L.F.	1.54	2.94		4.48	install 6" diameter non-insulated
	Demolish and Install	L.F.	1.54	4.90		6.44	flexible fiberglass fabric on corrosion
	Reinstall	L.F.		2.35		2.35	resistant metal ductwork.
	Clean	L.F.		1.92		1.92	
	Minimum Charge	Job		229		229	
8" Non-insulated							
	Demolish	L.F.		2.83		2.83	Cost includes material and labor to
	Install	L.F.	1.94	4.12		6.06	install 8" diameter non-insulated
	Demolish and Install	L.F.	1.94	6.95		8.89	flexible fiberglass fabric on corrosion
	Reinstall	L.F.		3.30		3.30	resistant metal ductwork.
	Clean	L.F.		2.56		2.56	
	Minimum Charge	Job		229		229	

Ductwork	Unit	Material	Labor	Equip.	Total	Specification
10″ Non-insulated						
Demolish	L.F.		3.63		3.63	Cost includes material and labor to
Install	L.F.	2.51	5.15		7.66	install 10″ diameter non-insulated
Demolish and Install	L.F.	2.51	8.78		11.29	flexible fiberglass fabric on corrosion
Reinstall	L.F.		4.12		4.12	resistant metal ductwork.
Clean	L.F.		3.20		3.20	
Minimum Charge	Job		229		229	
12″ Non-insulated						
Demolish	L.F.		5.10		5.10	Cost includes material and labor to
Install	L.F.	3	6.85		9.85	install 12″ diameter non-insulated
Demolish and Install	L.F.	3	11.95		14.95	flexible fiberglass fabric on corrosion
Reinstall	L.F.		5.49		5.49	resistant metal ductwork.
Clean	L.F.		3.84		3.84	
Minimum Charge	Job		229		229	
4″ Insulated						
Demolish	L.F.		1.50		1.50	Cost includes material and labor to
Install	L.F.	2.44	2.42		4.86	install 4″ diameter insulated flexible
Demolish and Install	L.F.	2.44	3.92		6.36	fiberglass fabric on corrosion resistant
Reinstall	L.F.		1.94		1.94	metal ductwork.
Clean	L.F.		1.28		1.28	
Minimum Charge	Job		229		229	
6″ Insulated						
Demolish	L.F.		1.96		1.96	Cost includes material and labor to
Install	L.F.	2.75	3.17		5.92	install 6″ diameter insulated flexible
Demolish and Install	L.F.	2.75	5.13		7.88	fiberglass fabric on corrosion resistant
Reinstall	L.F.		2.54		2.54	metal ductwork.
Clean	L.F.		1.92		1.92	
Minimum Charge	Job		229		229	
8″ Insulated						
Demolish	L.F.		2.83		2.83	Cost includes material and labor to
Install	L.F.	3.31	4.58		7.89	install 8″ diameter insulated flexible
Demolish and Install	L.F.	3.31	7.41		10.72	fiberglass fabric on corrosion resistant
Reinstall	L.F.		3.66		3.66	metal ductwork.
Clean	L.F.		2.56		2.56	
Minimum Charge	Job		229		229	
10″ Insulated						
Demolish	L.F.		3.63		3.63	Cost includes material and labor to
Install	L.F.	4.03	5.90		9.93	install 10″ diameter insulated flexible
Demolish and Install	L.F.	4.03	9.53		13.56	fiberglass fabric on corrosion resistant
Reinstall	L.F.		4.71		4.71	metal ductwork.
Clean	L.F.		3.20		3.20	
Minimum Charge	Job		229		229	
12″ Insulated						
Demolish	L.F.		5.10		5.10	Cost includes material and labor to
Install	L.F.	4.62	8.25		12.87	install 12″ diameter insulated flexible
Demolish and Install	L.F.	4.62	13.35		17.97	fiberglass fabric on corrosion resistant
Reinstall	L.F.		6.59		6.59	metal ductwork.
Clean	L.F.		3.84		3.84	
Minimum Charge	Job		229		229	

Heating		Unit	Material	Labor	Equip.	Total	Specification
Hot Water Baseboard							
	Demolish	L.F.		8.30		8.30	Includes material and labor to install
	Install	L.F.	8.40	14.55		22.95	baseboard radiation.
	Demolish and Install	L.F.	8.40	22.85		31.25	
	Reinstall	L.F.		11.63		11.63	
	Clean	L.F.	1.67	4.79		6.46	
	Minimum Charge	Job		238		238	
3'							
	Demolish	Ea.		26.50		26.50	Includes material and labor to install
	Install	Ea.	28	48.50		76.50	fin tube baseboard radiation in 3'
	Demolish and Install	Ea.	28	75		103	sections.
	Reinstall	Ea.		38.76		38.76	
	Clean	Ea.	.47	14.60		15.07	
	Minimum Charge	Job		238		238	
4'							
	Demolish	Ea.		35		35	Includes material and labor to install
	Install	Ea.	37	54.50		91.50	fin tube baseboard radiation in 4'
	Demolish and Install	Ea.	37	89.50		126.50	sections.
	Reinstall	Ea.		43.60		43.60	
	Clean	Ea.	.96	19.15		20.11	
	Minimum Charge	Job		238		238	
5'							
	Demolish	Ea.		44		44	Includes material and labor to install
	Install	Ea.	46	62.50		108.50	fin tube baseboard radiation in 5'
	Demolish and Install	Ea.	46	106.50		152.50	sections.
	Reinstall	Ea.		49.83		49.83	
	Clean	Ea.	.96	23.50		24.46	
	Minimum Charge	Job		238		238	
6'							
	Demolish	Ea.		53		53	Includes material and labor to install
	Install	Ea.	55.50	72.50		128	fin tube baseboard radiation in 6'
	Demolish and Install	Ea.	55.50	125.50		181	sections.
	Reinstall	Ea.		58.13		58.13	
	Clean	Ea.	.96	28		28.96	
	Minimum Charge	Job		238		238	
7'							
	Demolish	Ea.		58.50		58.50	Includes material and labor to install
	Install	Ea.	65	95		160	fin tube baseboard radiation in 7'
	Demolish and Install	Ea.	65	153.50		218.50	sections.
	Reinstall	Ea.		76.03		76.03	
	Clean	Ea.	1.20	34		35.20	
	Minimum Charge	Job		238		238	
9'							
	Demolish	Ea.		88		88	Includes material and labor to install
	Install	Ea.	83.50	136		219.50	fin tube baseboard radiation in 9'
	Demolish and Install	Ea.	83.50	224		307.50	sections.
	Reinstall	Ea.		108.62		108.62	
	Clean	Ea.	1.91	44		45.91	
	Minimum Charge	Job		238		238	

Heating		Unit	Material	Labor	Equip.	Total	Specification
50 MBH							
	Demolish	Ea.		43.50		43.50	Includes material and labor to install a
	Install	Ea.	1325	125		1450	cabinet space heater with an output of
	Demolish and Install	Ea.	1325	168.50		1493.50	50 MBH.
	Reinstall	Ea.		99.66		99.66	
	Clean	Ea.	1.20	38.50		39.70	
	Minimum Charge	Job		242		242	

Rough Mechanical

Heating

	Unit	Material	Labor	Equip.	Total	Specification
75 MBH						
Demolish	Ea.		43.50		43.50	Includes material and labor to install a
Install	Ea.	1350	145		1495	cabinet space heater with an output of
Demolish and Install	Ea.	1350	188.50		1538.50	75 MBH.
Reinstall	Ea.		116.27		116.27	
Clean	Ea.	1.20	38.50		39.70	
Minimum Charge	Job		242		242	
125 MBH						
Demolish	Ea.		52.50		52.50	Includes material and labor to install a
Install	Ea.	1650	174		1824	cabinet space heater with an output of
Demolish and Install	Ea.	1650	226.50		1876.50	125 MBH.
Reinstall	Ea.		139.52		139.52	
Clean	Ea.	1.20	38.50		39.70	
Minimum Charge	Job		242		242	
175 MBH						
Demolish	Ea.		65.50		65.50	Includes material and labor to install a
Install	Ea.	1875	249		2124	cabinet space heater with an output of
Demolish and Install	Ea.	1875	314.50		2189.50	175 MBH.
Reinstall	Ea.		199.31		199.31	
Clean	Ea.	1.20	38.50		39.70	
Minimum Charge	Job		242		242	

Furnace Unit

	Unit	Material	Labor	Equip.	Total	Specification
Wall (gas-fired)						
25 MBH w / Thermostat						
Demolish	Ea.		103		103	Includes material and labor to install a
Install	Ea.	670	165		835	gas fired hot air furnace rated at 25
Demolish and Install	Ea.	670	268		938	MBH.
Reinstall	Ea.		131.84		131.84	
Clean	Ea.	2.39	85		87.39	
Minimum Charge	Job		242		242	
35 MBH w / Thermostat						
Demolish	Ea.		103		103	Includes material and labor to install a
Install	Ea.	820	183		1003	gas fired hot air furnace rated at 35
Demolish and Install	Ea.	820	286		1106	MBH.
Reinstall	Ea.		146.49		146.49	
Clean	Ea.	2.39	85		87.39	
Minimum Charge	Job		242		242	
50 MBH w / Thermostat						
Demolish	Ea.		103		103	Includes material and labor to install a
Install	Ea.	1000	206		1206	gas fired hot air furnace rated at 50
Demolish and Install	Ea.	1000	309		1309	MBH.
Reinstall	Ea.		164.80		164.80	
Clean	Ea.	2.39	85		87.39	
Minimum Charge	Job		242		242	
60 MBH w / Thermostat						
Demolish	Ea.		103		103	Includes material and labor to install a
Install	Ea.	1125	229		1354	gas fired hot air furnace rated at 60
Demolish and Install	Ea.	1125	332		1457	MBH.
Reinstall	Ea.		183.11		183.11	
Clean	Ea.	2.39	85		87.39	
Minimum Charge	Job		242		242	

Furnace Unit	Unit	Material	Labor	Equip.	Total	Specification
Floor (gas-fired)						
30 MBH w / Thermostat						Includes material and labor to install a
Demolish	Ea.		103		103	gas fired hot air floor furnace rated at
Install	Ea.	890	165		1055	30 MBH.
Demolish and Install	Ea.	890	268		1158	
Reinstall	Ea.		131.84		131.84	
Clean	Ea.	2.39	85		87.39	
Minimum Charge	Job		242		242	
50 MBH w / Thermostat						Includes material and labor to install a
Demolish	Ea.		103		103	gas fired hot air floor furnace rated at
Install	Ea.	965	206		1171	50 MBH.
Demolish and Install	Ea.	965	309		1274	
Reinstall	Ea.		164.80		164.80	
Clean	Ea.	2.39	85		87.39	
Minimum Charge	Job		242		242	
Gas Forced Air						
50 MBH						Includes material and labor to install
Demolish	Ea.		103		103	an up flow gas fired hot air furnace
Install	Ea.	950	206		1156	rated at 50 MBH.
Demolish and Install	Ea.	950	309		1259	
Reinstall	Ea.		164.80		164.80	
Clean	Ea.	2.39	85		87.39	
Minimum Charge	Job		242		242	
80 MBH						Includes material and labor to install
Demolish	Ea.		103		103	an up flow gas fired hot air furnace
Install	Ea.	950	229		1179	rated at 80 MBH.
Demolish and Install	Ea.	950	332		1282	
Reinstall	Ea.		183.11		183.11	
Clean	Ea.	2.39	85		87.39	
Minimum Charge	Job		242		242	
100 MBH						Includes material and labor to install
Demolish	Ea.		103		103	an up flow gas fired hot air furnace
Install	Ea.	1100	258		1358	rated at 100 MBH.
Demolish and Install	Ea.	1100	361		1461	
Reinstall	Ea.		206		206	
Clean	Ea.	2.39	85		87.39	
Minimum Charge	Job		242		242	
120 MBH						Includes material and labor to install
Demolish	Ea.		103		103	an up flow gas fired hot air furnace
Install	Ea.	1150	275		1425	rated at 120 MBH.
Demolish and Install	Ea.	1150	378		1528	
Reinstall	Ea.		219.73		219.73	
Clean	Ea.	2.39	85		87.39	
Minimum Charge	Job		242		242	
Electric Forced Air						
31.4 MBH						Includes material and labor to install
Demolish	Ea.		103		103	an electric hot air furnace rated at
Install	Ea.	1700	233		1933	31.4 MBH.
Demolish and Install	Ea.	1700	336		2036	
Reinstall	Ea.		186.67		186.67	
Clean	Ea.	2.39	85		87.39	
Minimum Charge	Job		242		242	

Rough Mechanical

Furnace Unit

Furnace Unit		Unit	Material	Labor	Equip.	Total	Specification
47.1 MBH							Includes material and labor to install
	Demolish	Ea.		103		103	an electric hot air furnace rated at
	Install	Ea.	1925	244		2169	47.1 MBH.
	Demolish and Install	Ea.	1925	347		2272	
	Reinstall	Ea.		195.35		195.35	
	Clean	Ea.	2.39	85		87.39	
	Minimum Charge	Job		242		242	
62.9 MBH							Includes material and labor to install
	Demolish	Ea.		103		103	an electric hot air furnace rated at
	Install	Ea.	2125	263		2388	62.9 MBH.
	Demolish and Install	Ea.	2125	366		2491	
	Reinstall	Ea.		210		210	
	Clean	Ea.	2.39	85		87.39	
	Minimum Charge	Job		242		242	
78.5 MBH							Includes material and labor to install
	Demolish	Ea.		103		103	an electric hot air furnace rated at
	Install	Ea.	2525	269		2794	78.5 MBH.
	Demolish and Install	Ea.	2525	372		2897	
	Reinstall	Ea.		215.38		215.38	
	Clean	Ea.	2.39	85		87.39	
	Minimum Charge	Job		242		242	
110 MBH							Includes material and labor to install
	Demolish	Ea.		103		103	an electric hot air furnace rated at
	Install	Ea.	3625	284		3909	110 MBH.
	Demolish and Install	Ea.	3625	387		4012	
	Reinstall	Ea.		227.03		227.03	
	Clean	Ea.	2.39	85		87.39	
	Minimum Charge	Job		242		242	
A/C Junction Box							Includes labor and materials to install
	Install	Ea.	68	113		181	a heating system emergency shut-off
	Minimum Charge	Job		242		242	switch. Cost includes up to 40 feet of
							non-metallic cable.

Boiler

Boiler		Unit	Material	Labor	Equip.	Total	Specification
Gas-Fired							
60 MBH							Includes material and labor to install a
	Demolish	Ea.		880		880	gas fired cast iron boiler rated at 60
	Install	Ea.	2425	1575		4000	MBH.
	Demolish and Install	Ea.	2425	2455		4880	
	Reinstall	Ea.		1268.36		1268.36	
	Clean	Ea.	4.77	51		55.77	
	Minimum Charge	Job		242		242	
Gas-Fired							
125 MBH							Includes material and labor to install a
	Demolish	Ea.		2425		2425	gas fired cast iron boiler rated at 125
	Install	Ea.	4275	1950		6225	MBH.
	Demolish and Install	Ea.	4275	4375		8650	
	Reinstall	Ea.		1550.22		1550.22	
	Clean	Ea.	4.77	51		55.77	
	Minimum Charge	Job		242		242	

Rough Mechanical

Boiler

Boiler	Unit	Material	Labor	Equip.	Total	Specification
Gas-Fired						
400 MBH						
Demolish	Ea.		2425		2425	Includes material and labor to install a
Install	Ea.	5475	2725		8200	gas fired cast iron boiler rated at 400
Demolish and Install	Ea.	5475	5150		10625	MBH.
Reinstall	Ea.		2725		2725	
Clean	Ea.	4.77	51		55.77	
Minimum Charge	Job		242		242	

Heat Pump

Heat Pump	Unit	Material	Labor	Equip.	Total	Specification
2 Ton						
Demolish	Ea.		242		242	Includes material and labor to install a
Install	Ea.	2350	435		2785	2 ton heat pump.
Demolish and Install	Ea.	2350	677		3027	
Reinstall	Ea.		348.80		348.80	
Clean	Ea.	4.77	38.50		43.27	
Minimum Charge	Job		242		242	
3 Ton						
Demolish	Ea.		405		405	Includes material and labor to install a
Install	Ea.	2925	725		3650	3 ton heat pump.
Demolish and Install	Ea.	2925	1130		4055	
Reinstall	Ea.		581.33		581.33	
Clean	Ea.	4.77	38.50		43.27	
Minimum Charge	Job		242		242	
4 Ton						
Demolish	Ea.		605		605	Includes material and labor to install a
Install	Ea.	3475	1100		4575	4 ton heat pump.
Demolish and Install	Ea.	3475	1705		5180	
Reinstall	Ea.		872		872	
Clean	Ea.	4.77	38.50		43.27	
Minimum Charge	Job		242		242	
5 Ton						
Demolish	Ea.		970		970	Includes material and labor to install a
Install	Ea.	3775	1750		5525	5 ton heat pump.
Demolish and Install	Ea.	3775	2720		6495	
Reinstall	Ea.		1395.20		1395.20	
Clean	Ea.	4.77	38.50		43.27	
Minimum Charge	Job		242		242	
Thermostat						
Demolish	Ea.		13.45		13.45	Includes material and labor to install
Install	Ea.	177	60.50		237.50	an electric thermostat, 2 set back.
Demolish and Install	Ea.	177	73.95		250.95	
Reinstall	Ea.		48.44		48.44	
Clean	Ea.	.10	9.60		9.70	
Minimum Charge	Job		242		242	
A/C Junction Box						
Install	Ea.	675	350		1025	Includes labor and materials to install
Minimum Charge	Job		226		226	a heat pump circuit including up to 40 feet of non-metallic cable.

Heating		Unit	Material	Labor	Equip.	Total	Specification
Electric Baseboard							
	Demolish	L.F.		6.30		6.30	Includes material and labor to install
	Install	L.F.	14.95	15.05		30	electric baseboard heating elements.
	Demolish and Install	L.F.	14.95	21.35		36.30	
	Reinstall	L.F.		12.05		12.05	
	Clean	L.F.	1.67	4.79		6.46	
	Minimum Charge	Job		226		226	
2' 6"							
	Demolish	Ea.		21		21	Includes material and labor to install a
	Install	Ea.	44	56.50		100.50	2' 6" long section of electric
	Demolish and Install	Ea.	44	77.50		121.50	baseboard heating elements.
	Reinstall	Ea.		45.20		45.20	
	Clean	Ea.	.47	11.80		12.27	
	Minimum Charge	Job		226		226	
3'							
	Demolish	Ea.		23		23	Includes material and labor to install a
	Install	Ea.	50.50	56.50		107	3' long section of electric baseboard
	Demolish and Install	Ea.	50.50	79.50		130	heating elements.
	Reinstall	Ea.		45.20		45.20	
	Clean	Ea.	.47	14.60		15.07	
	Minimum Charge	Job		226		226	
4'							
	Demolish	Ea.		25		25	Includes material and labor to install a
	Install	Ea.	70.50	67.50		138	4' long section of electric baseboard
	Demolish and Install	Ea.	70.50	92.50		163	heating elements.
	Reinstall	Ea.		53.97		53.97	
	Clean	Ea.	.19	3.19		3.38	
	Minimum Charge	Job		226		226	
5'							
	Demolish	Ea.		28		28	Includes material and labor to install a
	Install	Ea.	75	79.50		154.50	5' long section of electric baseboard
	Demolish and Install	Ea.	75	107.50		182.50	heating elements.
	Reinstall	Ea.		63.44		63.44	
	Clean	Ea.	.96	23.50		24.46	
	Minimum Charge	Job		226		226	
6'							
	Demolish	Ea.		31.50		31.50	Includes material and labor to install a
	Install	Ea.	81.50	90.50		172	6' long section of electric baseboard
	Demolish and Install	Ea.	81.50	122		203.50	heating elements.
	Reinstall	Ea.		72.32		72.32	
	Clean	Ea.	.19	3.83		4.02	
	Minimum Charge	Job		226		226	
8'							
	Demolish	Ea.		42		42	Includes material and labor to install
	Install	Ea.	101	113		214	an 8' long section of electric
	Demolish and Install	Ea.	101	155		256	baseboard heating elements.
	Reinstall	Ea.		90.40		90.40	
	Clean	Ea.	.19	4.79		4.98	
	Minimum Charge	Job		226		226	
10'							
	Demolish	Ea.		50		50	Includes material and labor to install a
	Install	Ea.	212	137		349	10' long section of electric baseboard
	Demolish and Install	Ea.	212	187		399	heating elements.
	Reinstall	Ea.		109.58		109.58	
	Clean	Ea.	1.91	48		49.91	
	Minimum Charge	Job		226		226	

Rough Mechanical

Heating

Heating	Unit	Material	Labor	Equip.	Total	Specification
Electric Radiant Wall Panel						
Demolish	Ea.		33.50		33.50	Includes material and labor to install
Install	Ea.	430	90.50		520.50	an 18" x 23" electric radiant heat wall
Demolish and Install	Ea.	430	124		554	panel.
Reinstall	Ea.		72.32		72.32	
Clean	Ea.	.24	9.60		9.84	
Minimum Charge	Job		226		226	

Heating Control

Heating Control	Unit	Material	Labor	Equip.	Total	Specification
Thermostat						
Demolish	Ea.		13.45		13.45	Includes material and labor to install
Install	Ea.	177	60.50		237.50	an electric thermostat, 2 set back.
Demolish and Install	Ea.	177	73.95		250.95	
Reinstall	Ea.		48.44		48.44	
Clean	Ea.	.10	9.60		9.70	
Minimum Charge	Job		242		242	

Air Conditioning

Air Conditioning	Unit	Material	Labor	Equip.	Total	Specification
2 Ton						
Demolish	Ea.		440		440	Includes material and labor to install a
Install	Ea.	2250	750		3000	rooftop air conditioning unit, 2 ton.
Demolish and Install	Ea.	2250	1190		3440	No hoisting is included.
Reinstall	Ea.		752.37		752.37	
Clean	Ea.	4.77	38.50		43.27	
Minimum Charge	Job		242		242	
3 Ton						
Demolish	Ea.		440		440	Includes material and labor to install a
Install	Ea.	2375	990		3365	rooftop air conditioning unit, 3 ton.
Demolish and Install	Ea.	2375	1430		3805	No hoisting is included.
Reinstall	Ea.		992.04		992.04	
Clean	Ea.	4.77	38.50		43.27	
Minimum Charge	Job		242		242	
4 Ton						
Demolish	Ea.		440		440	Includes material and labor to install a
Install	Ea.	2800	1150		3950	rooftop air conditioning unit, 4 ton.
Demolish and Install	Ea.	2800	1590		4390	No hoisting is included.
Reinstall	Ea.		1150.40		1150.40	
Clean	Ea.	4.77	38.50		43.27	
Minimum Charge	Job		242		242	
5 Ton						
Demolish	Ea.		440		440	Includes material and labor to install a
Install	Ea.	2975	1250		4225	rooftop air conditioning unit, 5 ton.
Demolish and Install	Ea.	2975	1690		4665	No hoisting is included.
Reinstall	Ea.		1242.17		1242.17	
Clean	Ea.	4.77	38.50		43.27	
Minimum Charge	Job		242		242	
Compressor						
2 Ton						
Demolish	Ea.		405		405	Includes material and labor to install a
Install	Ea.	275	242		517	refrigeration compressor.
Demolish and Install	Ea.	275	647		922	
Reinstall	Ea.		193.76		193.76	
Clean	Ea.	4.77	38.50		43.27	
Minimum Charge	Job		242		242	

Air Conditioning		Unit	Material	Labor	Equip.	Total	Specification
2.5 Ton							
	Demolish	Ea.		405		405	Includes material and labor to install a
	Install	Ea.	325	262		587	refrigeration compressor.
	Demolish and Install	Ea.	325	667		992	
	Reinstall	Ea.		209.92		209.92	
	Clean	Ea.	4.77	38.50		43.27	
	Minimum Charge	Job		242		242	
3 Ton							
	Demolish	Ea.		405		405	Includes material and labor to install a
	Install	Ea.	360	274		634	refrigeration compressor.
	Demolish and Install	Ea.	360	679		1039	
	Reinstall	Ea.		219.06		219.06	
	Clean	Ea.	4.77	38.50		43.27	
	Minimum Charge	Job		242		242	
4 Ton							
	Demolish	Ea.		405		405	Includes material and labor to install a
	Install	Ea.	455	220		675	refrigeration compressor.
	Demolish and Install	Ea.	455	625		1080	
	Reinstall	Ea.		176.15		176.15	
	Clean	Ea.	4.77	38.50		43.27	
	Minimum Charge	Job		242		242	
5 Ton							
	Demolish	Ea.		405		405	Includes material and labor to install a
	Install	Ea.	500	300		800	refrigeration compressor.
	Demolish and Install	Ea.	500	705		1205	
	Reinstall	Ea.		239.95		239.95	
	Clean	Ea.	4.77	38.50		43.27	
	Minimum Charge	Job		242		242	
Condensing Unit							
2 Ton Air-cooled							
	Demolish	Ea.		115		115	Includes material and labor to install a
	Install	Ea.	1475	415		1890	2 ton condensing unit.
	Demolish and Install	Ea.	1475	530		2005	
	Reinstall	Ea.		332.19		332.19	
	Clean	Ea.	4.77	38.50		43.27	
	Minimum Charge	Job		242		242	
2.5 Ton Air-cooled							
	Demolish	Ea.		135		135	Includes material and labor to install a
	Install	Ea.	1550	515		2065	2.5 ton condensing unit.
	Demolish and Install	Ea.	1550	650		2200	
	Reinstall	Ea.		410.35		410.35	
	Clean	Ea.	4.77	38.50		43.27	
	Minimum Charge	Job		242		242	
3 Ton Air-cooled							
	Demolish	Ea.		161		161	Includes material and labor to install a
	Install	Ea.	1575	670		2245	3 ton condensing unit.
	Demolish and Install	Ea.	1575	831		2406	
	Reinstall	Ea.		536.62		536.62	
	Clean	Ea.	4.77	38.50		43.27	
	Minimum Charge	Job		242		242	
4 Ton Air-cooled							
	Demolish	Ea.		242		242	Includes material and labor to install a
	Install	Ea.	2075	970		3045	4 ton condensing unit.
	Demolish and Install	Ea.	2075	1212		3287	
	Reinstall	Ea.		775.11		775.11	
	Clean	Ea.	4.77	38.50		43.27	
	Minimum Charge	Job		242		242	

Rough Mechanical

Air Conditioning	Unit	Material	Labor	Equip.	Total	Specification
5 Ton Air-cooled						
Demolish	Ea.		365		365	Includes material and labor to install a
Install	Ea.	2475	1450		3925	5 ton condensing unit.
Demolish and Install	Ea.	2475	1815		4290	
Reinstall	Ea.		1162.67		1162.67	
Clean	Ea.	4.77	38.50		43.27	
Minimum Charge	Job		242		242	
Air Handler						
1,200 CFM						
Demolish	Ea.		291		291	Includes material and labor to install a
Install	Ea.	2825	670		3495	1200 CFM capacity air handling unit.
Demolish and Install	Ea.	2825	961		3786	
Reinstall	Ea.		536.62		536.62	
Clean	Ea.	4.77	38.50		43.27	
Minimum Charge	Job		242		242	
2,000 CFM						
Demolish	Ea.		291		291	Includes material and labor to install a
Install	Ea.	4725	795		5520	2000 CFM capacity air handling unit.
Demolish and Install	Ea.	4725	1086		5811	
Reinstall	Ea.		634.18		634.18	
Clean	Ea.	4.77	38.50		43.27	
Minimum Charge	Job		242		242	
3,000 CFM						
Demolish	Ea.		325		325	Includes material and labor to install a
Install	Ea.	5875	870		6745	3000 CFM capacity air handling unit.
Demolish and Install	Ea.	5875	1195		7070	
Reinstall	Ea.		697.60		697.60	
Clean	Ea.	4.77	38.50		43.27	
Minimum Charge	Job		242		242	
Evaporative Cooler						
4,300 CFM, 1/3 HP						
Demolish	Ea.		117		117	Includes material and labor to install
Install	Ea.	780	258		1038	an evaporative cooler.
Demolish and Install	Ea.	780	375		1155	
Reinstall	Ea.		206		206	
Clean	Ea.	1.91	38.50		40.41	
Minimum Charge	Job		242		242	
4,700 CFM, 1/2 HP						
Demolish	Ea.		117		117	Includes material and labor to install
Install	Ea.	780	266		1046	an evaporative cooler.
Demolish and Install	Ea.	780	383		1163	
Reinstall	Ea.		212.65		212.65	
Clean	Ea.	1.91	38.50		40.41	
Minimum Charge	Job		242		242	
5,600 CFM, 3/4 HP						
Demolish	Ea.		117		117	Includes material and labor to install
Install	Ea.	1550	275		1825	an evaporative cooler.
Demolish and Install	Ea.	1550	392		1942	
Reinstall	Ea.		219.73		219.73	
Clean	Ea.	1.91	38.50		40.41	
Minimum Charge	Job		242		242	
Master Cool Brand						
Demolish	Ea.		117		117	Includes material and labor to install
Install	Ea.	780	284		1064	an evaporative cooler.
Demolish and Install	Ea.	780	401		1181	
Reinstall	Ea.		227.31		227.31	
Clean	Ea.	1.91	38.50		40.41	
Minimum Charge	Job		242		242	

Rough Mechanical

Air Conditioning

	Unit	Material	Labor	Equip.	Total	Specification
Motor						
Demolish	Ea.		66		66	Includes material and labor to install
Install	Ea.	183	200		383	an evaporative cooler motor.
Demolish and Install	Ea.	183	266		449	
Reinstall	Ea.		160.28		160.28	
Clean	Ea.	1.91	38.50		40.41	
Minimum Charge	Job		242		242	
Water Pump						
Demolish	Ea.		66		66	Includes material and labor to install
Install	Ea.	51	115		166	an evaporative cooler water pump.
Demolish and Install	Ea.	51	181		232	
Reinstall	Ea.		91.60		91.60	
Clean	Ea.	1.91	38.50		40.41	
Minimum Charge	Job		242		242	
Fan Belt						
Demolish	Ea.		13.20		13.20	Includes material and labor to install
Install	Ea.	37	23		60	an evaporative cooler fan belt.
Demolish and Install	Ea.	37	36.20		73.20	
Reinstall	Ea.		18.32		18.32	
Minimum Charge	Job		242		242	
Pads (4 ea.)						
Demolish	Ea.		13.20		13.20	Includes material and labor to install
Install	Ea.	20	57.50		77.50	pre-fabricated roof pads for an
Demolish and Install	Ea.	20	70.70		90.70	evaporative cooler.
Reinstall	Ea.		45.80		45.80	
Clean	Ea.	1.91	38.50		40.41	
Minimum Charge	Job		242		242	
Service call						
Install	Job		229		229	Includes 4 hour minimum labor charge for an sheetmetal worker.

Window Mounted

	Unit	Material	Labor	Equip.	Total	Specification
Low Output BTU						
Install	Ea.	330	52		382	Includes material and labor to install a
Reinstall	Ea.		41.44		41.44	window air conditioning unit.
Clean	Ea.	.72	9.60		10.32	
Minimum Charge	Job		242		242	
Mid-range Output BTU						
Demolish	Ea.		36.50		36.50	Includes material and labor to install a
Install	Ea.	450	69		519	window air conditioning unit.
Demolish and Install	Ea.	450	105.50		555.50	
Reinstall	Ea.		55.25		55.25	
Clean	Ea.	.72	9.60		10.32	
Minimum Charge	Job		242		242	
High Output BTU						
Demolish	Ea.		46		46	Includes material and labor to install a
Install	Ea.	580	69		649	window air conditioning unit.
Demolish and Install	Ea.	580	115		695	
Reinstall	Ea.		55.25		55.25	
Clean	Ea.	.72	9.60		10.32	
Minimum Charge	Job		242		242	
Hotel-type Hot / Cold						
Demolish	Ea.		76.50		76.50	Includes material and labor to install
Install	Ea.	1150	291		1441	packaged air conditioning unit,
Demolish and Install	Ea.	1150	367.50		1517.50	15000 BTU cooling, 13900 BTU
Reinstall	Ea.		232.53		232.53	heating.
Clean	Ea.	.96	19.15		20.11	
Minimum Charge	Job		242		242	

Rough Mechanical

Air Conditioning

Air Conditioning	Unit	Material	Labor	Equip.	Total	Specification
Thermostat						
Demolish	Ea.		13.45		13.45	Includes material and labor to install
Install	Ea.	177	60.50		237.50	an electric thermostat, 2 set back.
Demolish and Install	Ea.	177	73.95		250.95	
Reinstall	Ea.		48.44		48.44	
Clean	Ea.	.10	9.60		9.70	
Minimum Charge	Job		242		242	
Concrete Pad						
Demolish	S.F.		2.13		2.13	Includes material and labor to install
Install	S.F.	2.55	4.78		7.33	air conditioner pad.
Demolish and Install	S.F.	2.55	6.91		9.46	
Reinstall	S.F.		3.82		3.82	
Clean	S.F.	.10	.61		.71	
Paint	S.F.	.18	.36		.54	
Minimum Charge	Job		242		242	
A/C Junction Box						
Install	Ea.	257	129		386	Includes labor and materials to install
Minimum Charge	Job		226		226	an air conditioning circuit including up to 40 feet of non-metallic cable.

Sprinkler System

Sprinkler System	Unit	Material	Labor	Equip.	Total	Specification
Exposed						
Wet Type						
Demolish	SF Flr.		.21		.21	Includes material and labor to install
Install	SF Flr.	2.26	2.06		4.32	an exposed wet pipe fire sprinkler
Demolish and Install	SF Flr.	2.26	2.27		4.53	system.
Reinstall	SF Flr.		2.06		2.06	
Minimum Charge	Job		238		238	
Dry Type						
Demolish	SF Flr.		.21		.21	Includes material and labor to install
Install	SF Flr.	2.60	2.06		4.66	an exposed dry pipe fire sprinkler
Demolish and Install	SF Flr.	2.60	2.27		4.87	system.
Reinstall	SF Flr.		2.06		2.06	
Minimum Charge	Job		238		238	
Concealed						
Wet Type						
Demolish	SF Flr.		.42		.42	Includes material and labor to install a
Install	SF Flr.	2.26	2.82		5.08	concealed wet pipe fire sprinkler
Demolish and Install	SF Flr.	2.26	3.24		5.50	system.
Reinstall	SF Flr.		2.82		2.82	
Minimum Charge	Job		238		238	
Dry Type						
Demolish	SF Flr.		.42		.42	Includes material and labor to install a
Install	SF Flr.	.02	2.82		2.84	concealed dry pipe fire sprinkler
Demolish and Install	SF Flr.	.02	3.24		3.26	system.
Reinstall	SF Flr.		2.82		2.82	
Minimum Charge	Job		238		238	

Junction Boxes	Cable	Switch Box

Electrical Per S.F.	Unit	Material	Labor	Equip.	Total	Specification
Residential						
Wiring, Lighting and Fixtures						Includes labor and material to replace house wiring, lighting fixtures, and built-in appliances. Apply S.F. cost to floor area including garages but not basements.
Install	S.F.	1.88	1.88		3.76	
Minimum Charge	Job		226		226	
Wiring Only						Includes labor and material to replace house wiring only. Apply S.F. cost to floor area including garages but not basements.
Install	S.F.	.24	.74		.98	

Main Service	Unit	Material	Labor	Equip.	Total	Specification
100 Amp.						Cost includes material and labor to install 100 Amp. residential service panel including 12 breaker interior panel, 10 single pole breakers and hook-up. Wiring is not included.
Demolish	Ea.		186		186	
Install	Ea.	650	380		1030	
Demolish and Install	Ea.	650	566		1216	
Reinstall	Ea.		303.87		303.87	
Clean	Ea.	.47	76.50		76.97	
Minimum Charge	Job		226		226	
150 Amp.						Cost includes material and labor to install 150 Amp. residential service, incl. 20 breaker exterior panel, main switch, 1 GFI and 14 single pole breakers, meter socket including hookup. Wiring is not included.
Demolish	Ea.		186		186	
Install	Ea.	1000	440		1440	
Demolish and Install	Ea.	1000	626		1626	
Reinstall	Ea.		351.07		351.07	
Clean	Ea.	.47	76.50		76.97	
Minimum Charge	Job		226		226	
200 Amp.						Cost includes material and labor to install 200 Amp. residential service, incl. 20 breaker exterior panel, main switch, 1 GFI and 18 single pole breakers, meter socket including hookup. Wiring is not included.
Demolish	Ea.		186		186	
Install	Ea.	1325	500		1825	
Demolish and Install	Ea.	1325	686		2011	
Reinstall	Ea.		401.78		401.78	
Clean	Ea.	.47	76.50		76.97	
Minimum Charge	Job		226		226	

Rough Electrical

Main Service	Unit	Material	Labor	Equip.	Total	Specification
Masthead						
Demolish	Ea.		31.50		31.50	Includes material and labor to install
Install	Ea.	130	188		318	galvanized steel conduit including
Demolish and Install	Ea.	130	219.50		349.50	masthead.
Reinstall	Ea.		150.67		150.67	
Minimum Charge	Job		226		226	
Allowance to Repair						
Install	Job		226		226	Minimum labor charge for residential
Minimum Charge	Job		226		226	wiring.

Insulation

Wall Insulation

Floor Insulation	Unit	Material	Labor	Equip.	Total	Specification
Kraft Faced Batt						
3-1/2″ (R-13)						
Demolish	S.F.		.14		.14	Cost includes material and labor to
Install	S.F.	.42	.59		1.01	install 3-1/2″ (R-13) kraft paper or foil
Demolish and Install	S.F.	.42	.73		1.15	faced roll and batt fiberglass
Minimum Charge	Job		207		207	insulation, joists 16″ O.C.
6″ (R-19)						
Demolish	S.F.		.14		.14	Cost includes material and labor to
Install	S.F.	.47	.69		1.16	install 6″ (R-19) kraft paper or foil
Demolish and Install	S.F.	.47	.83		1.30	faced roll and batt fiberglass
Minimum Charge	Job		207		207	insulation, joists 16″ O.C.
10″ (R-30)						
Demolish	S.F.		.14		.14	Cost includes material and labor to
Install	S.F.	.73	.83		1.56	install 10″ (R-30) kraft paper-faced roll
Demolish and Install	S.F.	.73	.97		1.70	and batt fiberglass insulation, joists
Minimum Charge	Job		207		207	16″ O.C.
12″ (R-38)						
Demolish	S.F.		.14		.14	Cost includes material and labor to
Install	S.F.	.79	.87		1.66	install 12″ (R-38) kraft paper-faced roll
Demolish and Install	S.F.	.79	1.01		1.80	and batt fiberglass insulation, joists
Minimum Charge	Job		207		207	16″ O.C.
Foil Faced Batt						
3-1/2″ (R-13)						
Demolish	S.F.		.14		.14	Cost includes material and labor to
Install	S.F.	.42	.59		1.01	install 3-1/2″ (R-13) kraft paper or foil
Demolish and Install	S.F.	.42	.73		1.15	faced roll and batt fiberglass
Minimum Charge	Job		207		207	insulation, joists 16″ O.C.
6″ (R-19)						
Demolish	S.F.		.14		.14	Cost includes material and labor to
Install	S.F.	.47	.69		1.16	install 6″ (R-19) kraft paper or foil
Demolish and Install	S.F.	.47	.83		1.30	faced roll and batt fiberglass
Minimum Charge	Job		207		207	insulation, joists 16″ O.C.
Unfaced Batt						
3-1/2″ (R-13)						
Demolish	S.F.		.14		.14	Cost includes material and labor to
Install	S.F.	.34	.69		1.03	install 3-1/2″ (R-13) unfaced roll and
Demolish and Install	S.F.	.34	.83		1.17	batt fiberglass insulation, joists 16″
Minimum Charge	Job		207		207	O.C.

Insulation

Floor Insulation

Floor Insulation		Unit	Material	Labor	Equip.	Total	Specification
6″ (R-19)							
	Demolish	S.F.		.14		.14	Cost includes material and labor to
	Install	S.F.	.39	.83		1.22	install 6″ (R-19) unfaced roll and batt
	Demolish and Install	S.F.	.39	.97		1.36	fiberglass insulation, joists 16″ O.C.
	Minimum Charge	Job		207		207	
10″ (R-30)							
	Demolish	S.F.		.14		.14	Cost includes material and labor to
	Install	S.F.	.68	.92		1.60	install 10″ (R-30) unfaced roll and batt
	Demolish and Install	S.F.	.68	1.06		1.74	fiberglass insulation, joists 16″ O.C.
	Minimum Charge	Job		207		207	
12″ (R-38)							
	Demolish	S.F.		.14		.14	Cost includes material and labor to
	Install	S.F.	.78	.97		1.75	install 12″ (R-38) unfaced roll and batt
	Demolish and Install	S.F.	.78	1.11		1.89	fiberglass insulation, joists 16″ O.C.
	Minimum Charge	Job		207		207	
Rigid Board							
1/2″							
	Demolish	S.F.		.14		.14	Includes material and labor to install
	Install	S.F.	.32	.52		.84	rigid foam insulation board foil faced
	Demolish and Install	S.F.	.32	.66		.98	two sides.
	Minimum Charge	Job		207		207	
3/4″							
	Demolish	S.F.		.14		.14	Includes material and labor to install
	Install	S.F.	.36	.52		.88	rigid foam insulation board foil faced
	Demolish and Install	S.F.	.36	.66		1.02	two sides.
	Minimum Charge	Job		207		207	
1-1/2″							
	Demolish	S.F.		.14		.14	Includes material and labor to install
	Install	S.F.	.70	.55		1.25	rigid foam insulation board foil faced
	Demolish and Install	S.F.	.70	.69		1.39	two sides.
	Minimum Charge	Job		207		207	
Support Wire							
	Demolish	S.F.		.06		.06	Includes material and labor to install
	Install	S.F.	.01	.12		.13	friction fit support wire.
	Demolish and Install	S.F.	.01	.18		.19	
	Minimum Charge	Job		207		207	
Vapor Barrier							
	Demolish	S.F.		.08		.08	Cost includes material and labor to
	Install	S.F.	.03	.11		.14	install 4 mil polyethylene vapor barrier
	Demolish and Install	S.F.	.03	.19		.22	10′ wide sheets with 6″ overlaps.
	Minimum Charge	Job		207		207	

Wall Insulation

Wall Insulation		Unit	Material	Labor	Equip.	Total	Specification
Kraft Faced Batt							
3-1/2″ (R-13)							
	Demolish	S.F.		.14		.14	Cost includes material and labor to
	Install	S.F.	.36	.31		.67	install 3-1/2″ (R-13) kraft paper-faced
	Demolish and Install	S.F.	.36	.45		.81	roll and batt fiberglass insulation, joist
	Minimum Charge	Job		207		207	or studs 16″ O.C.
6″ (R-19)							
	Demolish	S.F.		.14		.14	Cost includes material and labor to
	Install	S.F.	.42	.31		.73	install 6″ (R-19) kraft paper-faced roll
	Demolish and Install	S.F.	.42	.45		.87	and batt fiberglass insulation, joist or
	Minimum Charge	Job		207		207	studs 16″ O.C.

Insulation

Wall Insulation		Unit	Material	Labor	Equip.	Total	Specification
10″ (R-30)							
	Demolish	S.F.		.14		.14	Cost includes material and labor to
	Install	S.F.	.68	.36		1.04	install 10″ (R-30) kraft paper-faced roll
	Demolish and Install	S.F.	.68	.50		1.18	and batt fiberglass insulation, joist or
	Minimum Charge	Job		207		207	studs 16″ O.C.
12″ (R-38)							
	Demolish	S.F.		.14		.14	Cost includes material and labor to
	Install	S.F.	.79	.36		1.15	install 12″ (R-38) kraft paper-faced roll
	Demolish and Install	S.F.	.79	.50		1.29	and batt fiberglass insulation, joist or
	Minimum Charge	Job		207		207	studs 16″ O.C.
Foil Faced Batt							
3-1/2″ (R-13)							
	Demolish	S.F.		.14		.14	Cost includes material and labor to
	Install	S.F.	.37	.31		.68	install 3-1/2″ (R-13) foil faced roll and
	Demolish and Install	S.F.	.37	.45		.82	batt fiberglass insulation, joist or studs
	Minimum Charge	Job		207		207	16″ O.C.
6″ (R-19)							
	Demolish	S.F.		.14		.14	Cost includes material and labor to
	Install	S.F.	.44	.31		.75	install 6″ (R-19) foil faced roll and batt
	Demolish and Install	S.F.	.44	.45		.89	fiberglass insulation, joist or studs 16″
	Minimum Charge	Job		207		207	O.C.
Unfaced Batt							
3-1/2″ (R-13)							
	Demolish	S.F.		.14		.14	Cost includes material and labor to
	Install	S.F.	.34	.31		.65	install 3-1/2″ (R-13) unfaced roll and
	Demolish and Install	S.F.	.34	.45		.79	batt fiberglass insulation, joist or studs
	Minimum Charge	Job		207		207	16″ O.C.
6″ (R-19)							
	Demolish	S.F.		.14		.14	Cost includes material and labor to
	Install	S.F.	.39	.36		.75	install 6″ (R-19) unfaced roll and batt
	Demolish and Install	S.F.	.39	.50		.89	fiberglass insulation, joist or studs 16″
	Minimum Charge	Job		207		207	O.C.
10″ (R-30)							
	Demolish	S.F.		.14		.14	Cost includes material and labor to
	Install	S.F.	.66	.36		1.02	install 10″ (R-30) unfaced roll and batt
	Demolish and Install	S.F.	.66	.50		1.16	fiberglass insulation, joist or studs 16″
	Minimum Charge	Job		207		207	O.C.
12″ (R-38)							
	Demolish	S.F.		.14		.14	Cost includes material and labor to
	Install	S.F.	.78	.41		1.19	install 12″ (R-38) unfaced roll and batt
	Demolish and Install	S.F.	.78	.55		1.33	fiberglass insulation, joist or studs 16″
	Minimum Charge	Job		207		207	O.C.
Blown							
R-13							
	Demolish	S.F.		.14		.14	Includes material and labor to install
	Install	S.F.	.11	1.37	.55	2.03	fiberglass blown-in insulation in wall
	Demolish and Install	S.F.	.11	1.51	.55	2.17	with wood siding.
	Minimum Charge	Job		475	191	666	
R-19							
	Demolish	S.F.		.14		.14	Includes material and labor to install
	Install	S.F.	.13	1.58	.64	2.35	fiberglass blown-in insulation in wall
	Demolish and Install	S.F.	.13	1.72	.64	2.49	with wood siding.
	Minimum Charge	Job		475	191	666	

Insulation

Wall Insulation

	Unit	Material	Labor	Equip.	Total	Specification
Rigid Board						
1/2"						
Demolish	S.F.		.17		.17	Includes material and labor to install
Install	S.F.	.32	.52		.84	rigid foam insulation board, foil faced,
Demolish and Install	S.F.	.32	.69		1.01	two sides.
Minimum Charge	Job		207		207	
3/4"						
Demolish	S.F.		.17		.17	Includes material and labor to install
Install	S.F.	.36	.52		.88	rigid foam insulation board, foil faced,
Demolish and Install	S.F.	.36	.69		1.05	two sides.
Minimum Charge	Job		207		207	
1-1/2"						
Demolish	S.F.		.17		.17	Includes material and labor to install
Install	S.F.	.70	.57		1.27	rigid foam insulation board, foil faced,
Demolish and Install	S.F.	.70	.74		1.44	two sides.
Minimum Charge	Job		207		207	
Vapor Barrier						
Demolish	S.F.		.05		.05	Cost includes material and labor to
Install	S.F.	.03	.11		.14	install 4 mil polyethylene vapor barrier
Demolish and Install	S.F.	.03	.16		.19	10' wide sheets with 6" overlaps.
Minimum Charge	Job		207		207	

Ceiling Insulation

	Unit	Material	Labor	Equip.	Total	Specification
Kraft Faced Batt						
3-1/2" (R-13)						
Demolish	S.F.		.14		.14	Cost includes material and labor to
Install	S.F.	.36	.31		.67	install 3-1/2" (R-13) kraft paper-faced
Demolish and Install	S.F.	.36	.45		.81	roll and batt fiberglass insulation, joist
Minimum Charge	Job		207		207	or studs 16" O.C.
6" (R-19)						
Demolish	S.F.		.14		.14	Cost includes material and labor to
Install	S.F.	.42	.31		.73	install 6" (R-19) kraft paper-faced roll
Demolish and Install	S.F.	.42	.45		.87	and batt fiberglass insulation, joist or
Minimum Charge	Job		207		207	studs 16" O.C.
10" (R-30)						
Demolish	S.F.		.14		.14	Cost includes material and labor to
Install	S.F.	.68	.36		1.04	install 10" (R-30) kraft paper-faced roll
Demolish and Install	S.F.	.68	.50		1.18	and batt fiberglass insulation, joist or
Minimum Charge	Job		207		207	studs 16" O.C.
12" (R-38)						
Demolish	S.F.		.14		.14	Cost includes material and labor to
Install	S.F.	.79	.36		1.15	install 12" (R-38) kraft paper-faced roll
Demolish and Install	S.F.	.79	.50		1.29	and batt fiberglass insulation, joist or
Minimum Charge	Job		207		207	studs 16" O.C.
Foil Faced Batt						
3-1/2" (R-13)						
Demolish	S.F.		.14		.14	Cost includes material and labor to
Install	S.F.	.37	.31		.68	install 3-1/2" (R-13) foil faced roll and
Demolish and Install	S.F.	.37	.45		.82	batt fiberglass insulation, joist or studs
Minimum Charge	Job		207		207	16" O.C.

Insulation

Ceiling Insulation		Unit	Material	Labor	Equip.	Total	Specification
6″ (R-19)							
	Demolish	S.F.		.14		.14	Cost includes material and labor to
	Install	S.F.	.44	.31		.75	install 6″ (R-19) foil faced roll and batt
	Demolish and Install	S.F.	.44	.45		.89	fiberglass insulation, joist or studs 16″
	Minimum Charge	Job		207		207	O.C.
Unfaced Batt							
3-1/2″ (R-13)							
	Demolish	S.F.		.14		.14	Cost includes material and labor to
	Install	S.F.	.34	.31		.65	install 3-1/2″ (R-13) unfaced roll and
	Demolish and Install	S.F.	.34	.45		.79	batt fiberglass insulation, joist or studs
	Minimum Charge	Job		207		207	16″ O.C.
6″ (R-19)							
	Demolish	S.F.		.14		.14	Cost includes material and labor to
	Install	S.F.	.39	.36		.75	install 6″ (R-19) unfaced roll and batt
	Demolish and Install	S.F.	.39	.50		.89	fiberglass insulation, joist or studs 16″
	Minimum Charge	Job		207		207	O.C.
10″ (R-30)							
	Demolish	S.F.		.14		.14	Cost includes material and labor to
	Install	S.F.	.66	.36		1.02	install 10″ (R-30) unfaced roll and batt
	Demolish and Install	S.F.	.66	.50		1.16	fiberglass insulation, joist or studs 16″
	Minimum Charge	Job		207		207	O.C.
12″ (R-38)							
	Demolish	S.F.		.14		.14	Cost includes material and labor to
	Install	S.F.	.78	.41		1.19	install 12″ (R-38) unfaced roll and batt
	Demolish and Install	S.F.	.78	.55		1.33	fiberglass insulation, joist or studs 16″
	Minimum Charge	Job		207		207	O.C.
Blown							
5″							
	Demolish	S.F.		.43		.43	Includes material and labor to install
	Install	S.F.	.04	.25	.10	.39	fiberglass blown-in insulation.
	Demolish and Install	S.F.	.04	.68	.10	.82	
	Minimum Charge	Job		475	191	666	
6″							
	Demolish	S.F.		.43		.43	Includes material and labor to install
	Install	S.F.	.06	.32	.13	.51	fiberglass blown-in insulation.
	Demolish and Install	S.F.	.06	.75	.13	.94	
	Minimum Charge	Job		475	191	666	
9″							
	Demolish	S.F.		.43		.43	Includes material and labor to install
	Install	S.F.	.07	.43	.17	.67	fiberglass blown-in insulation.
	Demolish and Install	S.F.	.07	.86	.17	1.10	
	Minimum Charge	Job		475	191	666	
12″							
	Demolish	S.F.		.43		.43	Includes material and labor to install
	Install	S.F.	.10	.63	.26	.99	fiberglass blown-in insulation.
	Demolish and Install	S.F.	.10	1.06	.26	1.42	
	Minimum Charge	Job		475	191	666	
Rigid Board							
1/2″							
	Demolish	S.F.		.24		.24	Includes material and labor to install
	Install	S.F.	.32	.52		.84	rigid foam insulation board, foil faced,
	Demolish and Install	S.F.	.32	.76		1.08	two sides.
	Minimum Charge	Job		207		207	

Insulation

Ceiling Insulation

Ceiling Insulation		Unit	Material	Labor	Equip.	Total	Specification
3/4"							
	Demolish	S.F.		.24		.24	Includes material and labor to install
	Install	S.F.	.36	.52		.88	rigid foam insulation board, foil faced,
	Demolish and Install	S.F.	.36	.76		1.12	two sides.
	Minimum Charge	Job		207		207	
1-1/2"							
	Demolish	S.F.		.24		.24	Includes material and labor to install
	Install	S.F.	.70	.57		1.27	rigid foam insulation board, foil faced,
	Demolish and Install	S.F.	.70	.81		1.51	two sides.
	Minimum Charge	Job		207		207	

Exterior Insulation

Exterior Insulation		Unit	Material	Labor	Equip.	Total	Specification
Rigid Board							
1/2"							
	Demolish	S.F.		.13		.13	Includes material and labor to install
	Install	S.F.	.32	.52		.84	rigid foam insulation board foil faced
	Demolish and Install	S.F.	.32	.65		.97	two sides.
	Minimum Charge	Job		207		207	
3/4"							
	Demolish	S.F.		.13		.13	Includes material and labor to install
	Install	S.F.	.36	.52		.88	rigid foam insulation board foil faced
	Demolish and Install	S.F.	.36	.65		1.01	two sides.
	Minimum Charge	Job		207		207	
1-1/2"							
	Demolish	S.F.		.13		.13	Includes material and labor to install
	Install	S.F.	.70	.55		1.25	rigid foam insulation board foil faced
	Demolish and Install	S.F.	.70	.68		1.38	two sides.
	Minimum Charge	Job		207		207	
Vapor Barrier							
	Demolish	S.F.		.08		.08	Cost includes material and labor to
	Install	S.F.	.03	.11		.14	install 4 mil polyethylene vapor barrier
	Demolish and Install	S.F.	.03	.19		.22	10' wide sheets with 6" overlaps.
	Minimum Charge	Job		207		207	

Roof Insulation Board

Roof Insulation Board		Unit	Material	Labor	Equip.	Total	Specification
Fiberglass							
3/4" Fiberglass							
	Demolish	Sq.		44.50		44.50	Includes material and labor to install
	Install	Sq.	61.50	30.50		92	fiberglass board insulation 3/4" thick,
	Demolish and Install	Sq.	61.50	75		136.50	R-2.80 and C-0.36 values.
	Minimum Charge	Job		207		207	
1" Fiberglass							
	Demolish	Sq.		44.50		44.50	Includes material and labor to install
	Install	Sq.	87	34.50		121.50	fiberglass board insulation 1" thick,
	Demolish and Install	Sq.	87	79		166	R-4.20 and C-0.24 values.
	Minimum Charge	Job		207		207	
1-3/8" Fiberglass							
	Demolish	Sq.		44.50		44.50	Includes material and labor to install
	Install	Sq.	139	37.50		176.50	fiberglass board insulation 1-3/8"
	Demolish and Install	Sq.	139	82		221	thick, R-5.30 and C-0.19 values.
	Minimum Charge	Job		207		207	

Insulation

Roof Insulation Board		Unit	Material	Labor	Equip.	Total	Specification
1-5/8″ Fiberglass							
	Demolish	Sq.		44.50		44.50	Includes material and labor to install
	Install	Sq.	143	39.50		182.50	fiberglass board insulation 1-5/8″
	Demolish and Install	Sq.	143	84		227	thick, R-6.70 and C-0.15 values.
	Minimum Charge	Job		207		207	
2-1/4″ Fiberglass							
	Demolish	Sq.		44.50		44.50	Includes material and labor to install
	Install	Sq.	169	43.50		212.50	fiberglass board insulation 2-1/4″
	Demolish and Install	Sq.	169	88		257	thick, R-8.30 and C-0.12 values.
	Minimum Charge	Job		207		207	
Perlite							
1″ Perlite							
	Demolish	Sq.		44.50		44.50	Includes material and labor to install
	Install	Sq.	50.50	34.50		85	perlite board insulation 1″ thick,
	Demolish and Install	Sq.	50.50	79		129.50	R-2.80 and C-0.36 values.
	Minimum Charge	Job		207		207	
4″ Perlite							
	Demolish	Sq.		44.50		44.50	Includes material and labor to install
	Install	Sq.	202	66.50		268.50	perlite board insulation 4″ thick,
	Demolish and Install	Sq.	202	111		313	R-10.0 and C-0.10 values.
	Minimum Charge	Job		207		207	
1-1/2″ Perlite							
	Demolish	Sq.		44.50		44.50	Includes material and labor to install
	Install	Sq.	53	37.50		90.50	perlite board insulation 1-1/2″ thick,
	Demolish and Install	Sq.	53	82		135	R-4.20 and C-0.24 values.
	Minimum Charge	Job		207		207	
2″ Perlite							
	Demolish	Sq.		44.50		44.50	Includes material and labor to install
	Install	Sq.	88	46		134	perlite board insulation 2″ thick,
	Demolish and Install	Sq.	88	90.50		178.50	R-5.30 and C-0.19 values.
	Minimum Charge	Job		207		207	
2-1/2″ Perlite							
	Demolish	Sq.		44.50		44.50	Includes material and labor to install
	Install	Sq.	105	52		157	perlite board insulation 2-1/2″ thick,
	Demolish and Install	Sq.	105	96.50		201.50	R-6.70 and C-0.15 values.
	Minimum Charge	Job		207		207	
3″ Perlite							
	Demolish	Sq.		44.50		44.50	Includes material and labor to install
	Install	Sq.	152	55.50		207.50	perlite board insulation 3″ thick,
	Demolish and Install	Sq.	152	100		252	R-8.30 and C-0.12 values.
	Minimum Charge	Job		207		207	
Polystyrene							
2″ Polystyrene							
	Demolish	Sq.		44.50		44.50	Includes material and labor to install
	Install	Sq.	61.50	43.50		105	extruded polystyrene board, R5.0/ 2″
	Demolish and Install	Sq.	61.50	88		149.50	in thickness @25PSI compressive
	Minimum Charge	Job		207		207	strength.
1″ Polystyrene							
	Demolish	Sq.		44.50		44.50	Includes material and labor to install
	Install	Sq.	31	29.50		60.50	extruded polystyrene board, R5.0/ 1″
	Demolish and Install	Sq.	31	74		105	in thickness @25PSI compressive
	Minimum Charge	Job		207		207	strength.
1-1/2″ Polystyrene							
	Demolish	Sq.		44.50		44.50	Includes material and labor to install
	Install	Sq.	46	34.50		80.50	extruded polystyrene board, R5.0/
	Demolish and Install	Sq.	46	79		125	1-1/2″ in thickness @25PSI
	Minimum Charge	Job		207		207	compressive strength.

Insulation

Roof Insulation Board		Unit	Material	Labor	Equip.	Total	Specification
Urethane							
3/4″ Urethane							
	Demolish	Sq.		44.50		44.50	Includes material and labor to install
	Install	Sq.	48.50	26		74.50	urethane board insulation 3/4″ thick,
	Demolish and Install	Sq.	48.50	70.50		119	R-5.30 and C-0.19 values.
	Minimum Charge	Job		207		207	
1″ Urethane							
	Demolish	Sq.		44.50		44.50	Includes material and labor to install
	Install	Sq.	56	27.50		83.50	urethane board insulation 1″ thick,
	Demolish and Install	Sq.	56	72		128	R-6.70 and C-0.15 values.
	Minimum Charge	Job		207		207	
1-1/2″ Urethane							
	Demolish	Sq.		44.50		44.50	Includes material and labor to install
	Install	Sq.	72.50	32		104.50	urethane board insulation 1-1/2″
	Demolish and Install	Sq.	72.50	76.50		149	thick, R-10.1 and C-0.09 values.
	Minimum Charge	Job		207		207	
2″ Urethane							
	Demolish	Sq.		44.50		44.50	Includes material and labor to install
	Install	Sq.	86	37.50		123.50	urethane board insulation 2″ thick,
	Demolish and Install	Sq.	86	82		168	R-13.4 and C-0.06 values.
	Minimum Charge	Job		207		207	

Gypsum Wallboard　　　　　　**Tile Ceiling**　　　　　　**Gypsum Wallboard Ceiling**

Wall Plaster	Unit	Material	Labor	Equip.	Total	Specification
Interior						
Cement						
Demolish	S.Y.		5.65		5.65	Includes material and labor to install
Install	S.Y.	14.15	24	1.95	40.10	cement plaster on interior wood
Demolish and Install	S.Y.	14.15	29.65	1.95	45.75	framing with metal lath.
Clean	S.Y.		2.79		2.79	
Paint	S.Y.	2	4.74		6.74	
Minimum Charge	Job		185		185	
Acoustic						
Demolish	S.Y.		5.65		5.65	Includes material and labor to install
Install	S.Y.	10.75	28.50	1.95	41.20	acoustical cement plaster on interior
Demolish and Install	S.Y.	10.75	34.15	1.95	46.85	wood framing with metal lath.
Clean	S.Y.		2.79		2.79	
Paint	S.Y.	2	4.74		6.74	
Minimum Charge	Job		185		185	
Gypsum						
Demolish	S.Y.		5.65		5.65	Includes material and labor to install
Install	S.Y.	9.40	24.50	1.66	35.56	gypsum wall or ceiling plaster on
Demolish and Install	S.Y.	9.40	30.15	1.66	41.21	interior wood framing with metal lath.
Clean	S.Y.		2.79		2.79	
Paint	S.Y.	2	4.74		6.74	
Minimum Charge	Job		185		185	
Stucco						
Demolish	S.Y.		13.60		13.60	Includes material and labor to install
Install	S.Y.	6.40	33.50	2.29	42.19	stucco on wire mesh over wood
Demolish and Install	S.Y.	6.40	47.10	2.29	55.79	framing.
Clean	S.Y.		2.79		2.79	
Paint	S.Y.	2	4.74		6.74	
Minimum Charge	Job		185		185	
Thin Coat						
Veneer						
Demolish	S.Y.		5.65		5.65	Includes materials and labor to install
Install	S.Y.	.86	4.42	.36	5.64	thin coat veneer plaster.
Demolish and Install	S.Y.	.86	10.07	.36	11.29	
Clean	S.Y.		2.79		2.79	
Paint	S.Y.	2	4.74		6.74	
Minimum Charge	Job		185		185	

Walls / Ceilings

Wall Plaster

Wall Plaster		Unit	Material	Labor	Equip.	Total	Specification
Lath							
Metal							
	Demolish	S.Y.		1.34		1.34	Includes material and labor to install
	Install	S.Y.	4.40	4.71		9.11	wire lath on steel framed walls.
	Demolish and Install	S.Y.	4.40	6.05		10.45	
	Clean	S.Y.		2.79		2.79	
	Minimum Charge	Job		83		83	
Gypsum							
	Demolish	S.Y.		1.34		1.34	Includes material and labor to install
	Install	S.Y.	4.95	4.42		9.37	gypsum lath on walls.
	Demolish and Install	S.Y.	4.95	5.76		10.71	
	Clean	S.Y.		2.79		2.79	
	Minimum Charge	Job		185		185	
Repairs							
Fill in Small Cracks							
	Install	L.F.	.07	2.96		3.03	Includes labor and material to fill-in
	Minimum Charge	Job		185		185	hairline cracks up to 1/8" with filler, sand and prep for paint.
Repair up to 1" Crack							
	Install	L.F.	.28	3.70		3.98	Includes labor and material to fill-in
	Minimum Charge	Job		185		185	hairline cracks up to 1" with filler, sand and prep for paint.
Patch Small Hole (2")							
	Install	Ea.	.07	3.89		3.96	Includes labor and material to patch
	Minimum Charge	Job		185		185	up to a 2" diameter hole in plaster.
Patch Large Hole							
	Install	Ea.	8.15	123		131.15	Includes labor and material to patch
	Minimum Charge	Job		185		185	up to a 20" diameter hole in plaster.
Patch Plaster Section							
	Install	Ea.	2.31	3.70		6.01	Includes labor and material to repair
	Minimum Charge	Job		185		185	section of plaster wall, area less than 20 S.F.
Repair Inside Corner							
	Install	L.F.	3.26	9.25		12.51	Includes material and labor to patch
	Minimum Charge	Job		185		185	plaster corners.

Ceiling Plaster

Ceiling Plaster		Unit	Material	Labor	Equip.	Total	Specification
Interior							
Cement							
	Demolish	S.Y.		5.65		5.65	Includes material and labor to install
	Install	S.Y.	14.15	24	1.95	40.10	cement plaster on interior wood
	Demolish and Install	S.Y.	14.15	29.65	1.95	45.75	framing with metal lath.
	Clean	S.Y.		2.92		2.92	
	Paint	S.Y.	2	4.74		6.74	
	Minimum Charge	Job		185		185	
Acoustic							
	Demolish	S.Y.		5.65		5.65	Includes material and labor to install
	Install	S.Y.	10.75	28.50	1.95	41.20	acoustical cement plaster on interior
	Demolish and Install	S.Y.	10.75	34.15	1.95	46.85	wood framing with metal lath.
	Clean	S.Y.		2.92		2.92	
	Paint	S.Y.	2	4.74		6.74	
	Minimum Charge	Job		185		185	

Walls / Ceilings

Ceiling Plaster

	Unit	Material	Labor	Equip.	Total	Specification
Gypsum						
Demolish	S.Y.		5.65		5.65	Includes material and labor to install
Install	S.Y.	9.40	24.50	1.66	35.56	gypsum wall or ceiling plaster on
Demolish and Install	S.Y.	9.40	30.15	1.66	41.21	interior wood framing with metal lath.
Clean	S.Y.		2.92		2.92	
Paint	S.Y.	2	4.74		6.74	
Minimum Charge	Job		185		185	
Stucco						
Demolish	S.Y.		13.60		13.60	Includes material and labor to install
Install	S.Y.	6.40	33.50	2.29	42.19	stucco on wire mesh over wood
Demolish and Install	S.Y.	6.40	47.10	2.29	55.79	framing.
Clean	S.Y.		2.92		2.92	
Paint	S.Y.	2	4.74		6.74	
Minimum Charge	Job		185		185	
Thin Coat						
Veneer						
Demolish	S.Y.		5.65		5.65	Includes materials and labor to install
Install	S.Y.	.86	4.42	.36	5.64	thin coat veneer plaster.
Demolish and Install	S.Y.	.86	10.07	.36	11.29	
Clean	S.Y.		2.92		2.92	
Paint	S.Y.	2	4.74		6.74	
Minimum Charge	Job		185		185	
Lath						
Metal						
Demolish	S.Y.		1.34		1.34	Includes material and labor to install
Install	S.Y.	4.40	5.90		10.30	wire lath on steel framed ceilings.
Demolish and Install	S.Y.	4.40	7.24		11.64	
Minimum Charge	Job		185		185	
Gypsum						
Demolish	S.Y.		1.34		1.34	Includes material and labor to install
Install	S.Y.	4.95	3.68		8.63	gypsum lath on ceilings.
Demolish and Install	S.Y.	4.95	5.02		9.97	
Minimum Charge	Job		185		185	
Repairs						
Fill in Small Cracks						
Install	S.F.	.07	.67		.74	Includes labor and material to fill in
Minimum Charge	Job		370		370	hairline cracks up to 1/8" with filler, sand and prep for paint.

Gypsum Wallboard

	Unit	Material	Labor	Equip.	Total	Specification
Finished						
1/4"						
Demolish	S.F.		.34		.34	Cost includes material and labor to
Install	S.F.	.21	1.25		1.46	install 1/4" drywall, including joint
Demolish and Install	S.F.	.21	1.59		1.80	taping, premixed compound and
Clean	S.F.		.28		.28	screws.
Paint	S.F.	.22	.31		.53	
Minimum Charge	Job		207		207	
3/8"						
Demolish	S.F.		.34		.34	Cost includes material and labor to
Install	S.F.	.22	1.27		1.49	install 3/8" drywall including joint
Demolish and Install	S.F.	.22	1.61		1.83	tape, premixed compound and
Clean	S.F.		.28		.28	screws.
Paint	S.F.	.22	.31		.53	
Minimum Charge	Job		207		207	

Walls / Ceilings

Gypsum Wallboard		Unit	Material	Labor	Equip.	Total	Specification
1/2″							
	Demolish	S.F.		.34		.34	Cost includes material and labor to
	Install	S.F.	.22	1.28		1.50	install 1/2″ drywall including joint
	Demolish and Install	S.F.	.22	1.62		1.84	tape, premixed compound and
	Clean	S.F.		.28		.28	screws.
	Paint	S.F.	.22	.31		.53	
	Minimum Charge	Job		207		207	
1/2″ Water Resistant							
	Demolish	S.F.		.34		.34	Cost includes material and labor to
	Install	S.F.	.34	1.09		1.43	install 1/2″ WR drywall including joint
	Demolish and Install	S.F.	.34	1.43		1.77	tape, premixed compound and
	Clean	S.F.		.28		.28	screws.
	Paint	S.F.	.22	.31		.53	
	Minimum Charge	Job		207		207	
1/2″ Fire-rated							
	Demolish	S.F.		.34		.34	Cost includes material and labor to
	Install	S.F.	.26	1.28		1.54	install 1/2″ FR drywall including
	Demolish and Install	S.F.	.26	1.62		1.88	screws. Taping and finishing not
	Clean	S.F.		.28		.28	included.
	Paint	S.F.	.22	.31		.53	
	Minimum Charge	Job		207		207	
5/8″							
	Demolish	S.F.		.34		.34	Cost includes material and labor to
	Install	S.F.	.27	1.24		1.51	install 5/8″ drywall including joint
	Demolish and Install	S.F.	.27	1.58		1.85	tape, premixed compound and
	Clean	S.F.		.28		.28	screws.
	Paint	S.F.	.22	.31		.53	
	Minimum Charge	Job		207		207	
5/8″ Fire-rated							
	Demolish	S.F.		.34		.34	Cost includes material and labor to
	Install	S.F.	.29	1.45		1.74	install 5/8″ FR drywall, including joint
	Demolish and Install	S.F.	.29	1.79		2.08	taping, premixed compound and
	Clean	S.F.		.28		.28	screws.
	Paint	S.F.	.22	.31		.53	
	Minimum Charge	Job		207		207	
2-hour fire-rated							
	Demolish	S.F.		.85		.85	Cost includes material and labor to
	Install	S.F.	.61	2.89		3.50	install 2 layers of 5/8″ type X drywall
	Demolish and Install	S.F.	.61	3.74		4.35	including joint taping, premixed
	Clean	S.F.		.28		.28	compound and screws.
	Paint	S.F.	.22	.31		.53	
	Minimum Charge	Job		207		207	
Unfinished							
1/4″							
	Demolish	S.F.		.34		.34	Cost includes material and labor to
	Install	S.F.	.17	.44		.61	install 1/4″ drywall including screws.
	Demolish and Install	S.F.	.17	.78		.95	Taping and finishing not included.
	Clean	S.F.		.28		.28	
	Minimum Charge	Job		207		207	
3/8″							
	Demolish	S.F.		.34		.34	Cost includes material and labor to
	Install	S.F.	.18	.44		.62	install 3/8″ drywall including screws.
	Demolish and Install	S.F.	.18	.78		.96	Tape, finish or texture is not included.
	Clean	S.F.		.28		.28	
	Minimum Charge	Job		207		207	

Walls / Ceilings

Gypsum Wallboard		Unit	Material	Labor	Equip.	Total	Specification
1/2"							
	Demolish	S.F.		.34		.34	Cost includes material and labor to
	Install	S.F.	.18	.44		.62	install 1/2" drywall including screws.
	Demolish and Install	S.F.	.18	.78		.96	Taping and finishing not included.
	Clean	S.F.		.28		.28	
	Minimum Charge	Job		207		207	
1/2" Water Resistant							
	Demolish	S.F.		.34		.34	Cost includes material and labor to
	Install	S.F.	.30	.44		.74	install 1/2" WR drywall including
	Demolish and Install	S.F.	.30	.78		1.08	screws. Taping and finishing is not
	Clean	S.F.		.28		.28	included.
	Minimum Charge	Job		207		207	
1/2" Fire-rated							
	Demolish	S.F.		.34		.34	Cost includes labor and material to
	Install	S.F.	.18	.30		.48	install 1/2" FR drywall including
	Demolish and Install	S.F.	.18	.64		.82	screws. Tape, finish or texture is not
	Clean	S.F.		.28		.28	included.
	Minimum Charge	Job		207		207	
5/8"							
	Demolish	S.F.		.34		.34	Cost includes material and labor to
	Install	S.F.	.23	.50		.73	install 5/8" drywall including screws.
	Demolish and Install	S.F.	.23	.84		1.07	Taping and finishing not included.
	Clean	S.F.		.28		.28	
	Minimum Charge	Job		207		207	
5/8" Fire-rated							
	Demolish	S.F.		.34		.34	Cost includes material and labor to
	Install	S.F.	.25	.50		.75	install 5/8" FR drywall including
	Demolish and Install	S.F.	.25	.84		1.09	screws. Taping and finishing not
	Clean	S.F.		.28		.28	included.
	Minimum Charge	Job		207		207	
2-hour Fire-rated							
	Demolish	S.F.		.85		.85	Cost includes material and labor to
	Install	S.F.	.61	2.89		3.50	install 2 layers of 5/8" type X drywall
	Demolish and Install	S.F.	.61	3.74		4.35	including joint taping, premixed
	Clean	S.F.		.28		.28	compound and screws.
	Minimum Charge	Job		207		207	
Accessories							
Tape & Finish							
	Install	S.F.	.06	.41		.47	Includes labor and material for taping,
	Minimum Charge	Job		207		207	sanding and finish.
Texture							
Sprayed							
	Install	S.F.	.04	.44		.48	Includes labor and material to install
	Minimum Charge	Job		207		207	by spray, texture finish.
Trowel							
	Install	S.F.		.24		.24	Includes labor and material to apply
	Minimum Charge	Job		207		207	hand troweled texture.
Patch Hole in Gypsum Wallboard							
	Install	S.F.	.41	55.50		55.91	Includes labor and material to patch a
	Minimum Charge	Job		207		207	one square foot area of damaged
							drywall.
Furring Strips							
	Demolish	S.F.		.09		.09	Cost includes material and labor to
	Install	S.F.	.21	.92		1.13	install 1" x 2" furring strips, 16" O.C.
	Demolish and Install	S.F.	.21	1.01		1.22	per S.F. of surface area to be covered.
	Minimum Charge	Job		104		104	

Ceramic Wall Tile	Unit	Material	Labor	Equip.	Total	Specification
Thin Set						
2″ x 2″						
Demolish	S.F.		1.13		1.13	Cost includes material and labor to
Install	S.F.	7.50	6.15		13.65	install 2″ x 2″ ceramic tile in organic
Demolish and Install	S.F.	7.50	7.28		14.78	adhesive including cutting and grout.
Clean	S.F.		.58		.58	
Minimum Charge	Job		184		184	
4-1/4″ x 4-1/4″						
Demolish	S.F.		1.13		1.13	Cost includes material and labor to
Install	S.F.	2.42	3.46		5.88	install 4-1/4″ x 4-1/4″ ceramic tile in
Demolish and Install	S.F.	2.42	4.59		7.01	organic adhesive including grout.
Clean	S.F.		.58		.58	
Minimum Charge	Job		184		184	
6″ x 6″						
Demolish	S.F.		1.13		1.13	Cost includes material and labor to
Install	S.F.	2.81	3.75		6.56	install 6″ x 6″ ceramic tile in organic
Demolish and Install	S.F.	2.81	4.88		7.69	adhesive including and grout.
Clean	S.F.		.58		.58	
Minimum Charge	Job		184		184	
8″ x 8″						
Demolish	S.F.		1.13		1.13	Cost includes material and labor to
Install	S.F.	4	3.86		7.86	install 8″ x 8″ ceramic tile in organic
Demolish and Install	S.F.	4	4.99		8.99	adhesive including cutting and grout.
Clean	S.F.		.58		.58	
Minimum Charge	Job		184		184	
Thick Set						
2″ x 2″						
Demolish	S.F.		1.36		1.36	Cost includes material and labor to
Install	S.F.	6.70	7.35		14.05	install 2″ x 2″ ceramic tile in mortar
Demolish and Install	S.F.	6.70	8.71		15.41	bed including cutting and grout.
Clean	S.F.		.58		.58	
Minimum Charge	Job		184		184	
4-1/4″ x 4-1/4″						
Demolish	S.F.		1.36		1.36	Cost includes material and labor to
Install	S.F.	8.15	7.35		15.50	install 4-1/4″ x 4-1/4″ ceramic tile in
Demolish and Install	S.F.	8.15	8.71		16.86	mortar bed including cutting and
Clean	S.F.		.58		.58	grout.
Minimum Charge	Job		184		184	
6″ x 6″						
Demolish	S.F.		1.36		1.36	Cost includes material and labor to
Install	S.F.	10.55	6.70		17.25	install 6″ x 6″ ceramic tile in mortar
Demolish and Install	S.F.	10.55	8.06		18.61	bed including cutting and grout.
Clean	S.F.		.58		.58	
Minimum Charge	Job		184		184	
8″ x 8″						
Demolish	S.F.		1.36		1.36	Cost includes material and labor to
Install	S.F.	12.10	6.15		18.25	install 8″ x 8″ ceramic tile in mortar
Demolish and Install	S.F.	12.10	7.51		19.61	bed including cutting and grout.
Clean	S.F.		.58		.58	
Minimum Charge	Job		184		184	
Re-grout						
Install	S.F.	.15	3.68		3.83	Includes material and labor to regrout
Minimum Charge	Job		184		184	ceramic tile walls.

RSMeans Professional Development Seminars

RSMeans Seminars are approved for Continuing Education Units (CEUs) by both the American Institute of Architects Continuing Education Systems (AIA/CES) and AACE International Certification Board.

Seminar Topics Include:

- Practical Project Management for Construction Professionals
- Scheduling with MSProject for Construction Professionals
- Assessing Scope of Work for Facilities Construction Estimating
- Site Work and Heavy Construction Estimating
- Facilities Construction Estimating
- Job Order Contracting
- Mechanical and Electrical Estimating
- Facilities Maintenance and Repair Estimating
- Unit Price Estimating
- RSMeans Product Training (MeansCostWorks.com and RSMeans CostWorks CD)

Ask us about on-site product training.
Call 1-800-334-3509, option 2.

For more information and a seminar schedule visit
www.reedconstructiondata.com/rsmeans/seminars.

RSMeans

Your job is tough enough.

Finding your next project doesn't have to be.

SmartProject News is the easiest way to find and track projects coming up for bid.

Convenient.
Find projects faster with easy-to-use search features and e-mail notifications.

Unlimited.
Access all the projects in your area for one low, flat rate.

Flexible.
Choose from over 200 subscription options covering the U.S. and Canada.

Learn how SmartProject News can work for you.
Visit www.smartprojectnews.com today.

SmartProject News
C. Reed Construction Data®

Walls / Ceilings

Wall Tile		Unit	Material	Labor	Equip.	Total	Specification
Mirror							
Custom Cut Wall							
	Demolish	S.F.		.65		.65	Includes material and labor to install
	Install	S.F.	2.20	4.12		6.32	distortion-free float glass mirror, 1/8"
	Demolish and Install	S.F.	2.20	4.77		6.97	to 3/16" thick with cut and polished
	Clean	S.F.	.04	.18		.22	edges.
	Minimum Charge	Job		201		201	
Beveled Wall							
	Demolish	S.F.		.65		.65	Includes material and labor to install
	Install	S.F.	6.25	7.30		13.55	distortion-free float glass mirror, 1/8"
	Demolish and Install	S.F.	6.25	7.95		14.20	to 3/16" thick with beveled edges.
	Clean	S.F.	.04	.18		.22	
	Minimum Charge	Job		201		201	
Smoked Wall							
	Demolish	S.F.		.65		.65	Includes material and labor to install
	Install	S.F.	8.85	7.30		16.15	distortion-free smoked float glass
	Demolish and Install	S.F.	8.85	7.95		16.80	mirror, 1/8" to 3/16" thick with cut
	Clean	S.F.	.04	.18		.22	and polished edges.
	Minimum Charge	Job		201		201	
Marble							
Good Grade							
	Demolish	S.F.		2.13		2.13	Cost includes material and labor to
	Install	S.F.	9.90	16		25.90	install 3/8" x 12" x 12" marble tile in
	Demolish and Install	S.F.	9.90	18.13		28.03	mortar bed with grout.
	Clean	S.F.		.58		.58	
	Minimum Charge	Job		184		184	
Better Grade							
	Demolish	S.F.		2.13		2.13	Cost includes material and labor to
	Install	S.F.	11	16		27	install 3/8" x 12" x 12" marble, in
	Demolish and Install	S.F.	11	18.13		29.13	mortar bed with grout.
	Clean	S.F.		.58		.58	
	Minimum Charge	Job		184		184	
Premium Grade							
	Demolish	S.F.		2.13		2.13	Cost includes material and labor to
	Install	S.F.	20.50	16		36.50	install 3/8" x 12" x 12" marble, in
	Demolish and Install	S.F.	20.50	18.13		38.63	mortar bed with grout.
	Clean	S.F.		.58		.58	
	Minimum Charge	Job		184		184	
Glass Block							
	Demolish	S.F.		1.70		1.70	Cost includes material and labor to
	Install	S.F.	31.50	16.35		47.85	install 3-7/8" thick, 6" x 6" smooth
	Demolish and Install	S.F.	31.50	18.05		49.55	face glass block including mortar and
	Clean	S.F.		.58		.58	cleaning.
	Minimum Charge	Job		370		370	
Cork							
	Demolish	S.F.		.26		.26	Cost includes material and labor to
	Install	S.F.	4.92	1.49		6.41	install 3/16" thick cork tile and
	Demolish and Install	S.F.	4.92	1.75		6.67	installation.
	Clean	S.F.		.58		.58	
	Minimum Charge	Job		179		179	
Re-grout							
	Install	S.F.	.15	3.68		3.83	Includes material and labor to regrout
	Minimum Charge	Job		184		184	ceramic tile walls.

Walls / Ceilings

Wall Paneling	Unit	Material	Labor	Equip.	Total	Specification
Plywood						
Good Grade						
Demolish	S.F.		.34		.34	Cost includes material and labor to
Install	S.F.	.99	1.66		2.65	install 4' x 8' x 1/4" paneling,
Demolish and Install	S.F.	.99	2		2.99	including nails and adhesive.
Clean	S.F.		.28		.28	
Paint	S.F.	.32	.68		1	
Minimum Charge	Job		207		207	
Better Grade						
Demolish	S.F.		.34		.34	Cost includes material and labor to
Install	S.F.	1.50	1.97		3.47	install 4' x 8' x 1/4" plywood wall
Demolish and Install	S.F.	1.50	2.31		3.81	panel, including nails and adhesive.
Clean	S.F.		.28		.28	
Paint	S.F.	.32	.68		1	
Minimum Charge	Job		207		207	
Premium Grade						
Demolish	S.F.		.34		.34	Cost includes material and labor to
Install	S.F.	2.19	2.37		4.56	install 4' x 8' x 1/4" plywood wall
Demolish and Install	S.F.	2.19	2.71		4.90	panel, including nails and adhesive.
Clean	S.F.		.28		.28	
Paint	S.F.	.32	.68		1	
Minimum Charge	Job		207		207	
Hardboard						
Embossed Paneling						
Demolish	S.F.		.34		.34	Includes material and labor to install
Install	S.F.	.75	1.66		2.41	hardboard embossed paneling
Demolish and Install	S.F.	.75	2		2.75	including adhesives.
Clean	S.F.		.28		.28	
Minimum Charge	Job		207		207	
Plastic Molding						
Demolish	L.F.		.34		.34	Includes material and labor to install
Install	L.F.	.74	1.04		1.78	plastic trim for paneling.
Demolish and Install	L.F.	.74	1.38		2.12	
Clean	L.F.	.04	.18		.22	
Minimum Charge	Job		207		207	
Hardboard						
Embossed Brick						
Demolish	S.F.		.34		.34	Cost includes material and labor to
Install	S.F.	2.32	1.84		4.16	install 4' x 8' non-ceramic mineral
Demolish and Install	S.F.	2.32	2.18		4.50	brick-like veneer wall panels including
Clean	S.F.		.28		.28	adhesive.
Paint	S.F.	.23	.53		.76	
Minimum Charge	Job		207		207	
Embossed Ceramic Tile						
Demolish	S.F.		.34		.34	Includes material and labor to install
Install	S.F.	.75	1.66		2.41	hardboard embossed paneling
Demolish and Install	S.F.	.75	2		2.75	including adhesives.
Clean	S.F.		.28		.28	
Paint	S.F.	.23	.53		.76	
Minimum Charge	Job		207		207	
Pegboard						
Demolish	S.F.		.34		.34	Cost includes material and labor to
Install	S.F.	.46	1.66		2.12	install 4' x 8' x 1/4" pegboard panel,
Demolish and Install	S.F.	.46	2		2.46	including adhesive.
Clean	S.F.		.28		.28	
Paint	S.F.	.23	.53		.76	
Minimum Charge	Job		207		207	

Walls / Ceilings

Wall Paneling		Unit	Material	Labor	Equip.	Total	Specification
Furring Strips							
	Demolish	S.F.		.09		.09	Cost includes material and labor to
	Install	S.F.	.21	.92		1.13	install 1" x 2" furring strips, 16" O.C.
	Demolish and Install	S.F.	.21	1.01		1.22	per S.F. of surface area to be covered.
	Minimum Charge	Job		207		207	
Molding							
Unfinished Base							
	Demolish	L.F.		.57		.57	Cost includes material and labor to
	Install	L.F.	.60	1.25		1.85	install 1/2" x 2-1/2" pine or birch
	Demolish and Install	L.F.	.60	1.82		2.42	base molding.
	Reinstall	L.F.		1		1	
	Clean	L.F.	.04	.18		.22	
	Paint	L.F.	.06	.39		.45	
	Minimum Charge	Job		207		207	
Unfinished Corner							
	Demolish	L.F.		.57		.57	Includes material and labor to install
	Install	L.F.	2.35	1.73		4.08	unfinished pine corner molding.
	Demolish and Install	L.F.	2.35	2.30		4.65	
	Reinstall	L.F.		1.38		1.38	
	Clean	Ea.	1.20	28		29.20	
	Paint	L.F.	.14	.57		.71	
	Minimum Charge	Job		207		207	
Unfinished Cove							
	Demolish	L.F.		.57		.57	Cost includes material and labor to
	Install	L.F.	2.20	1.53		3.73	install 3/4" x 3-1/2" unfinished pine
	Demolish and Install	L.F.	2.20	2.10		4.30	cove molding.
	Reinstall	L.F.		1.23		1.23	
	Clean	Ea.	1.20	28		29.20	
	Paint	L.F.	.14	.57		.71	
	Minimum Charge	Job		207		207	
Unfinished Crown							
	Demolish	L.F.		.68		.68	Includes material and labor to install
	Install	L.F.	2.95	1.66		4.61	unfinished pine crown molding.
	Demolish and Install	L.F.	2.95	2.34		5.29	
	Reinstall	L.F.		1.33		1.33	
	Clean	L.F.	.06	.24		.30	
	Paint	L.F.	.10	.38		.48	
	Minimum Charge	Job		207		207	
Prefinished Base							
	Demolish	L.F.		.57		.57	Cost includes material and labor to
	Install	L.F.	1.26	1.33		2.59	install 9/16" x 3-5/16" prefinished
	Demolish and Install	L.F.	1.26	1.90		3.16	base molding.
	Reinstall	L.F.		1.06		1.06	
	Clean	L.F.	.04	.18		.22	
	Paint	L.F.	.06	.39		.45	
	Minimum Charge	Job		207		207	
Prefinished Corner							
	Demolish	L.F.		.57		.57	Includes material and labor to install
	Install	L.F.	2.64	1.73		4.37	inside or outside prefinished corner
	Demolish and Install	L.F.	2.64	2.30		4.94	molding.
	Reinstall	L.F.		1.38		1.38	
	Clean	L.F.		.12		.12	
	Paint	L.F.	.14	.57		.71	
	Minimum Charge	Job		207		207	

Walls / Ceilings

Wall Paneling

Wall Paneling	Unit	Material	Labor	Equip.	Total	Specification
Prefinished Crown						Cost includes material and labor to install 3/4" x 3-13/16" prefinished crown molding.
Demolish	L.F.		.68		.68	
Install	L.F.	1.65	1.66		3.31	
Demolish and Install	L.F.	1.65	2.34		3.99	
Reinstall	L.F.		1.33		1.33	
Clean	L.F.	.06	.24		.30	
Paint	L.F.	.10	.38		.48	
Minimum Charge	Job		207		207	

Wall Covering

Wall Covering	Unit	Material	Labor	Equip.	Total	Specification
Surface Prep						
Patch Walls						Includes labor and material to repair section of plaster wall, area less than 20 S.F.
Install	S.F.	.11	3.70		3.81	
Minimum Charge	Job		179		179	
Sizing						Includes labor and materials to apply wall sizing.
Install	S.F.	.07	.18		.25	
Minimum Charge	Job		179		179	
Good Grade						
Walls						Includes material and labor to install pre-pasted, vinyl-coated wallcovering.
Demolish	S.F.		.66		.66	
Install	S.F.	.99	.75		1.74	
Demolish and Install	S.F.	.99	1.41		2.40	
Clean	S.F.	.01	.07		.08	
Minimum Charge	Job		179		179	
Ceiling						Includes material and labor to install pre-pasted, vinyl-coated wallcovering.
Demolish	S.F.		.66		.66	
Install	S.F.	.99	.75		1.74	
Demolish and Install	S.F.	.99	1.41		2.40	
Clean	S.F.	.04	.18		.22	
Minimum Charge	Job		179		179	
Better Grade						
Walls						Includes material and labor to install pre-pasted, vinyl-coated wallcovering.
Demolish	S.F.		.66		.66	
Install	S.F.	1.11	.75		1.86	
Demolish and Install	S.F.	1.11	1.41		2.52	
Clean	S.F.	.01	.07		.08	
Minimum Charge	Job		179		179	
Ceiling						Includes material and labor to install pre-pasted, vinyl-coated wallcovering.
Demolish	S.F.		.66		.66	
Install	S.F.	1.11	.75		1.86	
Demolish and Install	S.F.	1.11	1.41		2.52	
Clean	S.F.	.04	.18		.22	
Minimum Charge	Job		179		179	
Premium Grade						
Walls						Includes material and labor to install pre-pasted, vinyl-coated wallcovering.
Demolish	S.F.		.83		.83	
Install	S.F.	1.40	.75		2.15	
Demolish and Install	S.F.	1.40	1.58		2.98	
Clean	S.F.	.01	.07		.08	
Minimum Charge	Job		179		179	
Ceiling						Includes material and labor to install pre-pasted, vinyl-coated wallcovering.
Demolish	S.F.		.83		.83	
Install	S.F.	1.40	.75		2.15	
Demolish and Install	S.F.	1.40	1.58		2.98	
Clean	S.F.	.04	.18		.22	
Minimum Charge	Job		179		179	

Wall Covering	Unit	Material	Labor	Equip.	Total	Specification
Mural						
Pre-printed						
Demolish	Ea.		106		106	Includes material and labor to install
Install	Ea.	262	269		531	wallcovering with a pre-printed mural.
Demolish and Install	Ea.	262	375		637	
Clean	Ea.		7.65		7.65	
Minimum Charge	Job		179		179	
Hand-painted						
Demolish	Ea.		106		106	Includes material and labor to install
Install	Ea.	525	540		1065	wallcovering with a hand-painted
Demolish and Install	Ea.	525	646		1171	mural.
Clean	Ea.		7.65		7.65	
Minimum Charge	Job		179		179	
Vinyl-coated						
Good Grade						
Demolish	Ea.		18.90		18.90	Includes material and labor to install
Install	Ea.	22	25		47	pre-pasted, vinyl-coated wallcovering.
Demolish and Install	Ea.	22	43.90		65.90	Based upon 30 S.F. rolls.
Clean	Ea.		7.65		7.65	
Minimum Charge	Job		179		179	
Better Grade						
Demolish	Ea.		18.90		18.90	Includes material and labor to install
Install	Ea.	29	25		54	pre-pasted, vinyl-coated wallcovering.
Demolish and Install	Ea.	29	43.90		72.90	Based upon 30 S.F. rolls.
Clean	Ea.		7.65		7.65	
Minimum Charge	Job		179		179	
Premium Grade						
Demolish	Ea.		18.90		18.90	Includes material and labor to install
Install	Ea.	51	25		76	pre-pasted, vinyl-coated wallcovering.
Demolish and Install	Ea.	51	43.90		94.90	Based upon 30 S.F. rolls.
Clean	Ea.		7.65		7.65	
Minimum Charge	Job		179		179	
Blank Underliner						
Demolish	Ea.		18.90		18.90	Includes material and labor to install
Install	Ea.	12.85	25.50		38.35	blank stock liner paper or bridging
Demolish and Install	Ea.	12.85	44.40		57.25	paper. Based upon 30 S.F. rolls.
Clean	Ea.		7.65		7.65	
Minimum Charge	Job		179		179	
Solid Vinyl						
Good Grade						
Demolish	Roll		22		22	Includes material and labor to install
Install	Ea.	29	25		54	pre-pasted, vinyl wallcovering. Based
Demolish and Install	Ea.	29	47		76	upon 30 S.F. rolls.
Clean	Ea.		7.65		7.65	
Minimum Charge	Job		179		179	
Better Grade						
Demolish	Roll		22		22	Includes material and labor to install
Install	Ea.	40.50	25		65.50	pre-pasted, vinyl wallcovering. Based
Demolish and Install	Ea.	40.50	47		87.50	upon 30 S.F. rolls.
Clean	Ea.		7.65		7.65	
Minimum Charge	Job		179		179	
Premium Grade						
Demolish	Roll		22		22	Includes material and labor to install
Install	Ea.	51.50	25		76.50	pre-pasted, vinyl wallcovering. Based
Demolish and Install	Ea.	51.50	47		98.50	upon 30 S.F. rolls.
Clean	Ea.		7.65		7.65	
Minimum Charge	Job		179		179	

Walls / Ceilings

Wall Covering		Unit	Material	Labor	Equip.	Total	Specification
Blank Underliner							
	Demolish	Ea.		18.90		18.90	Includes material and labor to install
	Install	Ea.	12.85	25.50		38.35	blank stock liner paper or bridging
	Demolish and Install	Ea.	12.85	44.40		57.25	paper. Based upon 30 S.F. rolls.
	Clean	Ea.		7.65		7.65	
	Minimum Charge	Job		179		179	
Grasscloth / String							
Good Grade							
	Demolish	Ea.		18.90		18.90	Includes material and labor to install
	Install	Ea.	41.50	32.50		74	grasscloth or string wallcovering.
	Demolish and Install	Ea.	41.50	51.40		92.90	Based upon 30 S.F. rolls.
	Clean	Ea.		10.20		10.20	
	Minimum Charge	Job		179		179	
Better Grade							
	Demolish	Ea.		18.90		18.90	Includes material and labor to install
	Install	Ea.	53.50	32.50		86	grasscloth or string wallcovering.
	Demolish and Install	Ea.	53.50	51.40		104.90	Based upon 30 S.F. rolls.
	Clean	Ea.		10.20		10.20	
	Minimum Charge	Job		179		179	
Premium Grade							
	Demolish	Ea.		18.90		18.90	Includes material and labor to install
	Install	Ea.	68	32.50		100.50	grasscloth or string wallcovering.
	Demolish and Install	Ea.	68	51.40		119.40	Based upon 30 S.F. rolls.
	Clean	Ea.		10.20		10.20	
	Minimum Charge	Job		179		179	
Blank Underliner							
	Demolish	Ea.		18.90		18.90	Includes material and labor to install
	Install	Ea.	12.85	25.50		38.35	blank stock liner paper or bridging
	Demolish and Install	Ea.	12.85	44.40		57.25	paper. Based upon 30 S.F. rolls.
	Clean	Ea.		7.65		7.65	
	Minimum Charge	Job		179		179	
Designer							
Premium Grade							
	Demolish	S.F.		.83		.83	Includes material and labor to install
	Install	Ea.	128	37.50		165.50	paperback vinyl, untrimmed and
	Demolish and Install	Ea.	128	38.33		166.33	hand-painted. Based upon 30 S.F.
	Clean	Ea.		7.65		7.65	rolls.
	Minimum Charge	Job		179		179	
Blank Underliner							
	Demolish	Ea.		18.90		18.90	Includes material and labor to install
	Install	Ea.	12.85	25.50		38.35	blank stock liner paper or bridging
	Demolish and Install	Ea.	12.85	44.40		57.25	paper. Based upon 30 S.F. rolls.
	Clean	Ea.		7.65		7.65	
	Minimum Charge	Job		179		179	
Foil							
	Demolish	Ea.		18.90		18.90	Includes material and labor to install
	Install	Ea.	43.50	32.50		76	foil coated wallcovering. Based upon
	Demolish and Install	Ea.	43.50	51.40		94.90	30 S.F. rolls.
	Clean	Ea.		7.65		7.65	
	Minimum Charge	Job		179		179	
Wallcovering Border							
Good Grade							
	Demolish	L.F.		1.24		1.24	Includes material and labor install
	Install	L.F.	2.17	1.38		3.55	vinyl-coated border 4" to 6" wide.
	Demolish and Install	L.F.	2.17	2.62		4.79	
	Clean	L.F.		.12		.12	
	Minimum Charge	Job		179		179	

Walls / Ceilings

Wall Covering

Wall Covering	Unit	Material	Labor	Equip.	Total	Specification
Better Grade						
Demolish	L.F.		1.24		1.24	Includes material and labor install
Install	L.F.	2.90	1.38		4.28	vinyl-coated border 4″ to 6″ wide.
Demolish and Install	L.F.	2.90	2.62		5.52	
Clean	L.F.		.12		.12	
Minimum Charge	Job		179		179	
Premium Grade						
Demolish	L.F.		1.24		1.24	Includes material and labor install
Install	L.F.	3.64	1.38		5.02	vinyl-coated border 4″ to 6″ wide.
Demolish and Install	L.F.	3.64	2.62		6.26	
Clean	L.F.		.12		.12	
Minimum Charge	Job		179		179	

Acoustical Ceiling

Acoustical Ceiling	Unit	Material	Labor	Equip.	Total	Specification
Complete System						
2′ x 2′ Square Edge						
Demolish	S.F.		.57		.57	Includes material and labor to install
Install	S.F.	1.87	1.28		3.15	T-bar grid acoustical ceiling system,
Demolish and Install	S.F.	1.87	1.85		3.72	random pinhole 5/8″ thick square
Reinstall	S.F.		1.02		1.02	edge tile.
Clean	S.F.	.06	.23		.29	
Minimum Charge	Job		207		207	
2′ x 2′ Reveal Edge						
Demolish	S.F.		.57		.57	Includes material and labor to install
Install	S.F.	2.73	1.66		4.39	T-bar grid acoustical ceiling system,
Demolish and Install	S.F.	2.73	2.23		4.96	random pinhole 5/8″ thick reveal
Reinstall	S.F.		1.33		1.33	edge tile.
Clean	S.F.	.06	.23		.29	
Minimum Charge	Job		207		207	
2′ x 2′ Fire-rated						
Demolish	S.F.		.57		.57	Includes material and labor to install
Install	S.F.	3.10	1.28		4.38	T-bar grid FR acoustical ceiling system,
Demolish and Install	S.F.	3.10	1.85		4.95	random pinhole 5/8″ thick square
Reinstall	S.F.		1.02		1.02	edge tile.
Clean	S.F.	.06	.23		.29	
Minimum Charge	Job		207		207	
2′ x 4′ Square Edge						
Demolish	S.F.		.57		.57	Cost includes material and labor to
Install	S.F.	1.60	1.09		2.69	install 2′ x 4′ T-bar grid acoustical
Demolish and Install	S.F.	1.60	1.66		3.26	ceiling system, random pinhole 5/8″
Reinstall	S.F.		.87		.87	thick square edge tile.
Clean	S.F.	.06	.23		.29	
Minimum Charge	Job		207		207	
2′ x 4′ Reveal Edge						
Demolish	S.F.		.57		.57	Includes material and labor to install
Install	S.F.	2.73	1.51		4.24	T-bar grid acoustical ceiling system,
Demolish and Install	S.F.	2.73	2.08		4.81	random pinhole 5/8″ thick reveal
Reinstall	S.F.		1.21		1.21	edge tile.
Clean	S.F.	.06	.23		.29	
Minimum Charge	Job		207		207	
2′ x 4′ Fire-rated						
Demolish	S.F.		.57		.57	Includes material and labor to install
Install	S.F.	3.10	1.28		4.38	T-bar grid FR acoustical ceiling system,
Demolish and Install	S.F.	3.10	1.85		4.95	random pinhole 5/8″ thick square
Reinstall	S.F.		1.02		1.02	edge tile.
Clean	S.F.	.06	.23		.29	
Minimum Charge	Job		207		207	

Acoustical Ceiling		Unit	Material	Labor	Equip.	Total	Specification
T-bar Grid							
2' x 2'							
	Demolish	S.F.		.67		.67	Includes material and labor to install
	Install	S.F.	.96	.64		1.60	T-bar grid acoustical ceiling
	Demolish and Install	S.F.	.96	1.31		2.27	suspension system.
	Reinstall	S.F.		.51		.51	
	Clean	S.F.	.06	.23		.29	
	Minimum Charge	Job		185		185	
2' x 4'							
	Demolish	S.F.		.67		.67	Includes material and labor to install
	Install	S.F.	.77	.52		1.29	T-bar grid acoustical ceiling
	Demolish and Install	S.F.	.77	1.19		1.96	suspension system.
	Reinstall	S.F.		.41		.41	
	Clean	S.F.	.06	.23		.29	
	Minimum Charge	Job		185		185	
Tile Panels							
2' x 2' Square Edge							
	Demolish	S.F.		.19		.19	Includes material and labor to install
	Install	S.F.	.83	.66		1.49	square edge panels 5/8" thick with
	Demolish and Install	S.F.	.83	.85		1.68	pinhole pattern. T-bar grid not
	Reinstall	S.F.		.53		.53	included.
	Clean	S.F.	.06	.23		.29	
	Minimum Charge	Job		207		207	
2' x 2' Reveal Edge							
	Demolish	S.F.		.19		.19	Includes material and labor to install
	Install	S.F.	1.60	.88		2.48	reveal edge panels 5/8" thick with
	Demolish and Install	S.F.	1.60	1.07		2.67	pinhole pattern. T-bar grid not
	Reinstall	S.F.		.71		.71	included.
	Clean	S.F.	.06	.23		.29	
	Minimum Charge	Job		207		207	
2' x 2' Fire-rated							
	Demolish	S.F.		.19		.19	Includes material and labor to install
	Install	S.F.	1.29	.61		1.90	FR square edge panels 5/8" thick with
	Demolish and Install	S.F.	1.29	.80		2.09	pinhole pattern. T-bar grid not
	Reinstall	S.F.		.49		.49	included.
	Clean	S.F.	.06	.23		.29	
	Minimum Charge	Job		207		207	
2' x 4' Square Edge							
	Demolish	S.F.		.19		.19	Includes material and labor to install
	Install	S.F.	.83	.66		1.49	square edge panels 5/8" thick with
	Demolish and Install	S.F.	.83	.85		1.68	pinhole pattern. T-bar grid not
	Reinstall	S.F.		.53		.53	included.
	Clean	S.F.	.06	.23		.29	
	Minimum Charge	Job		207		207	
2' x 4' Reveal Edge							
	Demolish	S.F.		.19		.19	Includes material and labor to install
	Install	S.F.	1.60	.88		2.48	reveal edge panels 5/8" thick with
	Demolish and Install	S.F.	1.60	1.07		2.67	pinhole pattern. T-bar grid not
	Reinstall	S.F.		.71		.71	included.
	Clean	S.F.	.06	.23		.29	
	Minimum Charge	Job		207		207	
2' x 4' Fire-rated							
	Demolish	S.F.		.19		.19	Includes material and labor to install
	Install	S.F.	1.29	.61		1.90	FR square edge panels 5/8" thick with
	Demolish and Install	S.F.	1.29	.80		2.09	pinhole pattern. T-bar grid not
	Reinstall	S.F.		.49		.49	included.
	Clean	S.F.	.06	.23		.29	
	Minimum Charge	Job		207		207	

Walls / Ceilings

Acoustical Ceiling		Unit	Material	Labor	Equip.	Total	Specification
Bleach Out Stains							
	Install	S.F.	.14	.31		.45	Includes labor and material to apply
	Minimum Charge	Job		207		207	laundry type chlorine bleach to remove light staining of acoustic tile material.
Adhesive Tile							
Good Grade							
	Demolish	S.F.		.76		.76	Cost includes material and labor to
	Install	S.F.	1.16	1.38		2.54	install 12″ x 12″ tile with embossed
	Demolish and Install	S.F.	1.16	2.14		3.30	texture pattern. Furring strips not
	Clean	S.F.	.04	.18		.22	included.
	Minimum Charge	Job		207		207	
Better Grade							
	Demolish	S.F.		.76		.76	Cost includes material and labor to
	Install	S.F.	1.65	1.38		3.03	install 12″ x 12″ tile with embossed
	Demolish and Install	S.F.	1.65	2.14		3.79	texture pattern. Furring strips not
	Clean	S.F.	.04	.18		.22	included.
	Minimum Charge	Job		207		207	
Premium Grade							
	Demolish	S.F.		.76		.76	Cost includes material and labor to
	Install	S.F.	5.45	1.38		6.83	install 12″ x 12″ tile with embossed
	Demolish and Install	S.F.	5.45	2.14		7.59	texture pattern. Furring strips not
	Clean	S.F.	.04	.18		.22	included.
	Minimum Charge	Job		207		207	
Bleach Out Stains							
	Install	S.F.	.14	.31		.45	Includes labor and material to apply
	Minimum Charge	Job		207		207	laundry type chlorine bleach to remove light staining of acoustic tile material.
Stapled Tile							
Good Grade							
	Demolish	S.F.		.45		.45	Cost includes material and labor to
	Install	S.F.	1.16	1.38		2.54	install 12″ x 12″ tile with embossed
	Demolish and Install	S.F.	1.16	1.83		2.99	texture pattern. Furring strips not
	Clean	S.F.	.04	.18		.22	included.
	Minimum Charge	Job		207		207	
Better Grade							
	Demolish	S.F.		.45		.45	Cost includes material and labor to
	Install	S.F.	1.65	1.38		3.03	install 12″ x 12″ tile with embossed
	Demolish and Install	S.F.	1.65	1.83		3.48	texture pattern. Furring strips not
	Clean	S.F.	.04	.18		.22	included.
	Minimum Charge	Job		207		207	
Premium Grade							
	Demolish	S.F.		.45		.45	Cost includes material and labor to
	Install	S.F.	5.45	1.38		6.83	install 12″ x 12″ tile with embossed
	Demolish and Install	S.F.	5.45	1.83		7.28	texture pattern. Furring strips not
	Clean	S.F.	.04	.18		.22	included.
	Minimum Charge	Job		207		207	
Bleach Out Stains							
	Install	S.F.	.14	.31		.45	Includes labor and material to apply
	Minimum Charge	Job		207		207	laundry type chlorine bleach to remove light staining of acoustic tile material.

Acoustical Ceiling	Unit	Material	Labor	Equip.	Total	Specification
Blown						
Scrape Off Existing						
Install	S.F.		.63		.63	Includes labor and material to remove existing blown acoustical ceiling material.
Minimum Charge	Job		207		207	
Seal Ceiling Gypsum Wallboard						
Install	S.F.	.07	.31		.38	Includes labor and material to seal existing drywall with shellac-based material.
Minimum Charge	Job		178		178	
Reblow Existing						
Install	S.F.	.04	.44		.48	Includes labor and material to install by spray, texture finish.
Minimum Charge	Job		500	70	570	
Bleach Out Stains						
Install	S.F.	.14	.31		.45	Includes labor and material to apply laundry type chlorine bleach to remove light staining of acoustic tile material.
Minimum Charge	Job		207		207	
New Blown						
Install	S.F.	.04	.44		.48	Includes labor and material to install by spray, texture finish.
Minimum Charge	Job		178		178	
Apply Glitter To						
Install	S.F.	.17	.16		.33	Includes labor and material to apply glitter material to existing or new drywall.
Minimum Charge	Job		178		178	
Furring Strips						
Demolish	S.F.		.09		.09	Cost includes material and labor to install 1" x 2" furring strips, 16" O.C. per S.F. of surface area to be covered.
Install	S.F.	.21	.92		1.13	
Demolish and Install	S.F.	.21	1.01		1.22	
Minimum Charge	Job		104		104	

Finished Stair

Bi-Fold Door

Raised Panel Door

Hollow Core Door	Unit	Material	Labor	Equip.	Total	Specification
Pre-hung Wood						
1' 6" x 6' 8"						
Demolish	Ea.		38.50		38.50	Cost includes material and labor to
Install	Ea.	151	23		174	install 1' 6" x 6' 8" pre-hung 1-3/8"
Demolish and Install	Ea.	151	61.50		212.50	lauan door with split pine jamb
Reinstall	Ea.		23.02		23.02	including casing, stops, and hinges.
Clean	Ea.	4.77	12.75		17.52	
Paint	Ea.	9.20	50.50		59.70	
Minimum Charge	Job		207		207	
2' x 6' 8"						
Demolish	Ea.		38.50		38.50	Cost includes material and labor to
Install	Ea.	161	24.50		185.50	install 2' x 6' 8" pre-hung 1-3/8"
Demolish and Install	Ea.	161	63		224	lauan door with split pine jamb
Reinstall	Ea.		24.38		24.38	including casing, stops, and hinges.
Clean	Ea.	4.77	12.75		17.52	
Paint	Ea.	9.20	50.50		59.70	
Minimum Charge	Job		207		207	
2' 4" x 6' 8"						
Demolish	Ea.		38.50		38.50	Cost includes material and labor to
Install	Ea.	163	24.50		187.50	install 2' 4" x 6' 8" pre-hung 1-3/8"
Demolish and Install	Ea.	163	63		226	lauan door with split pine jamb
Reinstall	Ea.		24.38		24.38	including casing, stops, and hinges.
Clean	Ea.	4.77	12.75		17.52	
Paint	Ea.	9.20	50.50		59.70	
Minimum Charge	Job		207		207	
2' 6" x 6' 8"						
Demolish	Ea.		38.50		38.50	Cost includes material and labor to
Install	Ea.	167	24.50		191.50	install 2' 6" x 6' 8" pre-hung 1-3/8"
Demolish and Install	Ea.	167	63		230	lauan door with split pine jamb
Reinstall	Ea.		24.38		24.38	including casing, stops, and hinges.
Clean	Ea.	4.77	12.75		17.52	
Paint	Ea.	9.20	50.50		59.70	
Minimum Charge	Job		207		207	
2' 8" x 6' 8"						
Demolish	Ea.		38.50		38.50	Cost includes material and labor to
Install	Ea.	165	24.50		189.50	install 2' 8" x 6' 8" pre-hung 1-3/8"
Demolish and Install	Ea.	165	63		228	lauan door with split pine jamb,
Reinstall	Ea.		24.38		24.38	including casing, stop and hinges.
Clean	Ea.	4.77	12.75		17.52	
Paint	Ea.	9.20	50.50		59.70	
Minimum Charge	Job		207		207	

Finish Carpentry

Hollow Core Door

	Unit	Material	Labor	Equip.	Total	Specification
3' x 6' 8"						
Demolish	Ea.		38.50		38.50	Cost includes material and labor to
Install	Ea.	171	26		197	install 3' x 6' 8" pre-hung 1-3/8"
Demolish and Install	Ea.	171	64.50		235.50	lauan door with split pine jamb
Reinstall	Ea.		25.90		25.90	including casing, stops, and hinges.
Clean	Ea.	4.77	12.75		17.52	
Paint	Ea.	9.20	50.50		59.70	
Minimum Charge	Job		207		207	
Pocket Type						
Demolish	Ea.		57.50		57.50	Cost includes material and labor to
Install	Ea.	44	46		90	install 2' 8" x 6' 8" lauan door.
Demolish and Install	Ea.	44	103.50		147.50	
Reinstall	Ea.		46.04		46.04	
Clean	Ea.	4.77	12.75		17.52	
Paint	Ea.	9.20	50.50		59.70	
Minimum Charge	Job		207		207	
Stain						
Install	Ea.	6.65	29.50		36.15	Includes labor and material to stain
Minimum Charge	Job		178		178	single door and trim on both sides.
Pre-hung Masonite						
1' 6" x 6' 8"						
Demolish	Ea.		38.50		38.50	Cost includes material and labor to
Install	Ea.	209	23		232	install 1' 6" x 6' 8" pre-hung 1-3/8"
Demolish and Install	Ea.	209	61.50		270.50	masonite door with split pine jamb
Reinstall	Ea.		23.02		23.02	including casing, stops, and hinges.
Clean	Ea.	4.77	12.75		17.52	
Paint	Ea.	9.20	50.50		59.70	
Minimum Charge	Job		207		207	
2' x 6' 8"						
Demolish	Ea.		38.50		38.50	Cost includes material and labor to
Install	Ea.	218	24.50		242.50	install 2' x 6' 8" pre-hung 1-3/8"
Demolish and Install	Ea.	218	63		281	masonite door with split pine jamb
Reinstall	Ea.		24.38		24.38	including casing, stops, and hinges.
Clean	Ea.	4.77	12.75		17.52	
Paint	Ea.	9.20	50.50		59.70	
Minimum Charge	Job		207		207	
2' 4" x 6' 8"						
Demolish	Ea.		38.50		38.50	Cost includes material and labor to
Install	Ea.	221	24.50		245.50	install 2' 4" x 6' 8" pre-hung 1-3/8"
Demolish and Install	Ea.	221	63		284	masonite door with split pine jamb
Reinstall	Ea.		24.38		24.38	including casing, stops, and hinges.
Clean	Ea.	4.77	12.75		17.52	
Paint	Ea.	9.20	50.50		59.70	
Minimum Charge	Job		207		207	
2' 8" x 6' 8"						
Demolish	Ea.		38.50		38.50	Cost includes material and labor to
Install	Ea.	224	24.50		248.50	install 2' 8" x 6' 8" pre-hung 1-3/8"
Demolish and Install	Ea.	224	63		287	masonite door with split pine jamb
Reinstall	Ea.		24.38		24.38	including casing, stops, and hinges.
Clean	Ea.	4.77	12.75		17.52	
Paint	Ea.	9.20	50.50		59.70	
Minimum Charge	Job		207		207	
3' x 6' 8"						
Demolish	Ea.		38.50		38.50	Cost includes material and labor to
Install	Ea.	229	26		255	install 3' x 6' 8" pre-hung 1-3/8"
Demolish and Install	Ea.	229	64.50		293.50	masonite door with split pine jamb
Reinstall	Ea.		25.90		25.90	including casing, stops, and hinges.
Clean	Ea.	4.77	12.75		17.52	
Paint	Ea.	9.20	50.50		59.70	
Minimum Charge	Job		207		207	

Hollow Core Door	Unit	Material	Labor	Equip.	Total	Specification
Pocket Type						
Demolish	Ea.		57.50		57.50	Cost includes material and labor to
Install	Ea.	44	46		90	install 2' 8" x 6' 8" lauan door.
Demolish and Install	Ea.	44	103.50		147.50	
Reinstall	Ea.		46.04		46.04	
Clean	Ea.	4.77	12.75		17.52	
Paint	Ea.	9.20	50.50		59.70	
Minimum Charge	Job		207		207	
Stain						
Install	Ea.	6.65	29.50		36.15	Includes labor and material to stain
Minimum Charge	Job		178		178	single door and trim on both sides.
Hollow Core Door Only						
1' 6" x 6' 8'						
Demolish	Ea.		8.20		8.20	Cost includes material and labor to
Install	Ea.	44.50	22		66.50	install 1' 6" x 6' 8" lauan hollow core
Demolish and Install	Ea.	44.50	30.20		74.70	door slab.
Reinstall	Ea.		21.81		21.81	
Clean	Ea.	1.99	9.60		11.59	
Paint	Ea.	4.86	44.50		49.36	
Minimum Charge	Job		207		207	
2' x 6' 8'						
Demolish	Ea.		8.20		8.20	Cost includes material and labor to
Install	Ea.	47.50	23		70.50	install 2' x 6' 8" lauan hollow core
Demolish and Install	Ea.	47.50	31.20		78.70	door slab.
Reinstall	Ea.		23.02		23.02	
Clean	Ea.	1.99	9.60		11.59	
Paint	Ea.	4.86	44.50		49.36	
Minimum Charge	Job		207		207	
2' 4" x 6' 8'						
Demolish	Ea.		8.20		8.20	Cost includes material and labor to
Install	Ea.	51.50	23		74.50	install 2' 4" x 6' 8" lauan hollow core
Demolish and Install	Ea.	51.50	31.20		82.70	door slab.
Reinstall	Ea.		23.02		23.02	
Clean	Ea.	1.99	9.60		11.59	
Paint	Ea.	4.86	44.50		49.36	
Minimum Charge	Job		207		207	
2' 8" x 6' 8'						
Demolish	Ea.		8.20		8.20	Cost includes material and labor to
Install	Ea.	53.50	23		76.50	install 2' 8" x 6' 8" lauan hollow core
Demolish and Install	Ea.	53.50	31.20		84.70	door slab.
Reinstall	Ea.		23.02		23.02	
Clean	Ea.	1.99	9.60		11.59	
Paint	Ea.	4.86	44.50		49.36	
Minimum Charge	Job		207		207	
3' x 6' 8'						
Demolish	Ea.		8.20		8.20	Cost includes material and labor to
Install	Ea.	55.50	24.50		80	install 3' x 6' 8" lauan hollow core
Demolish and Install	Ea.	55.50	32.70		88.20	door slab.
Reinstall	Ea.		24.38		24.38	
Clean	Ea.	1.99	9.60		11.59	
Paint	Ea.	4.86	44.50		49.36	
Minimum Charge	Job		207		207	
Pocket Type						
Demolish	Ea.		8.20		8.20	Cost includes material and labor to
Install	Ea.	44	46		90	install 2' 8" x 6' 8" lauan door.
Demolish and Install	Ea.	44	54.20		98.20	
Reinstall	Ea.		46.04		46.04	
Clean	Ea.	1.99	9.60		11.59	
Paint	Ea.	4.86	44.50		49.36	
Minimum Charge	Job		207		207	

Hollow Core Door		Unit	Material	Labor	Equip.	Total	Specification
Stain							
	Install	Ea.	3.69	39.50		43.19	Includes labor and materials to stain a flush style door on both sides by brush.
	Minimum Charge	Job		178		178	
Casing Trim							
Single Width							
	Demolish	Ea.		7.30		7.30	Cost includes material and labor to install 11/16" x 2-1/2" pine ranch style casing for one side of a standard door opening.
	Install	Opng.	25	34.50		59.50	
	Demolish and Install	Opng.	25	41.80		66.80	
	Reinstall	Opng.		27.63		27.63	
	Clean	Opng.	.68	3.06		3.74	
	Paint	Ea.	5.25	7.10		12.35	
	Minimum Charge	Job		207		207	
Double Width							
	Demolish	Ea.		8.70		8.70	Cost includes material and labor to install 11/16" x 2-1/2" pine ranch style door casing for one side of a double door opening.
	Install	Opng.	28.50	41.50		70	
	Demolish and Install	Opng.	28.50	50.20		78.70	
	Reinstall	Opng.		33.15		33.15	
	Clean	Opng.	.79	6.15		6.94	
	Paint	Ea.	5.25	8.05		13.30	
	Minimum Charge	Job		207		207	
Hardware							
Doorknob w / Lock							
	Demolish	Ea.		16.45		16.45	Includes material and labor to install privacy lockset.
	Install	Ea.	44.50	26		70.50	
	Demolish and Install	Ea.	44.50	42.45		86.95	
	Reinstall	Ea.		20.72		20.72	
	Clean	Ea.	.47	9.60		10.07	
	Minimum Charge	Job		207		207	
Doorknob							
	Demolish	Ea.		16.45		16.45	Includes material and labor to install residential passage lockset, keyless bored type.
	Install	Ea.	29	26		55	
	Demolish and Install	Ea.	29	42.45		71.45	
	Reinstall	Ea.		20.72		20.72	
	Clean	Ea.	.47	9.60		10.07	
	Minimum Charge	Job		207		207	
Deadbolt							
	Demolish	Ea.		14.40		14.40	Includes material and labor to install a deadbolt.
	Install	Ea.	70	29.50		99.50	
	Demolish and Install	Ea.	70	43.90		113.90	
	Reinstall	Ea.		23.68		23.68	
	Clean	Ea.	.47	9.60		10.07	
	Minimum Charge	Job		207		207	
Lever Handle							
	Demolish	Ea.		16.45		16.45	Includes material and labor to install residential passage lockset, keyless bored type with lever handle.
	Install	Ea.	38	41.50		79.50	
	Demolish and Install	Ea.	38	57.95		95.95	
	Reinstall	Ea.		33.15		33.15	
	Clean	Ea.	.47	9.60		10.07	
	Minimum Charge	Job		207		207	
Closer							
	Demolish	Ea.		8.65		8.65	Includes material and labor to install pneumatic light duty closer for interior type doors.
	Install	Ea.	144	64		208	
	Demolish and Install	Ea.	144	72.65		216.65	
	Reinstall	Ea.		51		51	
	Clean	Ea.	.24	12.75		12.99	
	Minimum Charge	Job		207		207	

Finish Carpentry

Hollow Core Door

	Unit	Material	Labor	Equip.	Total	Specification
Push Plate						
Demolish	Ea.		12.80		12.80	Includes material and labor to install
Install	Ea.	23.50	34.50		58	bronze push-pull plate.
Demolish and Install	Ea.	23.50	47.30		70.80	
Reinstall	Ea.		27.63		27.63	
Clean	Ea.	.47	9.60		10.07	
Minimum Charge	Job		207		207	
Kickplate						
Demolish	Ea.		12.80		12.80	Includes material and labor to install
Install	Ea.	28.50	27.50		56	aluminum kickplate, 10" x 28".
Demolish and Install	Ea.	28.50	40.30		68.80	
Reinstall	Ea.		22.10		22.10	
Clean	Ea.	.47	9.60		10.07	
Minimum Charge	Job		207		207	
Exit Sign						
Demolish	Ea.		23		23	Includes material and labor to install a
Install	Ea.	113	56.50		169.50	wall mounted interior electric exit sign.
Demolish and Install	Ea.	113	79.50		192.50	
Reinstall	Ea.		45.20		45.20	
Clean	Ea.	.03	7.05		7.08	
Minimum Charge	Job		207		207	
Jamb						
Demolish	Ea.		29		29	Includes material and labor to install
Install	Ea.	100	11.20		111.20	flat pine jamb with square cut heads
Demolish and Install	Ea.	100	40.20		140.20	and rabbeted sides for 6' 8" high and
Clean	Ea.	.15	7.65		7.80	3-9/16" door including trim sets for
Paint	Ea.	6.60	23.50		30.10	both sides.
Minimum Charge	Job		207		207	
Shave & Refit						
Install	Ea.		34.50		34.50	Includes labor to shave and rework
Minimum Charge	Job		207		207	door to fit opening at the job site.

Solid Core Door

	Unit	Material	Labor	Equip.	Total	Specification
Pre-hung Wood						
2' 4" x 6' 8"						
Demolish	Ea.		38.50		38.50	Cost includes material and labor to
Install	Ea.	244	24.50		268.50	install 2' 4" x 6' 8" pre-hung 1-3/4"
Demolish and Install	Ea.	244	63		307	door, 4-1/2" split jamb, including
Reinstall	Ea.		24.38		24.38	casing and stop, hinges, aluminum sill,
Clean	Ea.	4.77	12.75		17.52	weatherstripping.
Paint	Ea.	10.30	50.50		60.80	
Minimum Charge	Job		207		207	
2' 6" x 6' 8"						
Demolish	Ea.		38.50		38.50	Cost includes material and labor to
Install	Ea.	240	24.50		264.50	install 2' 6" x 6' 8" pre-hung 1-3/4"
Demolish and Install	Ea.	240	63		303	door, 4-1/2" split jamb, including
Reinstall	Ea.		24.38		24.38	casing and stop, hinges, aluminum sill,
Clean	Ea.	4.77	12.75		17.52	weatherstripping.
Paint	Ea.	10.30	50.50		60.80	
Minimum Charge	Job		207		207	

Finish Carpentry

Solid Core Door

	Unit	Material	Labor	Equip.	Total	Specification
2' 8" x 6' 8"						
Demolish	Ea.		38.50		38.50	Cost includes material and labor to
Install	Ea.	220	24.50		244.50	install 2' 8" x 6' 8" pre-hung 1-3/4"
Demolish and Install	Ea.	220	63		283	door, 4-1/2" split jamb, including
Reinstall	Ea.		24.38		24.38	casing and stop, hinges, aluminum sill,
Clean	Ea.	4.77	12.75		17.52	weatherstripping.
Paint	Ea.	10.30	50.50		60.80	
Minimum Charge	Job		207		207	
3' x 6' 8"						
Demolish	Ea.		38.50		38.50	Cost includes material and labor to
Install	Ea.	229	26		255	install 3' x 6' 8" pre-hung 1-3/4"
Demolish and Install	Ea.	229	64.50		293.50	door, including casing and stop,
Reinstall	Ea.		25.90		25.90	hinges, jamb, aluminum sill,
Clean	Ea.	4.77	12.75		17.52	weatherstripped.
Paint	Ea.	10.30	50.50		60.80	
Minimum Charge	Job		207		207	
3' 6" x 6' 8"						
Demolish	Ea.		38.50		38.50	Cost includes material and labor to
Install	Ea.	385	27.50		412.50	install 3' 6" x 6' 8" pre-hung 1-3/4"
Demolish and Install	Ea.	385	66		451	door, 4-1/2" split jamb, including
Reinstall	Ea.		27.63		27.63	casing and stop, hinges, aluminum sill,
Clean	Ea.	4.77	12.75		17.52	weatherstripping.
Paint	Ea.	10.30	50.50		60.80	
Minimum Charge	Job		207		207	
Raised Panel						
Demolish	Ea.		38.50		38.50	Cost includes material and labor to
Install	Ea.	480	23		503	install 3' x 6' 8" pre-hung 1-3/4"
Demolish and Install	Ea.	480	61.50		541.50	door, jamb, including casing and
Reinstall	Ea.		23.02		23.02	stop, hinges, aluminum sill,
Clean	Ea.	4.77	12.75		17.52	weatherstripping.
Paint	Ea.	10.30	118		128.30	
Minimum Charge	Job		207		207	
Stain						
Install	Ea.	6.65	29.50		36.15	Includes labor and material to stain
Minimum Charge	Job		178		178	single door and trim on both sides.

Bifold Door

	Unit	Material	Labor	Equip.	Total	Specification
Wood, Single						
3'						
Demolish	Ea.		29		29	Cost includes material and labor to
Install	Ea.	78.50	64		142.50	install 3' wide solid wood bi-fold door
Demolish and Install	Ea.	78.50	93		171.50	not including jamb, trim, track, and
Reinstall	Ea.		63.75		63.75	hardware.
Clean	Ea.	4.77	12.75		17.52	
Paint	Ea.	9.20	50.50		59.70	
Minimum Charge	Job		207		207	
5'						
Demolish	Ea.		29		29	Includes material and labor to install
Install	Ea.	116	75.50		191.50	pair of 2' 6" wide solid wood bi-fold
Demolish and Install	Ea.	116	104.50		220.50	doors not including jamb, trim, track,
Reinstall	Ea.		75.35		75.35	and hardware.
Clean	Ea.	2.09	22		24.09	
Paint	Ea.	33.50	89		122.50	
Minimum Charge	Job		207		207	

Finish Carpentry

Bifold Door

	Unit	Material	Labor	Equip.	Total	Specification
6'						
Demolish	Ea.		29		29	Includes material and labor to install
Install	Ea.	141	83		224	pair of 3' wide solid wood bi-fold
Demolish and Install	Ea.	141	112		253	doors not including jamb, trim, track,
Reinstall	Ea.		82.88		82.88	and hardware.
Clean	Ea.	2.39	25.50		27.89	
Paint	Ea.	33.50	89		122.50	
Minimum Charge	Job		207		207	
8'						
Demolish	Ea.		29		29	Includes material and labor to install
Install	Ea.	215	92		307	pair of 4' wide solid wood bi-fold
Demolish and Install	Ea.	215	121		336	doors not including jamb, trim, track,
Reinstall	Ea.		92.09		92.09	and hardware.
Clean	Ea.	3.29	30.50		33.79	
Paint	Ea.	17.60	89		106.60	
Minimum Charge	Job		207		207	

Mirrored

	Unit	Material	Labor	Equip.	Total	Specification
6'						
Demolish	Ea.		29		29	Includes material and labor to install
Install	Ea.	450	46		496	pair of 3' wide mirrored bi-fold doors
Demolish and Install	Ea.	450	75		525	including jamb, trim, track, and
Reinstall	Ea.		46.04		46.04	hardware.
Clean	Ea.	2.39	12.75		15.14	
Minimum Charge	Job		207		207	
8'						
Demolish	Ea.		29		29	Includes material and labor to install
Install	Ea.	710	69		779	pair of 4' wide mirrored bi-fold doors
Demolish and Install	Ea.	710	98		808	including jamb, trim, track, and
Reinstall	Ea.		69.07		69.07	hardware.
Clean	Ea.	3.29	15.30		18.59	
Minimum Charge	Job		207		207	

Louvered

	Unit	Material	Labor	Equip.	Total	Specification
3'						
Demolish	Ea.		29		29	Cost includes material and labor to
Install	Ea.	227	64		291	install 3' wide louvered bi-fold door
Demolish and Install	Ea.	227	93		320	not including jamb, trim, track, and
Reinstall	Ea.		63.75		63.75	hardware.
Clean	Ea.	4.77	12.75		17.52	
Paint	Ea.	9.20	50.50		59.70	
Minimum Charge	Job		207		207	
5'						
Demolish	Ea.		29		29	Includes material and labor to install
Install	Ea.	286	75.50		361.50	pair of 2' 6" wide louvered wood
Demolish and Install	Ea.	286	104.50		390.50	bi-fold doors not including jamb, trim,
Reinstall	Ea.		75.35		75.35	track, and hardware.
Clean	Ea.	2.09	22		24.09	
Paint	Ea.	33.50	89		122.50	
Minimum Charge	Job		207		207	
6'						
Demolish	Ea.		29		29	Includes material and labor to install
Install	Ea.	315	83		398	pair of 3' wide louvered wood bi-fold
Demolish and Install	Ea.	315	112		427	doors not including jamb, trim, track,
Reinstall	Ea.		82.88		82.88	and hardware.
Clean	Ea.	2.39	25.50		27.89	
Paint	Ea.	33.50	89		122.50	
Minimum Charge	Job		207		207	

Finish Carpentry

Bifold Door		Unit	Material	Labor	Equip.	Total	Specification
8'							Includes material and labor to install
	Demolish	Ea.		29		29	pair of 4' wide solid wood bi-fold
	Install	Ea.	490	83		573	doors not including jamb, trim, track,
	Demolish and Install	Ea.	490	112		602	and hardware.
	Reinstall	Ea.		82.88		82.88	
	Clean	Ea.	11.35	22		33.35	
	Paint	Ea.	17.60	89		106.60	
	Minimum Charge	Job		207		207	
Accordion Type							Includes material and labor to install
	Demolish	S.F.		1		1	vinyl folding accordion closet doors,
	Install	Ea.	43	83		126	including track and frame.
	Demolish and Install	Ea.	43	84		127	
	Reinstall	Ea.		82.88		82.88	
	Clean	S.F.	.01	.37		.38	
	Minimum Charge	Job		207		207	
Casing Trim							
Single Width							
	Demolish	Ea.		7.30		7.30	Cost includes material and labor to
	Install	Opng.	25	34.50		59.50	install 11/16" x 2-1/2" pine ranch
	Demolish and Install	Opng.	25	41.80		66.80	style casing for one side of a standard
	Reinstall	Opng.		27.63		27.63	door opening.
	Clean	Opng.	.68	3.06		3.74	
	Paint	Ea.	5.25	7.10		12.35	
	Minimum Charge	Job		207		207	
Double Width							
	Demolish	Ea.		8.70		8.70	Cost includes material and labor to
	Install	Opng.	28.50	41.50		70	install 11/16" x 2-1/2" pine ranch
	Demolish and Install	Opng.	28.50	50.20		78.70	style door casing for one side of a
	Reinstall	Opng.		33.15		33.15	double door opening.
	Clean	Opng.	.79	6.15		6.94	
	Paint	Ea.	5.25	8.05		13.30	
	Minimum Charge	Job		207		207	
Jamb							
	Demolish	Ea.		29		29	Includes material and labor to install
	Install	Ea.	100	11.20		111.20	flat pine jamb with square cut heads
	Demolish and Install	Ea.	100	40.20		140.20	and rabbeted sides for 6' 8" high and
	Clean	Ea.	.15	7.65		7.80	3-9/16" door including trim sets for
	Paint	Ea.	6.60	23.50		30.10	both sides.
	Minimum Charge	Job		104		104	
Stain							
	Install	Ea.	6.65	29.50		36.15	Includes labor and material to stain
	Minimum Charge	Job		178		178	single door and trim on both sides.
Shave & Refit							
	Install	Ea.		34.50		34.50	Includes labor to shave and rework
	Minimum Charge	Job		104		104	door to fit opening at the job site.

Finish Carpentry

Louver Door

Louver Door		Unit	Material	Labor	Equip.	Total	Specification
Full							
2' x 6' 8"							
	Demolish	Ea.		8.20		8.20	Cost includes material and labor to
	Install	Ea.	197	41.50		238.50	install 2' x 6' 8" pine full louver door,
	Demolish and Install	Ea.	197	49.70		246.70	jamb, hinges.
	Reinstall	Ea.		41.44		41.44	
	Clean	Ea.	8.85	38.50		47.35	
	Paint	Ea.	9.20	50.50		59.70	
	Minimum Charge	Job		207		207	
2' 8" x 6' 8"							
	Demolish	Ea.		8.20		8.20	Cost includes material and labor to
	Install	Ea.	218	41.50		259.50	install 2' 8" x 6' 8" pine full louver
	Demolish and Install	Ea.	218	49.70		267.70	door, jamb, hinges.
	Reinstall	Ea.		41.44		41.44	
	Clean	Ea.	8.85	38.50		47.35	
	Paint	Ea.	9.20	50.50		59.70	
	Minimum Charge	Job		207		207	
3' x 6' 8"							
	Demolish	Ea.		8.20		8.20	Cost includes material and labor to
	Install	Ea.	246	43.50		289.50	install 3' x 6' 8" pine full louver door,
	Demolish and Install	Ea.	246	51.70		297.70	jamb, hinges.
	Reinstall	Ea.		43.62		43.62	
	Clean	Ea.	8.85	38.50		47.35	
	Paint	Ea.	9.20	50.50		59.70	
	Minimum Charge	Job		207		207	
Half							
2' x 6' 8"							
	Demolish	Ea.		8.20		8.20	Cost includes material and labor to
	Install	Ea.	320	41.50		361.50	install 2' x 6' 8" pine half louver door,
	Demolish and Install	Ea.	320	49.70		369.70	jamb, hinges.
	Reinstall	Ea.		41.44		41.44	
	Clean	Ea.	8.85	38.50		47.35	
	Paint	Ea.	9.20	50.50		59.70	
	Minimum Charge	Job		207		207	
2' 8" x 6' 8"							
	Demolish	Ea.		8.20		8.20	Cost includes material and labor to
	Install	Ea.	340	41.50		381.50	install 2' 8" x 6' 8" pine half louver
	Demolish and Install	Ea.	340	49.70		389.70	door, jamb, hinges.
	Reinstall	Ea.		41.44		41.44	
	Clean	Ea.	8.85	38.50		47.35	
	Paint	Ea.	9.20	50.50		59.70	
	Minimum Charge	Job		207		207	
3' x 6' 8"							
	Demolish	Ea.		8.20		8.20	Cost includes material and labor to
	Install	Ea.	360	43.50		403.50	install 3' x 6' 8" pine half louver door,
	Demolish and Install	Ea.	360	51.70		411.70	jamb, hinges.
	Reinstall	Ea.		43.62		43.62	
	Clean	Ea.	8.85	38.50		47.35	
	Paint	Ea.	9.20	50.50		59.70	
	Minimum Charge	Job		207		207	
Jamb							
	Demolish	Ea.		29		29	Includes material and labor to install
	Install	Ea.	100	11.20		111.20	flat pine jamb with square cut heads
	Demolish and Install	Ea.	100	40.20		140.20	and rabbeted sides for 6' 8" high and
	Clean	Ea.	.15	7.65		7.80	3-9/16" door including trim sets for
	Paint	Ea.	6.60	23.50		30.10	both sides.
	Minimum Charge	Job		104		104	

Finish Carpentry

Louver Door		Unit	Material	Labor	Equip.	Total	Specification
Stain							
	Install	Ea.	6.65	29.50		36.15	Includes labor and material to stain
	Minimum Charge	Job		178		178	single door and trim on both sides.
Shave & Refit							
	Install	Ea.		34.50		34.50	Includes labor to shave and rework
	Minimum Charge	Job		178		178	door to fit opening at the job site.

Bypass Sliding Door		Unit	Material	Labor	Equip.	Total	Specification
Wood							
5'							
	Demolish	Ea.		38.50		38.50	Includes material and labor to install
	Install	Opng.	206	75.50		281.50	pair of 2' 6" wide lauan hollow core
	Demolish and Install	Opng.	206	114		320	wood bi-pass doors with jamb, track
	Reinstall	Opng.		75.35		75.35	hardware.
	Clean	Ea.	2.09	22		24.09	
	Paint	Ea.	33.50	89		122.50	
	Minimum Charge	Job		207		207	
6'							
	Demolish	Ea.		38.50		38.50	Includes material and labor to install
	Install	Opng.	230	83		313	pair of 3' wide lauan hollow core
	Demolish and Install	Opng.	230	121.50		351.50	wood bi-pass doors with jamb, track
	Reinstall	Opng.		82.88		82.88	and hardware.
	Clean	Ea.	2.39	25.50		27.89	
	Paint	Ea.	33.50	89		122.50	
	Minimum Charge	Job		207		207	
8'							
	Demolish	Ea.		38.50		38.50	Includes material and labor to install
	Install	Opng.	345	104		449	pair of 4' wide lauan hollow core
	Demolish and Install	Opng.	345	142.50		487.50	wood bi-pass doors with jamb, track
	Reinstall	Opng.		103.60		103.60	and hardware.
	Clean	Ea.	3.29	30.50		33.79	
	Paint	Ea.	17.60	89		106.60	
	Minimum Charge	Job		207		207	
Mirrored							
6'							
	Demolish	Ea.		38.50		38.50	Includes material and labor to install
	Install	Opng.	273	83		356	pair of 3' wide mirrored bi-pass doors
	Demolish and Install	Opng.	273	121.50		394.50	with jamb, trim, track hardware.
	Reinstall	Opng.		82.88		82.88	
	Clean	Ea.	2.39	12.75		15.14	
	Minimum Charge	Job		207		207	
8'							
	Demolish	Ea.		38.50		38.50	Includes material and labor to install
	Install	Opng.	475	92		567	pair of 4' wide mirrored bi-pass doors
	Demolish and Install	Opng.	475	130.50		605.50	with jamb, trim, track hardware.
	Reinstall	Opng.		92.09		92.09	
	Clean	Ea.	3.29	15.30		18.59	
	Minimum Charge	Job		207		207	

Finish Carpentry

Bypass Sliding Door

	Unit	Material	Labor	Equip.	Total	Specification
Casing Trim						
Single Width						
Demolish	Ea.		7.30		7.30	Cost includes material and labor to
Install	Opng.	25	34.50		59.50	install 11/16" x 2-1/2" pine ranch
Demolish and Install	Opng.	25	41.80		66.80	style casing for one side of a standard
Reinstall	Opng.		27.63		27.63	door opening.
Clean	Opng.	.68	3.06		3.74	
Paint	Ea.	5.25	7.10		12.35	
Minimum Charge	Job		207		207	
Double Width						
Demolish	Ea.		8.70		8.70	Cost includes material and labor to
Install	Opng.	28.50	41.50		70	install 11/16" x 2-1/2" pine ranch
Demolish and Install	Opng.	28.50	50.20		78.70	style door casing for one side of a
Reinstall	Opng.		33.15		33.15	double door opening.
Clean	Opng.	.79	6.15		6.94	
Paint	Ea.	5.25	8.05		13.30	
Minimum Charge	Job		207		207	
Jamb						
Demolish	Ea.		29		29	Includes material and labor to install
Install	Ea.	100	11.20		111.20	flat pine jamb with square cut heads
Demolish and Install	Ea.	100	40.20		140.20	and rabbeted sides for 6' 8" high and
Clean	Ea.	.15	7.65		7.80	3-9/16" door including trim sets for
Paint	Ea.	6.60	23.50		30.10	both sides.
Minimum Charge	Job		104		104	
Stain						
Install	Ea.	6.65	29.50		36.15	Includes labor and material to stain
Minimum Charge	Job		178		178	single door and trim on both sides.
Shave & Refit						
Install	Ea.		34.50		34.50	Includes labor to shave and rework
Minimum Charge	Job		104		104	door to fit opening at the job site.

Base Molding

	Unit	Material	Labor	Equip.	Total	Specification
One Piece						
1-5/8"						
Demolish	L.F.		.57		.57	Includes material and labor to install
Install	L.F.	.40	1.23		1.63	pine or birch base molding.
Demolish and Install	L.F.	.40	1.80		2.20	
Reinstall	L.F.		.98		.98	
Clean	L.F.	.04	.18		.22	
Paint	L.F.	.06	.39		.45	
Minimum Charge	Job		207		207	
2-1/2"						
Demolish	L.F.		.57		.57	Cost includes material and labor to
Install	L.F.	.60	1.25		1.85	install 1/2" x 2-1/2" pine or birch
Demolish and Install	L.F.	.60	1.82		2.42	base molding.
Reinstall	L.F.		1		1	
Clean	L.F.	.04	.18		.22	
Paint	L.F.	.06	.39		.45	
Minimum Charge	Job		207		207	

Finish Carpentry

Base Molding	Unit	Material	Labor	Equip.	Total	Specification
3-1/2"						
Demolish	L.F.		.57		.57	Cost includes material and labor to
Install	L.F.	.95	1.33		2.28	install 9/16" x 3-1/2" pine or birch
Demolish and Install	L.F.	.95	1.90		2.85	base molding.
Reinstall	L.F.		1.06		1.06	
Clean	L.F.	.04	.18		.22	
Paint	L.F.	.09	.42		.51	
Minimum Charge	Job		207		207	
6"						
Demolish	L.F.		.57		.57	Cost includes material and labor to
Install	L.F.	.82	1.33		2.15	install 1" x 6" pine or birch base
Demolish and Install	L.F.	.82	1.90		2.72	molding.
Reinstall	L.F.		1.06		1.06	
Clean	L.F.	.04	.26		.30	
Paint	L.F.	.10	.53		.63	
Minimum Charge	Job		207		207	
8"						
Demolish	L.F.		.68		.68	Cost includes material and labor to
Install	L.F.	1.11	1.33		2.44	install 1" x 8" pine or birch base
Demolish and Install	L.F.	1.11	2.01		3.12	molding.
Reinstall	L.F.		1.06		1.06	
Clean	L.F.	.06	.31		.37	
Paint	L.F.	.11	.59		.70	
Minimum Charge	Job		207		207	
Premium / Custom Grade						
Demolish	L.F.		.68		.68	Includes material and labor to install
Install	L.F.	3.24	3.98		7.22	custom 2 or 3 piece oak or other
Demolish and Install	L.F.	3.24	4.66		7.90	hardwood, stain grade trim.
Reinstall	L.F.		3.19		3.19	
Clean	L.F.	.06	.31		.37	
Paint	L.F.	.12	.59		.71	
Minimum Charge	Job		207		207	
One Piece Oak						
1-5/8"						
Demolish	L.F.		.57		.57	Cost includes material and labor to
Install	L.F.	1.05	1.23		2.28	install 1/2" x 1-5/8" oak base
Demolish and Install	L.F.	1.05	1.80		2.85	molding.
Reinstall	L.F.		.98		.98	
Clean	L.F.	.04	.18		.22	
Paint	L.F.	.11	.53		.64	
Minimum Charge	Job		207		207	
2-1/2"						
Demolish	L.F.		.57		.57	Cost includes material and labor to
Install	L.F.	1.47	1.25		2.72	install 1/2" x 2-1/2" oak base
Demolish and Install	L.F.	1.47	1.82		3.29	molding.
Reinstall	L.F.		1		1	
Clean	L.F.	.04	.18		.22	
Paint	L.F.	.12	.54		.66	
Minimum Charge	Job		207		207	
3-1/2"						
Demolish	L.F.		.57		.57	Cost includes material and labor to
Install	L.F.	1.78	1.28		3.06	install 1/2" x 3-1/2" oak base
Demolish and Install	L.F.	1.78	1.85		3.63	molding.
Reinstall	L.F.		1.02		1.02	
Clean	L.F.	.04	.18		.22	
Paint	L.F.	.12	.55		.67	
Minimum Charge	Job		207		207	

Finish Carpentry

Base Molding

	Unit	Material	Labor	Equip.	Total	Specification
6"						
Demolish	L.F.		.57		.57	Cost includes material and labor to
Install	L.F.	2.13	1.33		3.46	install 1" x 6" oak base molding.
Demolish and Install	L.F.	2.13	1.90		4.03	
Reinstall	L.F.		1.06		1.06	
Clean	L.F.	.06	.31		.37	
Paint	L.F.	.12	.57		.69	
Minimum Charge	Job		207		207	
8"						
Demolish	L.F.		.68		.68	Cost includes material and labor to
Install	L.F.	2.83	1.33		4.16	install 1" x 8" oak base molding.
Demolish and Install	L.F.	2.83	2.01		4.84	
Reinstall	L.F.		1.06		1.06	
Clean	L.F.	.06	.31		.37	
Paint	L.F.	.13	.59		.72	
Minimum Charge	Job		207		207	

Vinyl Base Molding

	Unit	Material	Labor	Equip.	Total	Specification
2-1/2"						
Demolish	L.F.		.57		.57	Cost includes material and labor to
Install	L.F.	1.16	1.17		2.33	install 2-1/2" vinyl or rubber cove
Demolish and Install	L.F.	1.16	1.74		2.90	base including adhesive.
Reinstall	L.F.		1.17		1.17	
Clean	L.F.		.28		.28	
Minimum Charge	Job		188		188	
4"						
Demolish	L.F.		.57		.57	Cost includes material and labor to
Install	L.F.	1.11	1.17		2.28	install 4" vinyl or rubber cove base
Demolish and Install	L.F.	1.11	1.74		2.85	including adhesive.
Reinstall	L.F.		1.17		1.17	
Clean	L.F.		.28		.28	
Minimum Charge	Job		188		188	
6"						
Demolish	L.F.		.57		.57	Cost includes material and labor to
Install	L.F.	1.71	1.17		2.88	install 6" vinyl or rubber cove base
Demolish and Install	L.F.	1.71	1.74		3.45	including adhesive.
Reinstall	L.F.		1.17		1.17	
Clean	L.F.		.28		.28	
Minimum Charge	Job		188		188	

Prefinished

	Unit	Material	Labor	Equip.	Total	Specification
Demolish	L.F.		.57		.57	Cost includes material and labor to
Install	L.F.	1.26	1.33		2.59	install 9/16" x 3-5/16" prefinished
Demolish and Install	L.F.	1.26	1.90		3.16	base molding.
Reinstall	L.F.		1.06		1.06	
Clean	L.F.	.04	.18		.22	
Paint	L.F.	.09	.42		.51	
Minimum Charge	Job		207		207	

Shoe

	Unit	Material	Labor	Equip.	Total	Specification
Demolish	L.F.		.57		.57	Includes material and labor to install
Install	L.F.	.40	1.23		1.63	pine or birch base molding.
Demolish and Install	L.F.	.40	1.80		2.20	
Reinstall	L.F.		.98		.98	
Clean	L.F.	.04	.18		.22	
Paint	L.F.	.14	.57		.71	
Minimum Charge	Job		207		207	

Finish Carpentry

Base Molding	Unit	Material	Labor	Equip.	Total	Specification
Carpeted						
Demolish	L.F.		.23		.23	Includes material and labor to install
Install	L.F.	1.49	2.23		3.72	carpet baseboard with adhesive.
Demolish and Install	L.F.	1.49	2.46		3.95	
Reinstall	L.F.		1.78		1.78	
Clean	L.F.		.12		.12	
Minimum Charge	Job		184		184	
Ceramic Tile						
Demolish	L.F.		1.24		1.24	Includes material and labor to install
Install	L.F.	4.08	5.15		9.23	thin set ceramic tile cove base
Demolish and Install	L.F.	4.08	6.39		10.47	including grout.
Clean	L.F.		.58		.58	
Minimum Charge	Job		184		184	
Quarry Tile						
Demolish	L.F.		1.24		1.24	Includes material and labor to install
Install	L.F.	6.15	5.95		12.10	quarry tile base including grout.
Demolish and Install	L.F.	6.15	7.19		13.34	
Clean	L.F.		.58		.58	
Minimum Charge	Job		184		184	
Caulk and Renail						
Install	L.F.	.01	.65		.66	Includes labor and material to renail
Minimum Charge	Job		207		207	base and caulk where necessary.

Molding	Unit	Material	Labor	Equip.	Total	Specification
Oak Base						
Demolish	L.F.		.57		.57	Cost includes material and labor to
Install	L.F.	1.47	1.25		2.72	install 1/2" x 2-1/2" oak base
Demolish and Install	L.F.	1.47	1.82		3.29	molding.
Reinstall	L.F.		1		1	
Clean	L.F.	.04	.18		.22	
Paint	L.F.	.12	.54		.66	
Minimum Charge	Job		207		207	
Shoe						
Demolish	L.F.		.57		.57	Includes material and labor to install
Install	L.F.	.40	1.23		1.63	pine or birch base molding.
Demolish and Install	L.F.	.40	1.80		2.20	
Reinstall	L.F.		.98		.98	
Clean	L.F.	.04	.18		.22	
Paint	L.F.	.14	.57		.71	
Minimum Charge	Job		207		207	
Quarter Round						
Demolish	L.F.		.57		.57	Includes material and labor to install
Install	L.F.	.77	1.63		2.40	pine base quarter round molding.
Demolish and Install	L.F.	.77	2.20		2.97	
Reinstall	L.F.		1.30		1.30	
Clean	L.F.	.04	.18		.22	
Paint	L.F.	.12	.89		1.01	
Minimum Charge	Job		207		207	
Chair Rail						
Demolish	L.F.		.57		.57	Cost includes material and labor to
Install	L.F.	1.85	1.53		3.38	install 5/8" x 2-1/2" oak chair rail
Demolish and Install	L.F.	1.85	2.10		3.95	molding.
Reinstall	L.F.		1.23		1.23	
Clean	L.F.	.04	.18		.22	
Paint	L.F.	.12	.89		1.01	
Minimum Charge	Job		207		207	

Finish Carpentry

Molding

	Unit	Material	Labor	Equip.	Total	Specification
Crown						
Demolish	L.F.		.57		.57	Includes material and labor to install
Install	L.F.	2.95	1.66		4.61	unfinished pine crown molding.
Demolish and Install	L.F.	2.95	2.23		5.18	
Reinstall	L.F.		1.33		1.33	
Clean	L.F.	.06	.24		.30	
Paint	L.F.	.12	.89		1.01	
Minimum Charge	Job		207		207	
Cove						
Demolish	L.F.		.57		.57	Cost includes material and labor to
Install	L.F.	2.40	1.63		4.03	install 1/2" x 2-3/4" pine cove
Demolish and Install	L.F.	2.40	2.20		4.60	molding.
Reinstall	L.F.		1.30		1.30	
Clean	L.F.	.04	.18		.22	
Paint	L.F.	.12	.89		1.01	
Minimum Charge	Job		207		207	
Corner						
Demolish	L.F.		.57		.57	Includes material and labor to install
Install	L.F.	1.89	.65		2.54	inside or outside pine corner molding.
Demolish and Install	L.F.	1.89	1.22		3.11	
Reinstall	L.F.		.52		.52	
Clean	L.F.	.04	.18		.22	
Paint	L.F.	.12	.89		1.01	
Minimum Charge	Job		207		207	
Picture						
Demolish	L.F.		.57		.57	Cost includes material and labor to
Install	L.F.	1.44	1.73		3.17	install 9/16" x 2-1/2" pine casing.
Demolish and Install	L.F.	1.44	2.30		3.74	
Reinstall	L.F.		1.38		1.38	
Clean	L.F.	.04	.18		.22	
Paint	L.F.	.12	.89		1.01	
Minimum Charge	Job		207		207	
Single Cased Opening						
Demolish	Ea.		29		29	Includes material and labor to install
Install	Ea.	24	26		50	flat pine jamb with square cut heads
Demolish and Install	Ea.	24	55		79	and rabbeted sides for 6' 8" high
Clean	Ea.	.33	6.40		6.73	opening including trim sets for both
Paint	Ea.	1.24	8.90		10.14	sides.
Minimum Charge	Job		207		207	
Double Cased Opening						
Demolish	Ea.		29		29	Includes material and labor to install
Install	Ea.	48.50	29.50		78	flat pine jamb with square cut heads
Demolish and Install	Ea.	48.50	58.50		107	and rabbeted sides for 6' 8" high
Clean	Ea.	.39	7.45		7.84	opening including trim sets for both
Paint	Ea.	1.43	10.45		11.88	sides.
Minimum Charge	Job		207		207	

Window Trim Set

	Unit	Material	Labor	Equip.	Total	Specification
Single						
Demolish	Ea.		7.55		7.55	Cost includes material and labor to
Install	Opng.	44.50	41.50		86	install 11/16" x 2-1/2" pine ranch
Demolish and Install	Opng.	44.50	49.05		93.55	style window casing.
Reinstall	Opng.		33.15		33.15	
Clean	Ea.	.47	4.38		4.85	
Paint	Ea.	1.16	8.45		9.61	
Minimum Charge	Job		207		207	

201

Finish Carpentry

Window Trim Set

	Unit	Material	Labor	Equip.	Total	Specification
Double						
Demolish	Ea.		8.50		8.50	Cost includes material and labor to
Install	Ea.	56.50	52		108.50	install 11/16" x 2-1/2" pine ranch
Demolish and Install	Ea.	56.50	60.50		117	style trim for casing one side of a
Reinstall	Ea.		41.44		41.44	double window opening.
Clean	Ea.	.86	5.10		5.96	
Paint	Ea.	1.95	14.20		16.15	
Minimum Charge	Job		207		207	
Triple						
Demolish	Ea.		9.75		9.75	Cost includes material and labor to
Install	Opng.	71	69		140	install 11/16" x 2-1/2" pine ranch
Demolish and Install	Opng.	71	78.75		149.75	style trim for casing one side of a
Reinstall	Opng.		55.25		55.25	triple window opening.
Clean	Ea.	1.20	6.15		7.35	
Paint	Ea.	2.73	19.75		22.48	
Minimum Charge	Job		207		207	
Window Casing Per L.F.						
Demolish	L.F.		.57		.57	Cost includes material and labor to
Install	L.F.	1.45	1.66		3.11	install 11/16" x 2-1/2" pine ranch
Demolish and Install	L.F.	1.45	2.23		3.68	style trim for casing.
Reinstall	L.F.		1.33		1.33	
Clean	L.F.	.04	.18		.22	
Paint	L.F.	.12	.89		1.01	
Minimum Charge	Job		207		207	

Window Sill

	Unit	Material	Labor	Equip.	Total	Specification
Wood						
Demolish	L.F.		.57		.57	Includes material and labor to install
Install	L.F.	2.92	2.07		4.99	flat, wood window stool.
Demolish and Install	L.F.	2.92	2.64		5.56	
Reinstall	L.F.		1.66		1.66	
Clean	L.F.	.04	.18		.22	
Paint	L.F.	.12	.89		1.01	
Minimum Charge	Job		207		207	
Marble						
Demolish	L.F.		.85		.85	Includes material and labor to install
Install	L.F.	11.50	8.65		20.15	marble window sills, 6" x 3/4" thick.
Demolish and Install	L.F.	11.50	9.50		21	
Reinstall	L.F.		6.93		6.93	
Clean	L.F.	.04	.18		.22	
Minimum Charge	Job		184		184	

Shelving

	Unit	Material	Labor	Equip.	Total	Specification
Pine						
18"						
Demolish	L.F.		.97		.97	Cost includes material and labor to
Install	L.F.	7.50	4.36		11.86	install 1" thick custom shelving board
Demolish and Install	L.F.	7.50	5.33		12.83	18" wide.
Reinstall	L.F.		3.49		3.49	
Clean	L.F.	.08	.51		.59	
Paint	L.F.	1.49	.56		2.05	
Minimum Charge	Job		207		207	

Finish Carpentry

Shelving

Shelving		Unit	Material	Labor	Equip.	Total	Specification
24"							
	Demolish	L.F.		.97		.97	Cost includes material and labor to
	Install	L.F.	9.95	4.88		14.83	install 1" thick custom shelving board.
	Demolish and Install	L.F.	9.95	5.85		15.80	
	Reinstall	L.F.		3.90		3.90	
	Clean	L.F.	.10	.77		.87	
	Paint	L.F.	2.02	.75		2.77	
	Minimum Charge	Job		207		207	
Particle Board							
	Demolish	L.F.		.90		.90	Cost includes material and labor to
	Install	L.F.	1.25	2.18		3.43	install 3/4" thick particle shelving
	Demolish and Install	L.F.	1.25	3.08		4.33	board 18" wide.
	Reinstall	L.F.		1.74		1.74	
	Clean	L.F.	.08	.51		.59	
	Paint	S.F.	.12	.83		.95	
	Minimum Charge	Job		207		207	
Plywood							
	Demolish	L.F.		.90		.90	Cost includes material and labor to
	Install	L.F.	.88	6.40		7.28	install 3/4" thick plywood shelving
	Demolish and Install	L.F.	.88	7.30		8.18	board.
	Reinstall	L.F.		5.10		5.10	
	Clean	L.F.	.08	.51		.59	
	Paint	S.F.	.12	.83		.95	
	Minimum Charge	Job		207		207	
Hardwood (oak)							
	Demolish	L.F.		.90		.90	Includes material and labor to install
	Install	L.F.	5.05	2.86		7.91	oak shelving, 1" x 12", incl. cleats and
	Demolish and Install	L.F.	5.05	3.76		8.81	bracing.
	Reinstall	L.F.		2.29		2.29	
	Clean	L.F.	.08	.51		.59	
	Paint	S.F.	.12	.83		.95	
	Minimum Charge	Job		207		207	
Custom Bookcase							
	Demolish	L.F.		11.35		11.35	Includes material and labor to install
	Install	L.F.	38	41.50		79.50	custom modular bookcase unit with
	Demolish and Install	L.F.	38	52.85		90.85	clear pine faced frames, shelves 12"
	Reinstall	L.F.		33.15		33.15	O.C., 7' high, 8" deep.
	Clean	L.F.	1.91	10.95		12.86	
	Paint	L.F.	1.60	27.50		29.10	
	Minimum Charge	Job		207		207	
Glass							
	Demolish	L.F.		.90		.90	Includes material and labor to install
	Install	L.F.	32.50	2.86		35.36	glass shelving, 1" x 12", incl. cleats
	Demolish and Install	L.F.	32.50	3.76		36.26	and bracing.
	Reinstall	L.F.		2.29		2.29	
	Clean	L.F.	.09	.47		.56	
	Minimum Charge	Job		201		201	

Closet Shelving

Closet Shelving		Unit	Material	Labor	Equip.	Total	Specification
Closet Shelf and Rod							
	Demolish	L.F.		.90		.90	Cost includes material and labor to
	Install	L.F.	2.94	6.90		9.84	install 1" thick custom shelving board
	Demolish and Install	L.F.	2.94	7.80		10.74	18" wide and 1" diameter clothes pole
	Reinstall	L.F.		5.53		5.53	with brackets 3' O.C.
	Clean	L.F.	.04	.38		.42	
	Paint	L.F.	.23	.89		1.12	
	Minimum Charge	Job		207		207	

Finish Carpentry

Closet Shelving

	Unit	Material	Labor	Equip.	Total	Specification
Clothing Rod						
Demolish	L.F.		.59		.59	Includes material and labor to install
Install	L.F.	2.60	2.07		4.67	fir closet pole, 1-5/8" diameter.
Demolish and Install	L.F.	2.60	2.66		5.26	
Reinstall	L.F.		1.66		1.66	
Clean	L.F.	.04	.53		.57	
Paint	L.F.	.22	.97		1.19	
Minimum Charge	Job		207		207	

Stair Assemblies

	Unit	Material	Labor	Equip.	Total	Specification
Straight Hardwood						
Demolish	Ea.		400		400	Includes material and labor to install
Install	Flight	1250	276		1526	factory cut and assembled straight
Demolish and Install	Flight	1250	676		1926	closed box stairs with oak treads and
Clean	Flight	4.77	26.50		31.27	prefinished stair rail with balusters.
Paint	Flight	21	47.50		68.50	
Minimum Charge	Job		207		207	
Clear Oak Tread						
Demolish	Ea.		10.45		10.45	Includes material and labor to install
Install	Ea.	82.50	23		105.50	1-1/4" thick clear oak treads per riser.
Demolish and Install	Ea.	82.50	33.45		115.95	
Clean	Ea.	.15	2.63		2.78	
Paint	Ea.	.69	2.63		3.32	
Minimum Charge	Job		207		207	
Landing						
Demolish	S.F.		3.55		3.55	Includes material and labor to install
Install	S.F.	9.90	23		32.90	clear oak landing.
Demolish and Install	S.F.	9.90	26.55		36.45	
Clean	S.F.		.38		.38	
Paint	S.F.	.44	.88		1.32	
Minimum Charge	Job		207		207	
Refinish / Stain						
Install	S.F.	1.41	2.36		3.77	Includes labor and material to sand
Minimum Charge	Job		178		178	and finish (3 passes) with two coats of
						urethane on a new floor.
Spiral Hardwood						
Demolish	Ea.		400		400	Cost includes material and labor to
Install	Flight	4000	555		4555	install 4' - 6' diameter spiral stairs with
Demolish and Install	Flight	4000	955		4955	oak treads, factory cut and assembled
Clean	Flight	4.77	26.50		31.27	with double handrails.
Paint	Flight	21	47.50		68.50	
Minimum Charge	Job		207		207	

Stairs

	Unit	Material	Labor	Equip.	Total	Specification
Disappearing						
Demolish	Ea.		21.50		21.50	Includes material and labor to install a
Install	Ea.	263	118		381	folding staircase.
Demolish and Install	Ea.	263	139.50		402.50	
Reinstall	Ea.		94.72		94.72	
Clean	Ea.	.72	19.15		19.87	
Minimum Charge	Job		207		207	

Finish Carpentry

Stair Components

Stair Components	Unit	Material	Labor	Equip.	Total	Specification
Handrail w / Balusters						
Demolish	L.F.		2.84		2.84	Includes material and labor to install
Install	L.F.	36	8.65		44.65	prefinished assembled stair rail with
Demolish and Install	L.F.	36	11.49		47.49	brackets, turned balusters and newel.
Clean	L.F.	.96	2.11		3.07	
Paint	L.F.	2.28	4.18		6.46	
Minimum Charge	Job		207		207	
Bannister						
Demolish	L.F.		2.84		2.84	Includes material and labor to install
Install	L.F.	38	6.90		44.90	built-up oak railings.
Demolish and Install	L.F.	38	9.74		47.74	
Clean	L.F.	.96	1.92		2.88	
Paint	L.F.	2.28	3.23		5.51	
Minimum Charge	Job		207		207	

Cabinets and Countertops

Wall and Base Cabinets

Countertop

Wall Cabinets	Unit	Material	Labor	Equip.	Total	Specification
Good Grade Laminated						
12" Wide, 1 Door						
Demolish	Ea.		8.50		8.50	Includes material and labor to install
Install	Ea.	165	37.50		202.50	good modular unit with melamine
Demolish and Install	Ea.	165	46		211	laminated to particle board, in
Reinstall	Ea.		30.14		30.14	textured colors or wood grain print
Clean	Ea.	.72	5.90		6.62	finish, hinges and pulls.
Paint	Ea.	.68	12.70		13.38	
Minimum Charge	Job		207		207	
15" Wide, 1 Door						
Demolish	Ea.		10.65		10.65	Includes material and labor to install
Install	Ea.	176	38.50		214.50	good modular unit with melamine
Demolish and Install	Ea.	176	49.15		225.15	laminated to particle board, in
Reinstall	Ea.		30.98		30.98	textured colors or wood grain print
Clean	Ea.	.89	7.30		8.19	finish, hinges and pulls.
Paint	Ea.	.86	16.15		17.01	
Minimum Charge	Job		207		207	
18" Wide, 1 Door						
Demolish	Ea.		12.85		12.85	Includes material and labor to install
Install	Ea.	194	39.50		233.50	good modular unit with melamine
Demolish and Install	Ea.	194	52.35		246.35	laminated to particle board, in
Reinstall	Ea.		31.72		31.72	textured colors or wood grain print
Clean	Ea.	1.08	8.75		9.83	finish, hinges and pulls.
Paint	Ea.	1.02	18.70		19.72	
Minimum Charge	Job		207		207	
21" Wide, 1 Door						
Demolish	Ea.		14.80		14.80	Includes material and labor to install
Install	Ea.	204	40		244	good modular unit with melamine
Demolish and Install	Ea.	204	54.80		258.80	laminated to particle board, in
Reinstall	Ea.		32.19		32.19	textured colors or wood grain print
Clean	Ea.	1.25	10.20		11.45	finish, hinges and pulls.
Paint	Ea.	1.20	22		23.20	
Minimum Charge	Job		207		207	
24" w / Blind Corner						
Demolish	Ea.		17		17	Includes material and labor to install
Install	Ea.	226	41		267	good modular unit with melamine
Demolish and Install	Ea.	226	58		284	laminated to particle board, in
Reinstall	Ea.		32.66		32.66	textured colors or wood grain print
Clean	Ea.	1.43	11.80		13.23	finish, hinges and pulls.
Paint	Ea.	1.36	25.50		26.86	
Minimum Charge	Job		207		207	

Cabinets and Countertops

Wall Cabinets	Unit	Material	Labor	Equip.	Total	Specification
27″ Wide, 2 Door						
Demolish	Ea.		18.90		18.90	Includes material and labor to install
Install	Ea.	249	42		291	good modular unit with melamine
Demolish and Install	Ea.	249	60.90		309.90	laminated to particle board, in
Reinstall	Ea.		33.49		33.49	textured colors or wood grain print
Clean	Ea.	1.62	13.30		14.92	finish, hinges and pulls.
Paint	Ea.	1.55	29.50		31.05	
Minimum Charge	Job		207		207	
30″ Wide, 2 Door						
Demolish	Ea.		21.50		21.50	Includes material and labor to install
Install	Ea.	257	43		300	good modular unit with melamine
Demolish and Install	Ea.	257	64.50		321.50	laminated to particle board, in
Reinstall	Ea.		34.35		34.35	textured colors or wood grain print
Clean	Ea.	1.79	14.60		16.39	finish, hinges and pulls.
Paint	Ea.	1.72	32.50		34.22	
Minimum Charge	Job		207		207	
36″ Wide, 2 Door						
Demolish	Ea.		25		25	Includes material and labor to install
Install	Ea.	289	44		333	good modular unit with melamine
Demolish and Install	Ea.	289	69		358	laminated to particle board, in
Reinstall	Ea.		35.27		35.27	textured colors or wood grain print
Clean	Ea.	2.15	18		20.15	finish, hinges and pulls.
Paint	Ea.	2.08	39.50		41.58	
Minimum Charge	Job		207		207	
48″ Wide, 2 Door						
Demolish	Ea.		34		34	Includes material and labor to install
Install	Ea.	365	45		410	good modular unit with melamine
Demolish and Install	Ea.	365	79		444	laminated to particle board, in
Reinstall	Ea.		36.03		36.03	textured colors or wood grain print
Clean	Ea.	2.87	23.50		26.37	finish, hinges and pulls.
Paint	Ea.	2.75	50.50		53.25	
Minimum Charge	Job		207		207	
Above-Appliance						
Demolish	Ea.		21.50		21.50	Includes material and labor to install
Install	Ea.	173	33.50		206.50	good modular unit with melamine
Demolish and Install	Ea.	173	55		228	laminated to particle board, in
Reinstall	Ea.		26.74		26.74	textured colors or wood grain print
Clean	Ea.	1.79	14.60		16.39	finish, hinges and pulls.
Paint	Ea.	1.72	32.50		34.22	
Minimum Charge	Job		207		207	
Better Grade Wood						
12″ Wide, 1 Door						
Demolish	Ea.		8.50		8.50	Includes material and labor to install
Install	Ea.	220	37.50		257.50	custom modular unit with solid
Demolish and Install	Ea.	220	46		266	hardwood faced frames, hardwood
Reinstall	Ea.		30.14		30.14	door frames and drawer fronts,
Clean	Ea.	.72	5.90		6.62	hardwood veneer on raised door
Paint	Ea.	.68	13.65		14.33	panels, hinges and pulls.
Minimum Charge	Job		207		207	
15″ Wide, 1 Door						
Demolish	Ea.		10.65		10.65	Includes material and labor to install
Install	Ea.	234	38.50		272.50	custom modular unit with solid
Demolish and Install	Ea.	234	49.15		283.15	hardwood faced frames, hardwood
Reinstall	Ea.		30.98		30.98	door frames and drawer fronts,
Clean	Ea.	.89	7.30		8.19	hardwood veneer on raised door
Paint	Ea.	.86	16.90		17.76	panels, hinges and pulls.
Minimum Charge	Job		207		207	

Cabinets and Countertops

Wall Cabinets	Unit	Material	Labor	Equip.	Total	Specification
18″ Wide, 1 Door						
Demolish	Ea.		12.85		12.85	Includes material and labor to install
Install	Ea.	257	39.50		296.50	custom modular unit with solid
Demolish and Install	Ea.	257	52.35		309.35	hardwood faced frames, hardwood
Reinstall	Ea.		31.72		31.72	door frames and drawer fronts,
Clean	Ea.	1.08	8.75		9.83	hardwood veneer on raised door
Paint	Ea.	1.02	21		22.02	panels, hinges and pulls.
Minimum Charge	Job		207		207	
21″ Wide, 1 Door						
Demolish	Ea.		14.80		14.80	Includes material and labor to install
Install	Ea.	271	40		311	custom modular unit with solid
Demolish and Install	Ea.	271	54.80		325.80	hardwood faced frames, hardwood
Reinstall	Ea.		32.19		32.19	door frames and drawer fronts,
Clean	Ea.	1.25	10.20		11.45	hardwood veneer on raised door
Paint	Ea.	1.20	23.50		24.70	panels, hinges and pulls.
Minimum Charge	Job		207		207	
24″ w / Blind Corner						
Demolish	Ea.		17		17	Includes material and labor to install
Install	Ea.	300	41		341	custom modular unit with solid
Demolish and Install	Ea.	300	58		358	hardwood faced frames, hardwood
Reinstall	Ea.		32.66		32.66	door frames and drawer fronts,
Clean	Ea.	1.43	11.80		13.23	hardwood veneer on raised door
Paint	Ea.	1.36	27.50		28.86	panels, hinges and pulls.
Minimum Charge	Job		207		207	
27″ Wide, 2 Door						
Demolish	Ea.		18.90		18.90	Includes material and labor to install
Install	Ea.	330	42		372	custom modular unit with solid
Demolish and Install	Ea.	330	60.90		390.90	hardwood faced frames, hardwood
Reinstall	Ea.		33.49		33.49	door frames and drawer fronts,
Clean	Ea.	1.62	13.30		14.92	hardwood veneer on raised door
Paint	Ea.	1.55	29.50		31.05	panels, hinges and pulls.
Minimum Charge	Job		207		207	
30″ Wide, 2 Door						
Demolish	Ea.		21.50		21.50	Includes material and labor to install
Install	Ea.	340	43		383	custom modular unit with solid
Demolish and Install	Ea.	340	64.50		404.50	hardwood faced frames, hardwood
Reinstall	Ea.		34.35		34.35	door frames and drawer fronts,
Clean	Ea.	1.79	14.60		16.39	hardwood veneer on raised door
Paint	Ea.	1.72	35.50		37.22	panels, hinges and pulls.
Minimum Charge	Job		207		207	
36″ Wide, 2 Door						
Demolish	Ea.		25		25	Includes material and labor to install
Install	Ea.	385	44		429	custom modular unit with solid
Demolish and Install	Ea.	385	69		454	hardwood faced frames, hardwood
Reinstall	Ea.		35.27		35.27	door frames and drawer fronts,
Clean	Ea.	2.15	18		20.15	hardwood veneer on raised door
Paint	Ea.	2.08	39.50		41.58	panels, hinges and pulls.
Minimum Charge	Job		207		207	
48″ Wide, 2 Door						
Demolish	Ea.		34		34	Includes material and labor to install
Install	Ea.	485	45		530	custom modular unit with solid
Demolish and Install	Ea.	485	79		564	hardwood faced frames, hardwood
Reinstall	Ea.		36.03		36.03	door frames and drawer fronts,
Clean	Ea.	2.87	23.50		26.37	hardwood veneer on raised door
Paint	Ea.	2.75	50.50		53.25	panels, hinges and pulls.
Minimum Charge	Job		207		207	

Cabinets and Countertops

Wall Cabinets		Unit	Material	Labor	Equip.	Total	Specification
Above-appliance							
	Demolish	Ea.		21.50		21.50	Includes material and labor to install
	Install	Ea.	231	33.50		264.50	custom modular unit with solid
	Demolish and Install	Ea.	231	55		286	hardwood faced frames, hardwood
	Reinstall	Ea.		26.74		26.74	door frames and drawer fronts,
	Clean	Ea.	1.79	14.60		16.39	hardwood veneer on raised door
	Paint	Ea.	1.72	35.50		37.22	panels, hinges and pulls.
	Minimum Charge	Job		207		207	
Premium Grade Wood							
12″ Wide, 1 Door							
	Demolish	Ea.		8.50		8.50	Includes material and labor to install
	Install	Ea.	264	37.50		301.50	premium modular unit with solid
	Demolish and Install	Ea.	264	46		310	hardwood faced frames, hardwood
	Reinstall	Ea.		30.14		30.14	door frames and drawer fronts,
	Clean	Ea.	.72	5.90		6.62	hardwood veneer on raised door
	Paint	Ea.	.68	14.80		15.48	panels, hinges and pulls.
	Minimum Charge	Job		207		207	
15″ Wide, 1 Door							
	Demolish	Ea.		10.65		10.65	Includes material and labor to install
	Install	Ea.	310	38.50		348.50	premium modular unit with solid
	Demolish and Install	Ea.	310	49.15		359.15	hardwood faced frames, hardwood
	Reinstall	Ea.		30.98		30.98	door frames and drawer fronts,
	Clean	Ea.	.89	7.30		8.19	hardwood veneer on raised door
	Paint	Ea.	.86	18.70		19.56	panels, hinges and pulls.
	Minimum Charge	Job		207		207	
18″ Wide, 1 Door							
	Demolish	Ea.		12.85		12.85	Includes material and labor to install
	Install	Ea.	310	39.50		349.50	premium modular unit with solid
	Demolish and Install	Ea.	310	52.35		362.35	hardwood faced frames, hardwood
	Reinstall	Ea.		31.72		31.72	door frames and drawer fronts,
	Clean	Ea.	1.08	8.75		9.83	hardwood veneer on raised door
	Paint	Ea.	1.02	22		23.02	panels, hinges and pulls.
	Minimum Charge	Job		207		207	
21″ Wide, 1 Door							
	Demolish	Ea.		14.80		14.80	Includes material and labor to install
	Install	Ea.	325	40		365	premium modular unit with solid
	Demolish and Install	Ea.	325	54.80		379.80	hardwood faced frames, hardwood
	Reinstall	Ea.		32.19		32.19	door frames and drawer fronts,
	Clean	Ea.	1.25	10.20		11.45	hardwood veneer on raised door
	Paint	Ea.	1.20	25.50		26.70	panels, hinges and pulls.
	Minimum Charge	Job		207		207	
24″ w / Blind Corner							
	Demolish	Ea.		17		17	Includes material and labor to install
	Install	Ea.	365	41		406	premium modular unit with solid
	Demolish and Install	Ea.	365	58		423	hardwood faced frames, hardwood
	Reinstall	Ea.		32.66		32.66	door frames and drawer fronts,
	Clean	Ea.	1.43	11.80		13.23	hardwood veneer on raised door
	Paint	Ea.	1.36	29.50		30.86	panels, hinges and pulls.
	Minimum Charge	Job		207		207	
27″ Wide, 2 Door							
	Demolish	Ea.		18.90		18.90	Includes material and labor to install
	Install	Ea.	330	42		372	premium modular unit with solid
	Demolish and Install	Ea.	330	60.90		390.90	hardwood faced frames, hardwood
	Reinstall	Ea.		33.49		33.49	door frames and drawer fronts,
	Clean	Ea.	1.62	13.30		14.92	hardwood veneer on raised door
	Paint	Ea.	1.55	32.50		34.05	panels, hinges and pulls.
	Minimum Charge	Job		207		207	

Cabinets and Countertops

Wall Cabinets	Unit	Material	Labor	Equip.	Total	Specification
30″ Wide, 2 Door						
Demolish	Ea.		21.50		21.50	Includes material and labor to install
Install	Ea.	415	43		458	premium modular unit with solid
Demolish and Install	Ea.	415	64.50		479.50	hardwood faced frames, hardwood
Reinstall	Ea.		34.35		34.35	door frames and drawer fronts,
Clean	Ea.	1.79	14.60		16.39	hardwood veneer on raised door
Paint	Ea.	1.72	35.50		37.22	panels, hinges and pulls.
Minimum Charge	Job		207		207	
36″ Wide, 2 Door						
Demolish	Ea.		25		25	Includes material and labor to install
Install	Ea.	460	44		504	premium modular unit with solid
Demolish and Install	Ea.	460	69		529	hardwood faced frames, hardwood
Reinstall	Ea.		35.27		35.27	door frames and drawer fronts,
Clean	Ea.	2.15	18		20.15	hardwood veneer on raised door
Paint	Ea.	2.08	44.50		46.58	panels, hinges and pulls.
Minimum Charge	Job		207		207	
48″ Wide, 2 Door						
Demolish	Ea.		34		34	Includes material and labor to install
Install	Ea.	585	45		630	premium modular unit with solid
Demolish and Install	Ea.	585	79		664	hardwood faced frames, hardwood
Reinstall	Ea.		36.03		36.03	door frames and drawer fronts,
Clean	Ea.	2.87	23.50		26.37	hardwood veneer on raised door
Paint	Ea.	2.75	59		61.75	panels, hinges and pulls.
Minimum Charge	Job		207		207	
Above-appliance						
Demolish	Ea.		21.50		21.50	Includes material and labor to install
Install	Ea.	276	33.50		309.50	premium modular unit with solid
Demolish and Install	Ea.	276	55		331	hardwood faced frames, hardwood
Reinstall	Ea.		26.74		26.74	door frames and drawer fronts,
Clean	Ea.	1.79	14.60		16.39	hardwood veneer on raised door
Paint	Ea.	1.72	35.50		37.22	panels, hinges, pulls.
Minimum Charge	Job		207		207	
Premium Hardwood						
12″ Wide, 1 Door						
Demolish	Ea.		8.50		8.50	Includes material and labor to install
Install	Ea.	288	37.50		325.50	premium hardwood modular unit with
Demolish and Install	Ea.	288	46		334	solid hardwood faced frames, drawer
Reinstall	Ea.		30.14		30.14	fronts, and door panels, steel drawer
Clean	Ea.	.72	5.90		6.62	guides, hinges, pulls, laminated
Paint	Ea.	.68	16.15		16.83	interior.
Minimum Charge	Job		207		207	
15″ Wide, 1 Door						
Demolish	Ea.		10.65		10.65	Includes material and labor to install
Install	Ea.	405	38.50		443.50	premium hardwood modular unit with
Demolish and Install	Ea.	405	49.15		454.15	solid hardwood faced frames, drawer
Reinstall	Ea.		30.98		30.98	fronts, and door panels, steel drawer
Clean	Ea.	.89	7.30		8.19	guides, hinges, pulls, laminated
Paint	Ea.	.86	19.75		20.61	interior.
Minimum Charge	Job		207		207	
18″ Wide, 1 Door						
Demolish	Ea.		12.85		12.85	Includes material and labor to install
Install	Ea.	335	39.50		374.50	premium hardwood modular unit with
Demolish and Install	Ea.	335	52.35		387.35	solid hardwood faced frames, drawer
Reinstall	Ea.		31.72		31.72	fronts, and door panels, steel drawer
Clean	Ea.	1.08	8.75		9.83	guides, hinges, pulls, laminated
Paint	Ea.	1.02	23.50		24.52	interior.
Minimum Charge	Job		207		207	

Cabinets and Countertops

Wall Cabinets	Unit	Material	Labor	Equip.	Total	Specification
21″ Wide, 1 Door						
Demolish	Ea.		14.80		14.80	Includes material and labor to install
Install	Ea.	350	40		390	premium hardwood modular unit with
Demolish and Install	Ea.	350	54.80		404.80	solid hardwood faced frames, drawer
Reinstall	Ea.		32.19		32.19	fronts, and door panels, steel drawer
Clean	Ea.	1.25	10.20		11.45	guides, hinges, pulls, laminated
Paint	Ea.	1.20	27.50		28.70	interior.
Minimum Charge	Job		207		207	
24″ w / Blind Corner						
Demolish	Ea.		17		17	Includes material and labor to install
Install	Ea.	395	41		436	premium hardwood modular unit with
Demolish and Install	Ea.	395	58		453	solid hardwood faced frames, drawer
Reinstall	Ea.		32.66		32.66	fronts, and door panels, steel drawer
Clean	Ea.	1.43	11.80		13.23	guides, hinges, pulls, laminated
Paint	Ea.	1.36	32.50		33.86	interior.
Minimum Charge	Job		207		207	
27″ Wide, 2 Door						
Demolish	Ea.		18.90		18.90	Includes material and labor to install
Install	Ea.	435	42		477	premium hardwood modular unit with
Demolish and Install	Ea.	435	60.90		495.90	solid hardwood faced frames, drawer
Reinstall	Ea.		33.49		33.49	fronts, and door panels, steel drawer
Clean	Ea.	1.62	13.30		14.92	guides, hinges, pulls, laminated
Paint	Ea.	1.55	35.50		37.05	interior.
Minimum Charge	Job		207		207	
30″ Wide, 2 Door						
Demolish	Ea.		21.50		21.50	Includes material and labor to install
Install	Ea.	450	43		493	premium hardwood modular unit with
Demolish and Install	Ea.	450	64.50		514.50	solid hardwood faced frames, drawer
Reinstall	Ea.		34.35		34.35	fronts, and door panels, steel drawer
Clean	Ea.	1.79	14.60		16.39	guides, hinges, pulls, laminated
Paint	Ea.	1.72	39.50		41.22	interior.
Minimum Charge	Job		207		207	
36″ Wide, 2 Door						
Demolish	Ea.		25		25	Includes material and labor to install
Install	Ea.	505	44		549	premium hardwood modular unit with
Demolish and Install	Ea.	505	69		574	solid hardwood faced frames, drawer
Reinstall	Ea.		35.27		35.27	fronts, and door panels, steel drawer
Clean	Ea.	2.15	18		20.15	guides, hinges, pulls, laminated
Paint	Ea.	2.08	50.50		52.58	interior.
Minimum Charge	Job		207		207	
48″ Wide, 2 Door						
Demolish	Ea.		34		34	Includes material and labor to install
Install	Ea.	640	45		685	premium hardwood modular unit with
Demolish and Install	Ea.	640	79		719	solid hardwood faced frames, drawer
Reinstall	Ea.		36.03		36.03	fronts, and door panels, steel drawer
Clean	Ea.	2.87	23.50		26.37	guides, hinges, pulls, laminated
Paint	Ea.	2.75	59		61.75	interior.
Minimum Charge	Job		207		207	
Above-appliance						
Demolish	Ea.		21.50		21.50	Includes material and labor to install
Install	Ea.	305	33.50		338.50	premium hardwood modular unit with
Demolish and Install	Ea.	305	55		360	solid hardwood faced frames, drawer
Reinstall	Ea.		26.74		26.74	fronts, and door panels, steel drawer
Clean	Ea.	1.79	14.60		16.39	guides, hinges, pulls, laminated
Paint	Ea.	1.72	39.50		41.22	interior.
Minimum Charge	Job		207		207	

Cabinets and Countertops

Wall Cabinets	Unit	Material	Labor	Equip.	Total	Specification
Medicine Cabinet						
Good Grade						
Demolish	Ea.		14.20		14.20	Cost includes material and labor to
Install	Ea.	154	29.50		183.50	install 14" x 18" recessed medicine
Demolish and Install	Ea.	154	43.70		197.70	cabinet with stainless steel frame,
Reinstall	Ea.		23.68		23.68	mirror. Light not included.
Clean	Ea.	.03	14.05		14.08	
Paint	Ea.	2.02	22		24.02	
Minimum Charge	Job		207		207	
Good Grade Lighted						
Demolish	Ea.		14.20		14.20	Cost includes material and labor to
Install	Ea.	395	34.50		429.50	install 14" x 18" recessed medicine
Demolish and Install	Ea.	395	48.70		443.70	cabinet with stainless steel frame,
Reinstall	Ea.		27.63		27.63	mirror and light.
Clean	Ea.	.03	14.05		14.08	
Paint	Ea.	2.02	22		24.02	
Minimum Charge	Job		207		207	
Better Grade						
Demolish	Ea.		14.20		14.20	Includes material and labor to install
Install	Ea.	275	29.50		304.50	recessed medicine cabinet with
Demolish and Install	Ea.	275	43.70		318.70	polished chrome frame and mirror.
Reinstall	Ea.		23.68		23.68	Light not included.
Clean	Ea.	.03	14.05		14.08	
Paint	Ea.	2.02	22		24.02	
Minimum Charge	Job		207		207	
Better Grade Lighted						
Demolish	Ea.		14.20		14.20	Includes material and labor to install
Install	Ea.	515	34.50		549.50	recessed medicine cabinet with
Demolish and Install	Ea.	515	48.70		563.70	polished chrome frame, mirror and
Reinstall	Ea.		27.63		27.63	light.
Clean	Ea.	.03	14.05		14.08	
Paint	Ea.	2.02	22		24.02	
Minimum Charge	Job		207		207	
Premium Grade						
Demolish	Ea.		14.20		14.20	Cost includes material and labor to
Install	Ea.	330	29.50		359.50	install 14" x 24" recessed medicine
Demolish and Install	Ea.	330	43.70		373.70	cabinet with beveled mirror, frameless
Reinstall	Ea.		23.68		23.68	swing door. Light not included.
Clean	Ea.	.03	14.05		14.08	
Paint	Ea.	2.02	22		24.02	
Minimum Charge	Job		207		207	
Premium Grade Light						
Demolish	Ea.		14.20		14.20	Cost includes material and labor to
Install	Ea.	570	34.50		604.50	install 36" x 30" surface mounted
Demolish and Install	Ea.	570	48.70		618.70	medicine cabinet with beveled tri-view
Reinstall	Ea.		27.63		27.63	mirror, frameless swing door and light.
Clean	Ea.	.03	14.05		14.08	
Paint	Ea.	2.02	22		24.02	
Minimum Charge	Job		207		207	
Bath Mirror						
Demolish	Ea.		10.65		10.65	Cost includes material and labor to
Install	Ea.	47	20.50		67.50	install 18" x 24" surface mount mirror
Demolish and Install	Ea.	47	31.15		78.15	with stainless steel frame.
Reinstall	Ea.		16.58		16.58	
Clean	Ea.	.03	.94		.97	
Minimum Charge	Job		207		207	

Cabinets and Countertops

Wall Cabinets

Wall Cabinets	Unit	Material	Labor	Equip.	Total	Specification
Garage						
Demolish	L.F.		8.50		8.50	Includes material and labor to install
Install	L.F.	81.50	20.50		102	good modular unit with melamine
Demolish and Install	L.F.	81.50	29		110.50	laminated to particle board, in
Reinstall	L.F.		16.58		16.58	textured colors or wood grain print
Clean	L.F.	.72	5.90		6.62	finish, hinges and pulls.
Paint	L.F.	.68	12.70		13.38	
Minimum Charge	Job		207		207	
Strip and Refinish						
Install	L.F.	4.10	44.50		48.60	Includes labor and material to strip,
Minimum Charge	Job		178		178	prep and refinish exterior of cabinets.

Tall Cabinets

Tall Cabinets	Unit	Material	Labor	Equip.	Total	Specification
Good Grade Laminated						
Demolish	L.F.		15.15		15.15	Includes material and labor to install
Install	L.F.	205	46		251	custom modular unit with solid
Demolish and Install	L.F.	205	61.15		266.15	hardwood faced frames, hardwood
Reinstall	L.F.		36.84		36.84	door frames and drawer fronts,
Clean	L.F.	1.91	10.95		12.86	hardwood veneer on raised door
Paint	L.F.	1.60	25.50		27.10	panels, hinges and pulls.
Minimum Charge	Job		207		207	
Better Grade Wood						
Demolish	L.F.		15.15		15.15	Includes material and labor to install
Install	L.F.	295	46		341	custom modular unit with solid
Demolish and Install	L.F.	295	61.15		356.15	hardwood faced frames, hardwood
Reinstall	L.F.		36.84		36.84	door frames and drawer fronts,
Clean	L.F.	1.91	10.95		12.86	hardwood veneer on raised door
Paint	L.F.	1.60	27.50		29.10	panels, hinges and pulls.
Minimum Charge	Job		207		207	
Premium Grade Wood						
Demolish	L.F.		15.15		15.15	Includes material and labor to install
Install	L.F.	420	46		466	premium modular unit with solid
Demolish and Install	L.F.	420	61.15		481.15	hardwood faced frames, hardwood
Reinstall	L.F.		36.84		36.84	door frames and drawer fronts,
Clean	L.F.	1.91	10.95		12.86	hardwood veneer on raised door
Paint	L.F.	1.60	29.50		31.10	panels, hinges and pulls.
Minimum Charge	Job		207		207	
Premium Hardwood						
Demolish	L.F.		15.15		15.15	Includes material and labor to install
Install	L.F.	590	46		636	premium hardwood modular unit with
Demolish and Install	L.F.	590	61.15		651.15	solid hardwood faced frames, drawer
Reinstall	L.F.		36.84		36.84	fronts, and door panels, steel drawer
Clean	L.F.	1.91	10.95		12.86	guides, hinges and pulls, laminated
Paint	L.F.	1.60	32.50		34.10	interior.
Minimum Charge	Job		207		207	

Cabinets and Countertops

Tall Cabinets	Unit	Material	Labor	Equip.	Total	Specification
Single Oven, 27" Wide						
Good Grade Laminated						Includes material and labor to install
Demolish	Ea.		34		34	good modular unit with melamine
Install	Ea.	710	104		814	laminated to particle board, in
Demolish and Install	Ea.	710	138		848	textured colors or wood grain print
Reinstall	Ea.		82.88		82.88	finish, hinges and pulls.
Clean	Ea.	6	19.15		25.15	
Paint	Ea.	2.68	57		59.68	
Minimum Charge	Job		207		207	
Better Grade Veneer						Includes material and labor to install
Demolish	Ea.		34		34	custom modular unit with solid
Install	Ea.	1275	104		1379	hardwood faced frames, hardwood
Demolish and Install	Ea.	1275	138		1413	door frames and drawer fronts,
Reinstall	Ea.		82.88		82.88	hardwood veneer on raised door
Clean	Ea.	6	19.15		25.15	panels, hinges and pulls.
Paint	Ea.	2.68	61		63.68	
Minimum Charge	Job		207		207	
Premium Grade Veneer						Includes material and labor to install
Demolish	Ea.		34		34	premium modular unit with solid
Install	Ea.	1125	104		1229	hardwood faced frames, hardwood
Demolish and Install	Ea.	1125	138		1263	door frames and drawer fronts,
Reinstall	Ea.		82.88		82.88	hardwood veneer on raised door
Clean	Ea.	6	19.15		25.15	panels, hinges and pulls.
Paint	Ea.	2.68	67		69.68	
Minimum Charge	Job		207		207	
Premium Hardwood						Includes material and labor to install
Demolish	Ea.		34		34	premium hardwood modular unit with
Install	Ea.	1250	104		1354	solid hardwood faced frames, drawer
Demolish and Install	Ea.	1250	138		1388	fronts, and door panels, steel drawer
Reinstall	Ea.		82.88		82.88	guides, hinges and pulls, laminated
Clean	Ea.	6	19.15		25.15	interior.
Paint	Ea.	2.68	72.50		75.18	
Minimum Charge	Job		207		207	
Single Oven, 30" Wide						
Good Grade Laminated						Includes material and labor to install
Demolish	Ea.		34		34	good modular unit with melamine
Install	Ea.	860	104		964	laminated to particle board, in
Demolish and Install	Ea.	860	138		998	textured colors or wood grain print
Reinstall	Ea.		82.88		82.88	finish, hinges and pulls.
Clean	Ea.	6	19.15		25.15	
Paint	Ea.	2.68	57		59.68	
Minimum Charge	Job		207		207	
Better Grade Veneer						Includes material and labor to install
Demolish	Ea.		34		34	custom modular unit with solid
Install	Ea.	925	104		1029	hardwood faced frames, hardwood
Demolish and Install	Ea.	925	138		1063	door frames and drawer fronts,
Reinstall	Ea.		82.88		82.88	hardwood veneer on raised door
Clean	Ea.	6	19.15		25.15	panels, hinges and pulls.
Paint	Ea.	2.68	57		59.68	
Minimum Charge	Job		207		207	

Cabinets and Countertops

Tall Cabinets	Unit	Material	Labor	Equip.	Total	Specification
Premium Grade Veneer						
Demolish	Ea.		34		34	Includes material and labor to install
Install	Ea.	1025	104		1129	premium modular unit with solid
Demolish and Install	Ea.	1025	138		1163	hardwood faced frames, hardwood
Reinstall	Ea.		82.88		82.88	door frames and drawer fronts,
Clean	Ea.	6	19.15		25.15	hardwood veneer on raised door
Paint	Ea.	2.68	57		59.68	panels, hinges and pulls.
Minimum Charge	Job		207		207	
Premium Hardwood						
Demolish	Ea.		34		34	Includes material and labor to install
Install	Ea.	1100	104		1204	premium hardwood modular unit with
Demolish and Install	Ea.	1100	138		1238	solid hardwood faced frames, drawer
Reinstall	Ea.		82.88		82.88	fronts, and door panels, steel drawer
Clean	Ea.	6	19.15		25.15	guides, hinges and pulls, laminated
Paint	Ea.	2.68	57		59.68	interior.
Minimum Charge	Job		207		207	
Utility 18″ W x 12″ D						
Good Grade Laminated						
Demolish	Ea.		34		34	Includes material and labor to install
Install	Ea.	425	83		508	good modular unit with melamine
Demolish and Install	Ea.	425	117		542	laminated to particle board, in
Reinstall	Ea.		66.30		66.30	textured colors or wood grain print
Clean	Ea.	1.41	9.30		10.71	finish, hinges and pulls.
Paint	Ea.	1.02	22		23.02	
Minimum Charge	Job		207		207	
Better Grade Veneer						
Demolish	Ea.		34		34	Includes material and labor to install
Install	Ea.	565	83		648	custom modular unit with solid
Demolish and Install	Ea.	565	117		682	hardwood faced frames, hardwood
Reinstall	Ea.		66.30		66.30	door frames and drawer fronts,
Clean	Ea.	1.41	9.30		10.71	hardwood veneer on raised door
Paint	Ea.	1.02	23.50		24.52	panels, hinges and pulls.
Minimum Charge	Job		207		207	
Premium Grade Veneer						
Demolish	Ea.		34		34	Includes material and labor to install
Install	Ea.	680	83		763	premium modular unit with solid
Demolish and Install	Ea.	680	117		797	hardwood faced frames, hardwood
Reinstall	Ea.		66.30		66.30	door frames and drawer fronts,
Clean	Ea.	1.41	9.30		10.71	hardwood veneer on raised door
Paint	Ea.	1.02	27.50		28.52	panels, hinges and pulls.
Minimum Charge	Job		207		207	
Premium Hardwood						
Demolish	Ea.		34		34	Includes material and labor to install
Install	Ea.	745	83		828	premium hardwood modular unit with
Demolish and Install	Ea.	745	117		862	solid hardwood faced frames, drawer
Reinstall	Ea.		66.30		66.30	fronts, and door panels, steel drawer
Clean	Ea.	1.41	9.30		10.71	guides, hinges and pulls, laminated
Paint	Ea.	1.02	29.50		30.52	interior.
Minimum Charge	Job		207		207	

Cabinets and Countertops

Tall Cabinets	Unit	Material	Labor	Equip.	Total	Specification
Utility 24″ W x 24″ D						
Good Grade Laminated						
Demolish	Ea.		34		34	Includes material and labor to install
Install	Ea.	600	104		704	good modular unit with melamine
Demolish and Install	Ea.	600	138		738	laminated to particle board, in
Reinstall	Ea.		82.88		82.88	textured colors or wood grain print
Clean	Ea.	1.84	12.25		14.09	finish, hinges and pulls.
Paint	Ea.	1.36	29.50		30.86	
Minimum Charge	Job		207		207	
Better Grade Veneer						
Demolish	Ea.		34		34	Includes material and labor to install
Install	Ea.	800	104		904	custom modular unit with solid
Demolish and Install	Ea.	800	138		938	hardwood faced frames, hardwood
Reinstall	Ea.		82.88		82.88	door frames and drawer fronts,
Clean	Ea.	1.84	12.25		14.09	hardwood veneer on raised door
Paint	Ea.	1.36	32.50		33.86	panels, hinges and pulls.
Minimum Charge	Job		207		207	
Premium Grade Veneer						
Demolish	Ea.		34		34	Includes material and labor to install
Install	Ea.	955	104		1059	premium modular unit with solid
Demolish and Install	Ea.	955	138		1093	hardwood faced frames, hardwood
Reinstall	Ea.		82.88		82.88	door frames and drawer fronts,
Clean	Ea.	1.84	12.25		14.09	hardwood veneer on raised door
Paint	Ea.	1.36	35.50		36.86	panels, hinges and pulls.
Minimum Charge	Job		207		207	
Premium Hardwood						
Demolish	Ea.		34		34	Includes material and labor to install
Install	Ea.	1050	104		1154	premium hardwood modular unit with
Demolish and Install	Ea.	1050	138		1188	solid hardwood faced frames, drawer
Reinstall	Ea.		82.88		82.88	fronts, and door panels, steel drawer
Clean	Ea.	1.84	12.25		14.09	guides, hinges and pulls, laminated
Paint	Ea.	1.36	39.50		40.86	interior.
Minimum Charge	Job		207		207	
Plain Shelves						
Install	Ea.	27.50	23		50.50	Includes labor and material to install
Rotating Shelves						tall cabinet shelving, per set.
Install	Ea.	142	20.50		162.50	Includes labor and material to install
Strip and Refinish						lazy susan shelving for wall cabinet.
Install	L.F.	8.20	71		79.20	Includes labor and material to strip,
Minimum Charge	Job		178		178	prep and refinish exterior of cabinets.
Stain						
Install	L.F.	.26	3.23		3.49	Includes labor and material to replace
Minimum Charge	Job		178		178	normal prep and stain on doors and
						exterior cabinets.

Cabinets and Countertops

Base Cabinets	Unit	Material	Labor	Equip.	Total	Specification
Good Grade Laminated						
12″ w, 1 Door, 1 Drawer						
Demolish	Ea.		8.50		8.50	Includes material and labor to install
Install	Ea.	193	33.50		226.50	good modular unit with melamine
Demolish and Install	Ea.	193	42		235	laminate, textured colors or wood
Reinstall	Ea.		26.74		26.74	grain print finish including hinges and
Clean	Ea.	.96	6.15		7.11	pulls.
Paint	Ea.	.68	14.80		15.48	
Minimum Charge	Job		207		207	
15″ w, 1 Door, 1 Drawer						
Demolish	Ea.		10.65		10.65	Includes material and labor to install
Install	Ea.	198	34.50		232.50	good modular unit with melamine
Demolish and Install	Ea.	198	45.15		243.15	laminate, textured colors or wood
Reinstall	Ea.		27.63		27.63	grain print finish including hinges and
Clean	Ea.	1.20	7.65		8.85	pulls.
Paint	Ea.	.86	18.70		19.56	
Minimum Charge	Job		207		207	
18″ w, 1 Door, 1 Drawer						
Demolish	Ea.		12.60		12.60	Includes material and labor to install
Install	Ea.	217	35.50		252.50	good modular unit with melamine
Demolish and Install	Ea.	217	48.10		265.10	laminate, textured colors or wood
Reinstall	Ea.		28.46		28.46	grain print finish including hinges and
Clean	Ea.	1.41	9.30		10.71	pulls.
Paint	Ea.	1.02	22		23.02	
Minimum Charge	Job		207		207	
21″ w, 1 Door, 1 Drawer						
Demolish	Ea.		14.80		14.80	Includes material and labor to install
Install	Ea.	230	36.50		266.50	good modular unit with melamine
Demolish and Install	Ea.	230	51.30		281.30	laminate, textured colors or wood
Reinstall	Ea.		29.21		29.21	grain print finish including hinges and
Clean	Ea.	1.71	10.95		12.66	pulls.
Paint	Ea.	1.20	25.50		26.70	
Minimum Charge	Job		207		207	
24″ w, 1 Door, 1 Drawer						
Demolish	Ea.		17		17	Includes material and labor to install
Install	Ea.	254	37		291	good modular unit with melamine
Demolish and Install	Ea.	254	54		308	laminate, textured colors or wood
Reinstall	Ea.		29.73		29.73	grain print finish including hinges and
Clean	Ea.	1.84	12.25		14.09	pulls.
Paint	Ea.	1.36	29.50		30.86	
Minimum Charge	Job		207		207	
30″ Wide Sink Base						
Demolish	Ea.		21.50		21.50	Includes material and labor to install
Install	Ea.	259	38.50		297.50	good modular unit with melamine
Demolish and Install	Ea.	259	60		319	laminate, textured colors or wood
Reinstall	Ea.		30.98		30.98	grain print finish including hinges and
Clean	Ea.	2.39	15.30		17.69	pulls.
Paint	Ea.	1.72	35.50		37.22	
Minimum Charge	Job		207		207	
36″ Wide Sink Base						
Demolish	Ea.		26		26	Includes material and labor to install
Install	Ea.	292	41		333	good modular unit with melamine
Demolish and Install	Ea.	292	67		359	laminate, textured colors or wood
Reinstall	Ea.		32.66		32.66	grain print finish including hinges and
Clean	Ea.	2.65	18		20.65	pulls.
Paint	Ea.	2.08	44.50		46.58	
Minimum Charge	Job		207		207	

Cabinets and Countertops

Base Cabinets

Base Cabinets	Unit	Material	Labor	Equip.	Total	Specification
36" Blind Corner						Includes material and labor to install
Demolish	Ea.		26		26	good modular unit with melamine
Install	Ea.	455	46		501	laminate, textured colors or wood
Demolish and Install	Ea.	455	72		527	grain print finish including hinges and
Reinstall	Ea.		36.84		36.84	pulls.
Clean	Ea.	2.65	18		20.65	
Paint	Ea.	2.08	44.50		46.58	
Minimum Charge	Job		207		207	
42" w, 2 Door, 2 Drawer						Includes material and labor to install
Demolish	Ea.		31		31	good modular unit with melamine
Install	Ea.	365	42		407	laminate, textured colors or wood
Demolish and Install	Ea.	365	73		438	grain print finish including hinges and
Reinstall	Ea.		33.49		33.49	pulls.
Clean	Ea.	3.41	22		25.41	
Paint	Ea.	2.38	50.50		52.88	
Minimum Charge	Job		207		207	
Clean Interior						Includes labor and materials to clean
Clean	L.F.	.96	4.64		5.60	the interior of a 27" cabinet.
Minimum Charge	Job		153		153	

Better Grade Wood

Better Grade Wood	Unit	Material	Labor	Equip.	Total	Specification
12" w, 1 Door, 1 Drawer						Includes material and labor to install
Demolish	Ea.		8.50		8.50	custom modular unit including solid
Install	Ea.	257	33.50		290.50	hardwood faced frames, hardwood
Demolish and Install	Ea.	257	42		299	door frames and drawer fronts,
Reinstall	Ea.		26.74		26.74	hardwood veneer on raised door
Clean	Ea.	.96	6.15		7.11	panels, hinges and pulls.
Paint	Ea.	.68	16.15		16.83	
Minimum Charge	Job		207		207	
15" w, 1 Door, 1 Drawer						Includes material and labor to install
Demolish	Ea.		10.65		10.65	custom modular unit including solid
Install	Ea.	264	34.50		298.50	hardwood faced frames, hardwood
Demolish and Install	Ea.	264	45.15		309.15	door frames and drawer fronts,
Reinstall	Ea.		27.63		27.63	hardwood veneer on raised door
Clean	Ea.	1.20	7.65		8.85	panels, hinges and pulls.
Paint	Ea.	.86	21		21.86	
Minimum Charge	Job		207		207	
18" w, 1 Door, 1 Drawer						Includes material and labor to install
Demolish	Ea.		12.60		12.60	custom modular unit including solid
Install	Ea.	289	35.50		324.50	hardwood faced frames, hardwood
Demolish and Install	Ea.	289	48.10		337.10	door frames and drawer fronts,
Reinstall	Ea.		28.46		28.46	hardwood veneer on raised door
Clean	Ea.	1.41	9.30		10.71	panels, hinges and pulls.
Paint	Ea.	1.02	23.50		24.52	
Minimum Charge	Job		207		207	
21" w, 1 Door, 1 Drawer						Includes material and labor to install
Demolish	Ea.		14.80		14.80	custom modular unit including solid
Install	Ea.	305	36.50		341.50	hardwood faced frames, hardwood
Demolish and Install	Ea.	305	51.30		356.30	door frames and drawer fronts,
Reinstall	Ea.		29.21		29.21	door frames and drawer fronts,
Clean	Ea.	1.71	10.95		12.66	hardwood veneer on raised door
Paint	Ea.	1.20	27.50		28.70	panels, hinges and pulls.
Minimum Charge	Job		207		207	

Cabinets and Countertops

Base Cabinets	Unit	Material	Labor	Equip.	Total	Specification
24" w, 1 Door, 1 Drawer						
Demolish	Ea.		17		17	Includes material and labor to install
Install	Ea.	340	37		377	custom modular unit including solid
Demolish and Install	Ea.	340	54		394	hardwood faced frames, hardwood
Reinstall	Ea.		29.73		29.73	door frames and drawer fronts,
Clean	Ea.	1.84	12.25		14.09	hardwood veneer on raised door
Paint	Ea.	1.36	32.50		33.86	panels, hinges and pulls.
Minimum Charge	Job		207		207	
30" Wide Sink Base						
Demolish	Ea.		21.50		21.50	Includes material and labor to install
Install	Ea.	345	38.50		383.50	custom modular unit including solid
Demolish and Install	Ea.	345	60		405	hardwood faced frames, hardwood
Reinstall	Ea.		30.98		30.98	door frames and drawer fronts,
Clean	Ea.	2.39	15.30		17.69	hardwood veneer on raised door
Paint	Ea.	1.72	39.50		41.22	panels, hinges and pulls.
Minimum Charge	Job		207		207	
36" Wide Sink Base						
Demolish	Ea.		26		26	Includes material and labor to install
Install	Ea.	390	41		431	custom modular unit including solid
Demolish and Install	Ea.	390	67		457	hardwood faced frames, hardwood
Reinstall	Ea.		32.66		32.66	door frames and drawer fronts,
Clean	Ea.	2.65	18		20.65	hardwood veneer on raised door
Paint	Ea.	2.08	50.50		52.58	panels, hinges and pulls.
Minimum Charge	Job		207		207	
36" Blind Corner						
Demolish	Ea.		26		26	Includes material and labor to install
Install	Ea.	605	46		651	custom modular unit including solid
Demolish and Install	Ea.	605	72		677	hardwood faced frames, hardwood
Reinstall	Ea.		36.84		36.84	door frames and drawer fronts,
Clean	Ea.	2.65	18		20.65	hardwood veneer on raised door
Paint	Ea.	2.08	50.50		52.58	panels, hinges and pulls.
Minimum Charge	Job		207		207	
42" w, 2 Door, 2 Drawer						
Demolish	Ea.		31		31	Includes material and labor to install
Install	Ea.	480	42		522	modular unit including solid hardwood
Demolish and Install	Ea.	480	73		553	faced frames, hardwood door frames
Reinstall	Ea.		33.49		33.49	and drawer fronts, hardwood veneer
Clean	Ea.	3.41	22		25.41	on raised door panels, hinges and
Paint	Ea.	2.38	59		61.38	pulls.
Minimum Charge	Job		207		207	
Clean Interior						
Clean	L.F.	.96	4.64		5.60	Includes labor and materials to clean
Minimum Charge	Job		153		153	the interior of a 27" cabinet.
Premium Grade Wood						
12" w, 1 Door, 1 Drawer						
Demolish	Ea.		8.50		8.50	Includes material and labor to install
Install	Ea.	310	16.70		326.70	premium hardwood modular unit with
Demolish and Install	Ea.	310	25.20		335.20	solid hardwood faced frames, drawer
Reinstall	Ea.		13.37		13.37	fronts, and door panels, steel drawer
Clean	Ea.	.96	6.15		7.11	guides, hinges, pulls and laminated
Paint	Ea.	.68	17.75		18.43	interior.
Minimum Charge	Job		207		207	

Cabinets and Countertops

Base Cabinets

	Unit	Material	Labor	Equip.	Total	Specification
15" w, 1 Door, 1 Drawer						
Demolish	Ea.		10.65		10.65	Includes material and labor to install
Install	Ea.	320	34.50		354.50	premium modular unit including solid
Demolish and Install	Ea.	320	45.15		365.15	hardwood faced frames, hardwood
Reinstall	Ea.		27.63		27.63	door frames and drawer fronts,
Clean	Ea.	1.20	7.65		8.85	hardwood veneer on raised door
Paint	Ea.	.86	22		22.86	panels, hinges and pulls.
Minimum Charge	Job		207		207	
18" w, 1 Door, 1 Drawer						
Demolish	Ea.		12.60		12.60	Includes material and labor to install
Install	Ea.	345	35.50		380.50	premium modular unit including solid
Demolish and Install	Ea.	345	48.10		393.10	hardwood faced frames, hardwood
Reinstall	Ea.		28.46		28.46	door frames and drawer fronts,
Clean	Ea.	1.41	9.30		10.71	hardwood veneer on raised door
Paint	Ea.	1.02	27.50		28.52	panels, hinges and pulls.
Minimum Charge	Job		207		207	
21" w, 1 Door, 1 Drawer						
Demolish	Ea.		14.80		14.80	Includes material and labor to install
Install	Ea.	375	36.50		411.50	premium modular unit including solid
Demolish and Install	Ea.	375	51.30		426.30	hardwood faced frames, hardwood
Reinstall	Ea.		29.21		29.21	door frames and drawer fronts,
Clean	Ea.	1.71	10.95		12.66	hardwood veneer on raised door
Paint	Ea.	1.20	29.50		30.70	panels, hinges and pulls.
Minimum Charge	Job		207		207	
24" w, 1 Door, 1 Drawer						
Demolish	Ea.		17		17	Includes material and labor to install
Install	Ea.	405	37		442	premium modular unit including solid
Demolish and Install	Ea.	405	54		459	hardwood faced frames, hardwood
Reinstall	Ea.		29.73		29.73	door frames and drawer fronts,
Clean	Ea.	1.84	12.25		14.09	hardwood veneer on raised door
Paint	Ea.	1.36	35.50		36.86	panels, hinges and pulls.
Minimum Charge	Job		207		207	
30" Wide Sink Base						
Demolish	Ea.		21.50		21.50	Includes material and labor to install
Install	Ea.	415	38.50		453.50	premium modular unit including solid
Demolish and Install	Ea.	415	60		475	hardwood faced frames, hardwood
Reinstall	Ea.		30.98		30.98	door frames and drawer fronts,
Clean	Ea.	2.39	15.30		17.69	hardwood veneer on raised door
Paint	Ea.	1.72	44.50		46.22	panels, hinges and pulls.
Minimum Charge	Job		207		207	
36" Wide Sink Base						
Demolish	Ea.		26		26	Includes material and labor to install
Install	Ea.	470	41		511	premium modular unit including solid
Demolish and Install	Ea.	470	67		537	hardwood faced frames, hardwood
Reinstall	Ea.		32.66		32.66	door frames and drawer fronts,
Clean	Ea.	2.65	18		20.65	hardwood veneer on raised door
Paint	Ea.	2.08	50.50		52.58	panels, hinges and pulls.
Minimum Charge	Job		207		207	
36" Blind Corner						
Demolish	Ea.		26		26	Includes material and labor to install
Install	Ea.	730	46		776	premium modular unit including solid
Demolish and Install	Ea.	730	72		802	hardwood faced frames, hardwood
Reinstall	Ea.		36.84		36.84	door frames and drawer fronts,
Clean	Ea.	2.65	18		20.65	hardwood veneer on raised door
Paint	Ea.	2.08	50.50		52.58	panels, hinges and pulls.
Minimum Charge	Job		207		207	

Cabinets and Countertops

Base Cabinets	Unit	Material	Labor	Equip.	Total	Specification
42″ w, 2 Door, 2 Drawer						Includes material and labor to install
Demolish	Ea.		31		31	premium modular unit including solid
Install	Ea.	640	42		682	hardwood faced frames, hardwood
Demolish and Install	Ea.	640	73		713	door frames and drawer fronts,
Reinstall	Ea.		33.49		33.49	hardwood veneer on raised door
Clean	Ea.	3.41	22		25.41	panels, hinges and pulls.
Paint	Ea.	2.38	59		61.38	
Minimum Charge	Job		207		207	
Clean Interior						
Clean	L.F.	.96	4.64		5.60	Includes labor and materials to clean
Minimum Charge	Job		153		153	the interior of a 27″ cabinet.
Premium Hardwood						
12″ w, 1 Door, 1 Drawer						
Demolish	Ea.		8.50		8.50	Includes material and labor to install
Install	Ea.	335	33.50		368.50	premium hardwood modular unit with
Demolish and Install	Ea.	335	42		377	solid hardwood faced frames, drawer
Reinstall	Ea.		26.74		26.74	fronts, and door panels, steel drawer
Clean	Ea.	.96	6.15		7.11	guides, hinges, pulls and laminated
Paint	Ea.	.68	19.75		20.43	interior.
Minimum Charge	Job		207		207	
15″ w, 1 Door, 1 Drawer						
Demolish	Ea.		10.65		10.65	Includes material and labor to install
Install	Ea.	345	34.50		379.50	premium hardwood modular unit with
Demolish and Install	Ea.	345	45.15		390.15	solid hardwood faced frames, drawer
Reinstall	Ea.		27.63		27.63	fronts, and door panels, steel drawer
Clean	Ea.	1.20	7.65		8.85	guides, hinges, pulls and laminated
Paint	Ea.	.86	25.50		26.36	interior.
Minimum Charge	Job		207		207	
18″ w, 1 Door, 1 Drawer						
Demolish	Ea.		12.60		12.60	Includes material and labor to install
Install	Ea.	380	35.50		415.50	premium hardwood modular unit with
Demolish and Install	Ea.	380	48.10		428.10	solid hardwood faced frames, drawer
Reinstall	Ea.		28.46		28.46	fronts, and door panels, steel drawer
Clean	Ea.	1.41	9.30		10.71	guides, hinges, pulls and laminated
Paint	Ea.	1.02	29.50		30.52	interior.
Minimum Charge	Job		207		207	
21″ w, 1 Door, 1 Drawer						
Demolish	Ea.		14.80		14.80	Includes material and labor to install
Install	Ea.	400	36.50		436.50	premium hardwood modular unit with
Demolish and Install	Ea.	400	51.30		451.30	solid hardwood faced frames, drawer
Reinstall	Ea.		29.21		29.21	fronts, and door panels, steel drawer
Clean	Ea.	1.71	10.95		12.66	guides, hinges, pulls and laminated
Paint	Ea.	1.20	32.50		33.70	interior.
Minimum Charge	Job		207		207	
24″ w, 1 Door, 1 Drawer						
Demolish	Ea.		17		17	Includes material and labor to install
Install	Ea.	445	37		482	premium hardwood modular unit with
Demolish and Install	Ea.	445	54		499	solid hardwood faced frames, drawer
Reinstall	Ea.		29.73		29.73	fronts, and door panels, steel drawer
Clean	Ea.	1.84	12.25		14.09	guides, hinges and pulls, laminated
Paint	Ea.	1.36	39.50		40.86	interior.
Minimum Charge	Job		207		207	

Cabinets and Countertops

Base Cabinets	Unit	Material	Labor	Equip.	Total	Specification
30″ Wide Sink Base						
Demolish	Ea.		21.50		21.50	Includes material and labor to install
Install	Ea.	450	38.50		488.50	premium hardwood modular unit with
Demolish and Install	Ea.	450	60		510	solid hardwood faced frames, drawer
Reinstall	Ea.		30.98		30.98	fronts, and door panels, steel drawer
Clean	Ea.	2.39	15.30		17.69	guides, hinges, pulls and laminated
Paint	Ea.	1.72	44.50		46.22	interior.
Minimum Charge	Job		207		207	
36″ Wide Sink Base						
Demolish	Ea.		26		26	Includes material and labor to install
Install	Ea.	505	41		546	premium hardwood modular unit with
Demolish and Install	Ea.	505	67		572	solid hardwood faced frames, drawer
Reinstall	Ea.		32.66		32.66	fronts, and door panels, steel drawer
Clean	Ea.	2.65	18		20.65	guides, hinges, pulls and laminated
Paint	Ea.	2.08	59		61.08	interior.
Minimum Charge	Job		207		207	
36″ Blind Corner						
Demolish	Ea.		26		26	Includes material and labor to install
Install	Ea.	800	46		846	premium hardwood modular unit with
Demolish and Install	Ea.	800	72		872	solid hardwood faced frames, drawer
Reinstall	Ea.		36.84		36.84	fronts, and door panels, steel drawer
Clean	Ea.	2.65	18		20.65	guides, hinges, pulls and laminated
Paint	Ea.	2.08	59		61.08	interior.
Minimum Charge	Job		207		207	
42″ w, 2 Door, 2 Drawer						
Demolish	Ea.		31		31	Includes material and labor to install
Install	Ea.	840	42		882	premium hardwood modular unit with
Demolish and Install	Ea.	840	73		913	solid hardwood faced frames, drawer
Reinstall	Ea.		33.49		33.49	fronts, and door panels, steel drawer
Clean	Ea.	3.41	22		25.41	guides, hinges, pulls and laminated
Paint	Ea.	2.38	71		73.38	interior.
Minimum Charge	Job		207		207	
Clean Interior						
Clean	L.F.	.96	4.64		5.60	Includes labor and materials to clean
Minimum Charge	Job		153		153	the interior of a 27″ cabinet.
Island						
24″ Wide						
Demolish	Ea.		17		17	Includes material and labor to install
Install	Ea.	530	34.50		564.50	custom modular unit with solid
Demolish and Install	Ea.	530	51.50		581.50	hardwood faced frames, hardwood
Reinstall	Ea.		27.63		27.63	door frames and drawer fronts,
Clean	Ea.	2.65	18		20.65	hardwood veneer on raised door
Paint	Ea.	2.05	50.50		52.55	panels, hinges and pulls.
Minimum Charge	Job		207		207	
30″ Wide						
Demolish	Ea.		21.50		21.50	Includes material and labor to install
Install	Ea.	590	43		633	custom modular unit with solid
Demolish and Install	Ea.	590	64.50		654.50	hardwood faced frames, hardwood
Reinstall	Ea.		34.53		34.53	door frames and drawer fronts,
Clean	Ea.	3.41	22		25.41	hardwood veneer on raised door
Paint	Ea.	2.57	59		61.57	panels, hinges and pulls.
Minimum Charge	Job		207		207	

Cabinets and Countertops

Base Cabinets	Unit	Material	Labor	Equip.	Total	Specification
36" Wide						
Demolish	Ea.		26		26	Includes material and labor to install
Install	Ea.	880	52		932	custom modular unit with solid
Demolish and Install	Ea.	880	78		958	hardwood faced frames, hardwood
Reinstall	Ea.		41.44		41.44	door frames and drawer fronts,
Clean	Ea.	3.98	28		31.98	hardwood veneer on raised door
Paint	Ea.	3.11	71		74.11	panels, hinges and pulls.
Minimum Charge	Job		207		207	
48" Wide						
Demolish	Ea.		34		34	Includes material and labor to install
Install	Ea.	1050	69		1119	custom modular unit with solid
Demolish and Install	Ea.	1050	103		1153	hardwood faced frames, hardwood
Reinstall	Ea.		55.25		55.25	door frames and drawer fronts,
Clean	Ea.	4.77	34		38.77	hardwood veneer on raised door
Paint	Ea.	3.56	89		92.56	panels, hinges and pulls.
Minimum Charge	Job		207		207	
60" Wide						
Demolish	Ea.		38		38	Includes material and labor to install
Install	Ea.	1175	86.50		1261.50	custom modular unit with solid
Demolish and Install	Ea.	1175	124.50		1299.50	hardwood faced frames, hardwood
Reinstall	Ea.		69.07		69.07	door frames and drawer fronts,
Clean	Ea.	6	44		50	hardwood veneer on raised door
Paint	Ea.	3.56	118		121.56	panels, hinges and pulls.
Minimum Charge	Job		207		207	
Clean Interior						
Clean	L.F.	.96	4.64		5.60	Includes labor and materials to clean
Minimum Charge	Job		153		153	the interior of a 27" cabinet.
Liquor Bar						
Demolish	L.F.		8.50		8.50	Includes material and labor to install
Install	L.F.	167	41.50		208.50	custom modular unit with solid
Demolish and Install	L.F.	167	50		217	hardwood faced frames, hardwood
Reinstall	L.F.		33.15		33.15	door frames and drawer fronts,
Clean	L.F.	.96	6.40		7.36	hardwood veneer on raised door
Paint	L.F.	5.50	16.15		21.65	panels, hinges and pulls.
Minimum Charge	Job		207		207	
Clean Interior						
Clean	L.F.	.96	4.64		5.60	Includes labor and materials to clean
Minimum Charge	Job		153		153	the interior of a 27" cabinet.
Seal Interior						
Install	L.F.	.51	5.80		6.31	Includes labor and materials to seal a
Minimum Charge	Job		178		178	cabinet interior.
Back Bar						
Demolish	L.F.		8.50		8.50	Includes material and labor to install
Install	L.F.	167	41.50		208.50	custom modular unit with solid
Demolish and Install	L.F.	167	50		217	hardwood faced frames, hardwood
Reinstall	L.F.		33.15		33.15	door frames and drawer fronts,
Clean	L.F.	.96	6.40		7.36	hardwood veneer on raised door
Paint	L.F.	5.50	16.15		21.65	panels, hinges and pulls.
Minimum Charge	Job		207		207	
Clean Interior						
Clean	L.F.	.96	4.64		5.60	Includes labor and materials to clean
Minimum Charge	Job		153		153	the interior of a 27" cabinet.

Cabinets and Countertops

Base Cabinets

Base Cabinets		Unit	Material	Labor	Equip.	Total	Specification
Seal Interior							
	Install	L.F.	.51	5.80		6.31	Includes labor and materials to seal a
	Minimum Charge	Job		178		178	cabinet interior.
Storage (garage)							
	Demolish	L.F.		8.50		8.50	Includes material and labor to install
	Install	L.F.	125	41.50		166.50	good modular unit with melamine
	Demolish and Install	L.F.	125	50		175	laminate, textured colors or wood
	Reinstall	L.F.		33.15		33.15	grain print finish including hinges and
	Clean	L.F.	.96	6.40		7.36	pulls.
	Paint	L.F.	5.50	16.15		21.65	
	Minimum Charge	Job		207		207	
Clean Interior							
	Clean	L.F.	.96	4.64		5.60	Includes labor and materials to clean
	Minimum Charge	Job		153		153	the interior of a 27" cabinet.
Seal Interior							
	Install	L.F.	.51	5.80		6.31	Includes labor and materials to seal a
	Minimum Charge	Job		178		178	cabinet interior.
Built-in Desk							
	Demolish	L.F.		8.50		8.50	Includes material and labor to install
	Install	L.F.	167	41.50		208.50	custom modular unit with solid
	Demolish and Install	L.F.	167	50		217	hardwood faced frames, hardwood
	Reinstall	L.F.		33.15		33.15	door frames and drawer fronts,
	Clean	L.F.	.96	6.40		7.36	hardwood veneer on raised door
	Paint	L.F.	5.50	16.15		21.65	panels, hinges and pulls.
	Minimum Charge	Job		207		207	
Built-in Bookcase							
	Demolish	L.F.		11.35		11.35	Includes material and labor to install
	Install	L.F.	38	41.50		79.50	custom modular bookcase unit with
	Demolish and Install	L.F.	38	52.85		90.85	clear pine faced frames, shelves 12"
	Reinstall	L.F.		33.15		33.15	O.C., 7' high, 8" deep.
	Clean	L.F.	1.91	10.95		12.86	
	Paint	L.F.	1.60	27.50		29.10	
	Minimum Charge	Job		207		207	
Strip and Refinish							
	Install	L.F.	4.10	44.50		48.60	Includes labor and material to strip,
	Minimum Charge	Job		178		178	prep and refinish exterior of cabinets.
Stain							
	Install	L.F.	.58	1.65		2.23	Includes labor and material to stain
	Minimum Charge	Job		207		207	door and exterior of cabinets.

Countertop

Countertop		Unit	Material	Labor	Equip.	Total	Specification
Laminated							
With Splash							
	Demolish	L.F.		5.65		5.65	Includes material and labor to install
	Install	L.F.	35	14.80		49.80	one piece laminated top with 4"
	Demolish and Install	L.F.	35	20.45		55.45	backsplash.
	Reinstall	L.F.		11.84		11.84	
	Clean	L.F.	.12	.77		.89	
	Minimum Charge	Job		207		207	

Cabinets and Countertops

Countertop		Unit	Material	Labor	Equip.	Total	Specification
Roll Top							
	Demolish	L.F.		5.65		5.65	Includes material and labor to install
	Install	L.F.	12.10	13.80		25.90	one piece laminated top with rolled
	Demolish and Install	L.F.	12.10	19.45		31.55	drip edge (post formed) and
	Reinstall	L.F.		11.05		11.05	backsplash.
	Clean	L.F.	.18	1.16		1.34	
	Minimum Charge	Job		207		207	
Ceramic Tile							
	Demolish	S.F.		2.84		2.84	Cost includes material and labor to
	Install	S.F.	18.15	8.30		26.45	install 4-1/4" x 4-1/4" to 6" x 6"
	Demolish and Install	S.F.	18.15	11.14		29.29	glazed tile set in mortar bed and grout
	Clean	S.F.	.09	.58		.67	on particle board substrate.
	Minimum Charge	Job		184		184	
Cultured Marble							
	Demolish	L.F.		5.65		5.65	Includes material and labor to install
	Install	L.F.	49.50	40.50		90	marble countertop, 24" wide, no
	Demolish and Install	L.F.	49.50	46.15		95.65	backsplash.
	Reinstall	L.F.		32.58		32.58	
	Clean	L.F.	.18	1.16		1.34	
	Minimum Charge	Job		184		184	
With Splash							
	Demolish	L.F.		5.65		5.65	Includes material and labor to install
	Install	L.F.	57	40.50		97.50	marble countertop, 24" wide, with
	Demolish and Install	L.F.	57	46.15		103.15	backsplash.
	Reinstall	L.F.		32.58		32.58	
	Clean	L.F.	.18	1.16		1.34	
	Minimum Charge	Job		184		184	
Quarry Tile							
	Demolish	S.F.		2.84		2.84	Includes material and labor to install
	Install	S.F.	9	8.30		17.30	quarry tile countertop with no
	Demolish and Install	S.F.	9	11.14		20.14	backsplash.
	Clean	S.F.	.09	.58		.67	
	Minimum Charge	Job		184		184	
With Splash							
	Demolish	S.F.		2.84		2.84	Includes material and labor to install
	Install	S.F.	12	9.20		21.20	quarry tile countertop with backsplash.
	Demolish and Install	S.F.	12	12.04		24.04	
	Clean	S.F.	.09	.58		.67	
	Minimum Charge	Job		184		184	
Butcher Block							
	Demolish	S.F.		2.84		2.84	Includes material and labor to install
	Install	S.F.	40.50	7.40		47.90	solid laminated maple countertop with
	Demolish and Install	S.F.	40.50	10.24		50.74	no backsplash.
	Reinstall	S.F.		5.92		5.92	
	Clean	S.F.	.03	.24		.27	
	Minimum Charge	Job		207		207	
Solid Surface							
	Demolish	L.F.		5.65		5.65	Includes material and labor to install
	Install	L.F.	49	29.50		78.50	solid surface counter top 22" deep.
	Demolish and Install	L.F.	49	35.15		84.15	
	Reinstall	L.F.		23.68		23.68	
	Clean	L.F.	.18	1.16		1.34	
	Minimum Charge	Job		207		207	

Cabinets and Countertops

Vanity Cabinets

Vanity Cabinets	Unit	Material	Labor	Equip.	Total	Specification
Good Grade Laminated						
24″ Wide, 2 Door						
Demolish	Ea.		17		17	Includes material and labor to install
Install	Ea.	191	41.50		232.50	modular unit with melamine laminated
Demolish and Install	Ea.	191	58.50		249.50	to particle board, textured colors or
Reinstall	Ea.		33.15		33.15	wood grain print finish, hinges and
Clean	Ea.	1.84	12.25		14.09	pulls.
Paint	Ea.	1.36	29.50		30.86	
Minimum Charge	Job		207		207	
30″ Wide, 2 Door						
Demolish	Ea.		21.50		21.50	Includes material and labor to install
Install	Ea.	221	52		273	modular unit with melamine laminated
Demolish and Install	Ea.	221	73.50		294.50	to particle board, textured colors or
Reinstall	Ea.		41.44		41.44	wood grain print finish, hinges and
Clean	Ea.	2.39	15.30		17.69	pulls.
Paint	Ea.	1.72	35.50		37.22	
Minimum Charge	Job		207		207	
36″ Wide, 2 Door						
Demolish	Ea.		26		26	Includes material and labor to install
Install	Ea.	294	62		356	modular unit with melamine laminated
Demolish and Install	Ea.	294	88		382	to particle board, textured colors or
Reinstall	Ea.		49.74		49.74	wood grain print finish, hinges and
Clean	Ea.	2.65	18		20.65	pulls.
Paint	Ea.	2.08	44.50		46.58	
Minimum Charge	Job		207		207	
42″ w, 3 Doors / Drawer						
Demolish	Ea.		31		31	Includes material and labor to install
Install	Ea.	425	67		492	modular unit with melamine laminated
Demolish and Install	Ea.	425	98		523	to particle board, textured colors or
Reinstall	Ea.		53.56		53.56	wood grain print finish, hinges and
Clean	Ea.	3.41	22		25.41	pulls.
Paint	Ea.	2.38	50.50		52.88	
Minimum Charge	Job		207		207	
48″ w, 3 Doors / Drawer						
Demolish	Ea.		34		34	Includes material and labor to install
Install	Ea.	350	72.50		422.50	modular unit with melamine laminated
Demolish and Install	Ea.	350	106.50		456.50	to particle board, textured colors or
Reinstall	Ea.		58.01		58.01	wood grain print finish, hinges and
Clean	Ea.	4.77	34		38.77	pulls.
Paint	Ea.	3.56	89		92.56	
Minimum Charge	Job		207		207	
Clean Interior						
Install	L.F.	.96	6.40		7.36	Includes labor and materials to clean
Minimum Charge	Job		153		153	base cabinetry.
Better Grade Wood						
24″ Wide, 2 Door						
Demolish	Ea.		17		17	Includes material and labor to install
Install	Ea.	256	41.50		297.50	custom modular unit with solid
Demolish and Install	Ea.	256	58.50		314.50	hardwood faced frames, hardwood
Reinstall	Ea.		33.15		33.15	door frames and drawer fronts,
Clean	Ea.	1.84	12.25		14.09	hardwood veneer on raised door
Paint	Ea.	1.36	32.50		33.86	panels, hinges and pulls.
Minimum Charge	Job		207		207	

Cabinets and Countertops

Vanity Cabinets	Unit	Material	Labor	Equip.	Total	Specification
30" Wide, 2 Door						
Demolish	Ea.		21.50		21.50	Includes material and labor to install
Install	Ea.	295	52		347	custom modular unit with solid
Demolish and Install	Ea.	295	73.50		368.50	hardwood faced frames, hardwood
Reinstall	Ea.		41.44		41.44	door frames and drawer fronts,
Clean	Ea.	2.39	15.30		17.69	hardwood veneer on raised door
Paint	Ea.	1.72	39.50		41.22	panels, hinges and pulls.
Minimum Charge	Job		207		207	
36" Wide, 2 Door						
Demolish	Ea.		26		26	Includes material and labor to install
Install	Ea.	390	62		452	custom modular unit with solid
Demolish and Install	Ea.	390	88		478	hardwood faced frames, hardwood
Reinstall	Ea.		49.74		49.74	door frames and drawer fronts,
Clean	Ea.	2.65	18		20.65	hardwood veneer on raised door
Paint	Ea.	2.08	50.50		52.58	panels, hinges and pulls.
Minimum Charge	Job		207		207	
42" w, 3 Doors / Drawer						
Demolish	Ea.		31		31	Includes material and labor to install
Install	Ea.	425	67		492	custom modular unit with solid
Demolish and Install	Ea.	425	98		523	hardwood faced frames, hardwood
Reinstall	Ea.		53.56		53.56	door frames and drawer fronts,
Clean	Ea.	3.41	22		25.41	hardwood veneer on raised door
Paint	Ea.	2.38	59		61.38	panels, hinges and pulls.
Minimum Charge	Job		207		207	
48" w, 3 Doors / Drawer						
Demolish	Ea.		34		34	Includes material and labor to install
Install	Ea.	470	72.50		542.50	custom modular unit with solid
Demolish and Install	Ea.	470	106.50		576.50	hardwood faced frames, hardwood
Reinstall	Ea.		58.01		58.01	door frames and drawer fronts,
Clean	Ea.	4.77	34		38.77	hardwood veneer on raised door
Paint	Ea.	3.56	89		92.56	panels, hinges and pulls.
Minimum Charge	Job		207		207	
Clean Interior						
Install	L.F.	.96	6.40		7.36	Includes labor and materials to clean
Minimum Charge	Job		153		153	base cabinetry.
Premium Grade Wood						
24" Wide, 2 Door						
Demolish	Ea.		17		17	Includes material and labor to install
Install	Ea.	294	41.50		335.50	premium modular unit with solid
Demolish and Install	Ea.	294	58.50		352.50	hardwood faced frames, hardwood
Reinstall	Ea.		33.15		33.15	door frames and drawer fronts,
Clean	Ea.	1.84	12.25		14.09	hardwood veneer on raised door
Paint	Ea.	1.36	35.50		36.86	panels, hinges and pulls.
Minimum Charge	Job		207		207	
30" Wide, 2 Door						
Demolish	Ea.		21.50		21.50	Includes material and labor to install
Install	Ea.	340	52		392	premium modular unit with solid
Demolish and Install	Ea.	340	73.50		413.50	hardwood faced frames, hardwood
Reinstall	Ea.		41.44		41.44	door frames and drawer fronts,
Clean	Ea.	2.39	15.30		17.69	hardwood veneer on raised door
Paint	Ea.	1.72	44.50		46.22	panels, hinges and pulls.
Minimum Charge	Job		207		207	

Cabinets and Countertops

Vanity Cabinets	Unit	Material	Labor	Equip.	Total	Specification
36″ Wide, 2 Door						
Demolish	Ea.		26		26	Includes material and labor to install
Install	Ea.	450	62		512	premium modular unit with solid
Demolish and Install	Ea.	450	88		538	hardwood faced frames, hardwood
Reinstall	Ea.		49.74		49.74	door frames and drawer fronts,
Clean	Ea.	2.65	18		20.65	hardwood veneer on raised door
Paint	Ea.	2.08	50.50		52.58	panels, hinges and pulls.
Minimum Charge	Job		207		207	
42″ w, 3 Doors / Drawer						
Demolish	Ea.		31		31	Includes material and labor to install
Install	Ea.	485	67		552	premium modular unit with solid
Demolish and Install	Ea.	485	98		583	hardwood faced frames, hardwood
Reinstall	Ea.		53.56		53.56	door frames and drawer fronts,
Clean	Ea.	3.41	22		25.41	hardwood veneer on raised door
Paint	Ea.	2.38	59		61.38	panels, hinges and pulls.
Minimum Charge	Job		207		207	
48″ w, 3 Doors / Drawer						
Demolish	Ea.		34		34	Includes material and labor to install
Install	Ea.	540	72.50		612.50	premium modular unit with solid
Demolish and Install	Ea.	540	106.50		646.50	hardwood faced frames, hardwood
Reinstall	Ea.		58.01		58.01	door frames and drawer fronts,
Clean	Ea.	4.77	34		38.77	hardwood veneer on raised door
Paint	Ea.	3.56	89		92.56	panels, hinges and pulls.
Minimum Charge	Job		207		207	
Clean Interior						
Install	L.F.	.96	6.40		7.36	Includes labor and materials to clean
Minimum Charge	Job		153		153	base cabinetry.
Premium Hardwood						
24″ Wide, 2 Door						
Demolish	Ea.		17		17	Includes material and labor to install
Install	Ea.	320	41.50		361.50	premium modular unit with solid
Demolish and Install	Ea.	320	58.50		378.50	hardwood faced frames, hardwood
Reinstall	Ea.		33.15		33.15	door frames and drawer fronts,
Clean	Ea.	1.84	12.25		14.09	hardwood veneer on raised door
Paint	Ea.	1.36	39.50		40.86	panels, hinges and pulls.
Minimum Charge	Job		207		207	
30″ Wide, 2 Door						
Demolish	Ea.		21.50		21.50	Includes material and labor to install
Install	Ea.	595	52		647	premium modular unit with solid
Demolish and Install	Ea.	595	73.50		668.50	hardwood faced frames, hardwood
Reinstall	Ea.		41.44		41.44	door frames and drawer fronts,
Clean	Ea.	2.39	15.30		17.69	hardwood veneer on raised door
Paint	Ea.	1.72	44.50		46.22	panels, hinges and pulls.
Minimum Charge	Job		207		207	
36″ Wide, 2 Door						
Demolish	Ea.		26		26	Includes material and labor to install
Install	Ea.	785	62		847	premium modular unit with solid
Demolish and Install	Ea.	785	88		873	hardwood faced frames, hardwood
Reinstall	Ea.		49.74		49.74	door frames and drawer fronts,
Clean	Ea.	2.65	18		20.65	hardwood veneer on raised door
Paint	Ea.	2.08	59		61.08	panels, hinges and pulls.
Minimum Charge	Job		207		207	

Cabinets and Countertops

Vanity Cabinets

Vanity Cabinets	Unit	Material	Labor	Equip.	Total	Specification
42″ w, 3 Doors / Drawer						
Demolish	Ea.		31		31	Includes material and labor to install
Install	Ea.	555	67		622	premium modular unit with solid
Demolish and Install	Ea.	555	98		653	hardwood faced frames, hardwood
Reinstall	Ea.		53.56		53.56	door frames and drawer fronts,
Clean	Ea.	3.41	22		25.41	hardwood veneer on raised door
Paint	Ea.	2.38	71		73.38	panels, hinges and pulls.
Minimum Charge	Job		207		207	
48″ w, 3 Doors / Drawer						
Demolish	Ea.		34		34	Includes material and labor to install
Install	Ea.	610	72.50		682.50	premium modular unit with solid
Demolish and Install	Ea.	610	106.50		716.50	hardwood faced frames, hardwood
Reinstall	Ea.		58.01		58.01	door frames and drawer fronts,
Clean	Ea.	4.77	34		38.77	hardwood veneer on raised door
Paint	Ea.	3.56	89		92.56	panels, hinges and pulls.
Minimum Charge	Job		207		207	
Clean Interior						
Install	L.F.	.96	6.40		7.36	Includes labor and materials to clean
Minimum Charge	Job		153		153	base cabinetry.
Strip and Refinish						
Install	L.F.	4.10	44.50		48.60	Includes labor and material to strip,
Minimum Charge	Job		178		178	prep and refinish exterior of cabinets.

Vanity Cabinet Tops

Vanity Cabinet Tops	Unit	Material	Labor	Equip.	Total	Specification
Cultured Marble Top						
Demolish	L.F.		5.65		5.65	Includes material and labor to install
Install	L.F.	45	24		69	cultured marble vanity top with
Demolish and Install	L.F.	45	29.65		74.65	integral sink, 22″ deep.
Reinstall	L.F.		19.16		19.16	
Clean	L.F.	.18	1.16		1.34	
Minimum Charge	Job		184		184	
Laminated Top						
Demolish	L.F.		3.40		3.40	Includes material and labor to install
Install	L.F.	35	14.80		49.80	one piece laminated top with 4″
Demolish and Install	L.F.	35	18.20		53.20	backsplash.
Reinstall	L.F.		11.84		11.84	
Clean	L.F.	.12	.77		.89	
Minimum Charge	Job		207		207	
Solid Surface						
Demolish	L.F.		5.65		5.65	Includes material and labor to install
Install	L.F.	68	30.50		98.50	solid surface vanity top with integral
Demolish and Install	L.F.	68	36.15		104.15	sink installed, 22″ deep.
Reinstall	L.F.		24.56		24.56	
Clean	L.F.	.18	1.16		1.34	
Minimum Charge	Job		207		207	

Painting

Roller Handle

Paint Brush

Paint Preparation, Walls		Unit	Material	Labor	Equip.	Total	Specification
Cover / Protect Floors							
	Install	S.F.	.56	.14		.70	Includes material and labor to install
	Minimum Charge	Job		179		179	plastic masking sheet on large uninterrupted areas.
Cover / Protect Walls							
	Install	S.F.	.03	.14		.17	Includes material and labor to install
	Minimum Charge	Job		179		179	plastic masking sheet on walls.
Clean Walls							
Light							
	Clean	S.F.		.11		.11	Includes labor to wash gypsum
	Minimum Charge	Job		179		179	drywall or plaster wall surfaces.
Heavy							
	Clean	S.F.		.14		.14	Includes labor and material for heavy
	Minimum Charge	Job		179		179	cleaning (multiple applications) with detergent and solvent.
Prep Walls							
	Paint	S.F.	.04	.18		.22	Includes labor and material to prepare
	Minimum Charge	Job		179		179	for painting including scraping, patching and puttying.
Sand Walls							
	Paint	S.F.		.12		.12	Includes labor to sand gypsum drywall
	Minimum Charge	Job		179		179	wall surfaces.
Seal Walls							
Large Area							
	Paint	S.F.	.07	.26		.33	Includes labor and material to paint
	Minimum Charge	Job		179		179	with primer / sealer by roller.
Spot							
	Paint	S.F.	.07	.31		.38	Includes labor and material to seal
	Minimum Charge	Job		179		179	existing drywall with shellac-based material.

Paint Preparation, Ceilings		Unit	Material	Labor	Equip.	Total	Specification
Cover / Protect Floors							
	Install	S.F.	.56	.14		.70	Includes material and labor to install
	Minimum Charge	Job		179		179	plastic masking sheet on large uninterrupted areas.

Painting

Paint Preparation, Ceilings

Paint Preparation, Ceilings		Unit	Material	Labor	Equip.	Total	Specification
Cover / Protect Walls							
	Install	S.F.	.03	.14		.17	Includes material and labor to install plastic masking sheet on walls.
	Minimum Charge	Job		179		179	
Prep Ceiling							
	Paint	S.F.	.07	.67		.74	Includes labor and material to fill in hairline cracks up to 1/8" with filler, sand and prep for paint.
	Minimum Charge	Job		179		179	
Sand Ceiling							
	Paint	S.F.		.16		.16	Includes labor to sand gypsum drywall ceiling surfaces.
	Minimum Charge	Job		179		179	
Seal Ceiling							
Large Area							
	Paint	S.F.	.14	.27		.41	Includes labor and material to paint ceiling, one coat flat latex.
	Minimum Charge	Job		178		178	
Spot							
	Paint	S.F.	.07	.31		.38	Includes labor and material to seal existing drywall with shellac-based material.
	Minimum Charge	Job		178		178	

Paint / Texture, Walls

Paint / Texture, Walls		Unit	Material	Labor	Equip.	Total	Specification
Texture Walls							
Spray							
	Install	S.F.	.04	.44		.48	Includes labor and material to install by spray, texture finish.
	Minimum Charge	Job		178		178	
Trowel							
	Install	S.F.		.24		.24	Includes labor and material to apply hand troweled texture.
	Minimum Charge	Job		178		178	
Paint Walls 1 Coat							
	Paint	S.F.	.14	.27		.41	Includes labor and material to paint, one coat flat latex.
	Minimum Charge	Job		178		178	
Paint Walls 2 Coats							
	Paint	S.F.	.13	.44		.57	Includes labor and material to paint, two coats flat latex.
	Minimum Charge	Job		178		178	
Paint Walls 3 Coats							
	Paint	S.F.	.21	.55		.76	Includes labor and material to paint, three coats flat latex.
	Minimum Charge	Job		178		178	
Clean and Seal							
	Paint	S.F.	.53	.95		1.48	Includes labor and material to do light cleaning, sealing with 2 coats of latex paint.
	Minimum Charge	Job		178		178	

Paint / Texture, Ceilings

Paint / Texture, Ceilings		Unit	Material	Labor	Equip.	Total	Specification
Texture Ceiling							
Spray							
	Install	S.F.	.04	.44		.48	Includes labor and material to install by spray, texture finish.
	Minimum Charge	Job		178		178	
Trowel							
	Install	S.F.		.24		.24	Includes labor and material to apply hand troweled texture.
	Minimum Charge	Job		178		178	

Painting

Paint / Texture, Ceilings		Unit	Material	Labor	Equip.	Total	Specification
Paint Ceiling, 1 Coat							
	Paint	S.F.	.14	.27		.41	Includes labor and material to paint
	Minimum Charge	Job		178		178	ceiling, one coat flat latex.
Paint Ceiling, 2 Coats							
	Paint	S.F.	.29	.44		.73	Includes labor and material to paint
	Minimum Charge	Job		178		178	two coats flat latex paint.
Paint Ceiling, 3 Coats							
	Paint	S.F.	.43	.52		.95	Includes labor and material to paint
	Minimum Charge	Job		178		178	ceiling, three coats flat latex.
Clean and Seal							
	Paint	S.F.	.43	.75		1.18	Includes labor and material for light
	Minimum Charge	Job		178		178	cleaning, sealing and paint 3 coats of flat latex paint.

Plank Flooring	Wood Strip Flooring	Tile Flooring

Wood Plank Flooring		Unit	Material	Labor	Equip.	Total	Specification
Maple							
2-1/4″							
	Demolish	S.F.		1.36		1.36	Includes material and labor to install
	Install	S.F.	4.69	2.07		6.76	unfinished T&G maple flooring,
	Demolish and Install	S.F.	4.69	3.43		8.12	25/32″ thick, 2-1/4″ wide, random
	Reinstall	S.F.		1.65		1.65	3′ to 16′ lengths including felt
	Clean	S.F.		.38		.38	underlayment, nailed in place over
	Paint	S.F.	1.41	2.36		3.77	prepared subfloor.
	Minimum Charge	Job		207		207	
3-1/4″							
	Demolish	S.F.		1.36		1.36	Includes material and labor to install
	Install	S.F.	3.97	2.07		6.04	unfinished T&G maple flooring,
	Demolish and Install	S.F.	3.97	3.43		7.40	33/32″ thick, 3-1/4″ wide, random
	Reinstall	S.F.		1.65		1.65	3′ to 16′ lengths including felt
	Clean	S.F.		.38		.38	underlayment, nailed in place over
	Paint	S.F.	1.41	2.36		3.77	prepared subfloor.
	Minimum Charge	Job		207		207	
Sand and Finish							
	Install	S.F.	.95	.77		1.72	Includes labor and material to sand (3
	Minimum Charge	Job		207		207	passes) and finish and two coats of
							urethane existing floor.
Oak							
2-1/4″							
	Demolish	S.F.		1.36		1.36	Includes material and labor to install
	Install	S.F.	3.10	2.07		5.17	unfinished T&G oak flooring, 25/32″
	Demolish and Install	S.F.	3.10	3.43		6.53	thick, 2-1/4″ wide, random 3′ to 16′
	Reinstall	S.F.		1.65		1.65	lengths including felt underlayment,
	Clean	S.F.		.38		.38	nailed in place over prepared
	Paint	S.F.	1.41	2.36		3.77	subfloor.
	Minimum Charge	Job		207		207	
3-1/4″							
	Demolish	S.F.		1.36		1.36	Includes material and labor to install
	Install	S.F.	4.46	1.46		5.92	unfinished T&G oak flooring, 25/32″
	Demolish and Install	S.F.	4.46	2.82		7.28	thick, 3-1/4″ wide, random 3′ to 16′
	Reinstall	S.F.		1.17		1.17	lengths including felt underlayment,
	Clean	S.F.		.38		.38	nailed in place over prepared
	Paint	S.F.	1.41	2.36		3.77	subfloor.
	Minimum Charge	Job		207		207	

Wood Plank Flooring		Unit	Material	Labor	Equip.	Total	Specification
Sand and Finish							
	Install	S.F.	1.41	2.36		3.77	Includes labor and material to sand
	Minimum Charge	Job		207		207	and finish (3 passes) with two coats of
							urethane on a new floor.
Walnut							
3″ to 7″							
	Demolish	S.F.		1.36		1.36	Includes material and labor to install
	Install	S.F.	9.50	1.46		10.96	unfinished T&G walnut flooring,
	Demolish and Install	S.F.	9.50	2.82		12.32	25/32″ thick, random 3′ to 16′
	Reinstall	S.F.		1.17		1.17	lengths including felt underlayment,
	Clean	S.F.		.38		.38	nailed in place over prepared
	Paint	S.F.	1.41	2.36		3.77	subfloor.
	Minimum Charge	Job		207		207	
Sand and Finish							
	Install	S.F.	1.41	2.36		3.77	Includes labor and material to sand
	Minimum Charge	Job		207		207	and finish (3 passes) with two coats of
							urethane on a new floor.
Pine							
2-1/4″							
	Demolish	S.F.		1.36		1.36	Includes material and labor to install
	Install	S.F.	7.60	1.56		9.16	unfinished T&G pine flooring, 25/32″
	Demolish and Install	S.F.	7.60	2.92		10.52	thick, 2-1/4″ wide, random 3′ to 16′
	Reinstall	S.F.		1.25		1.25	lengths including felt underlayment,
	Clean	S.F.		.38		.38	nailed in place over prepared
	Paint	S.F.	.95	.77		1.72	subfloor.
	Minimum Charge	Job		207		207	
Sand and Finish							
	Install	S.F.	1.41	2.36		3.77	Includes labor and material to sand
	Minimum Charge	Job		207		207	and finish (3 passes) with two coats of
							urethane on a new floor.
Prefinished Oak							
2-1/4″							
	Demolish	S.F.		1.36		1.36	Includes material and labor to install
	Install	S.F.	4.32	2.07		6.39	prefinished T&G oak flooring, 2-1/4″
	Demolish and Install	S.F.	4.32	3.43		7.75	wide, random 3′ to 16′ lengths
	Reinstall	S.F.		1.65		1.65	including felt underlayment, nailed in
	Clean	S.F.		.38		.38	place over prepared subfloor.
	Minimum Charge	Job		207		207	
3-1/4″							
	Demolish	S.F.		1.36		1.36	Includes material and labor to install
	Install	S.F.	4.56	1.90		6.46	prefinished T&G oak flooring, 25/32″
	Demolish and Install	S.F.	4.56	3.26		7.82	thick, 3″ to 7″ wide, random 3′ to 16′
	Reinstall	S.F.		1.52		1.52	lengths including felt underlayment,
	Clean	S.F.		.38		.38	nailed in place over prepared
	Minimum Charge	Job		207		207	subfloor.
Sand and Finish New							
	Install	S.F.	.95	1.04		1.99	Includes labor and material to sand (3
	Minimum Charge	Job		207		207	passes) and finish, two coats of
							urethane, new floor.
Refinish Existing							
	Install	S.F.	.95	.77		1.72	Includes labor and material to sand (3
	Minimum Charge	Job		207		207	passes) and finish and two coats of
							urethane existing floor.

Flooring

Wood Plank Flooring

		Unit	Material	Labor	Equip.	Total	Specification
Urethane Coat							
	Install	S.F.	.17	.19		.36	Includes labor and material to install
	Minimum Charge	Job		207		207	two coats of urethane, on existing floor.
Clean and Wax							
	Clean	S.F.	.03	.24		.27	Includes labor and material to wash
	Minimum Charge	Job		207		207	and wax a hardwood floor.
Underlayment Per S.F.							
	Demolish	S.F.		.61		.61	Cost includes material and labor to
	Install	S.F.	.73	.55		1.28	install 1/4" lauan subfloor, standard
	Demolish and Install	S.F.	.73	1.16		1.89	interior grade, nailed every 6".
	Clean	S.F.		.30		.30	
	Minimum Charge	Job		207		207	

Wood Parquet Tile Floor

		Unit	Material	Labor	Equip.	Total	Specification
Oak							
9" x 9"							
	Demolish	S.F.		1.02		1.02	Includes material and labor to install
	Install	S.F.	5.10	3.32		8.42	prefinished oak 9" x 9" parquet block
	Demolish and Install	S.F.	5.10	4.34		9.44	flooring, 5/16" thick, installed in
	Reinstall	S.F.		2.65		2.65	mastic.
	Clean	S.F.		.38		.38	
	Paint	S.F.	1.41	2.36		3.77	
	Minimum Charge	Job		207		207	
13" x 13"							
	Demolish	S.F.		1.02		1.02	Includes material and labor to install
	Install	S.F.	9.35	2.59		11.94	prefinished oak 13" x 13" parquet
	Demolish and Install	S.F.	9.35	3.61		12.96	block flooring, 5/16" thick, installed in
	Reinstall	S.F.		2.07		2.07	mastic.
	Clean	S.F.		.38		.38	
	Paint	S.F.	1.41	2.36		3.77	
	Minimum Charge	Job		207		207	
Cherry							
9" x 9"							
	Demolish	S.F.		1.02		1.02	Includes material and labor to install
	Install	S.F.	8.55	3.32		11.87	prefinished cherry 9" x 9" parquet
	Demolish and Install	S.F.	8.55	4.34		12.89	block flooring, 5/16" thick, installed in
	Reinstall	S.F.		3.32		3.32	mastic.
	Clean	S.F.		.38		.38	
	Paint	S.F.	1.41	2.36		3.77	
	Minimum Charge	Job		207		207	
13" x 13"							
	Demolish	S.F.		1.02		1.02	Includes material and labor to install
	Install	S.F.	9.75	2.59		12.34	prefinished cherry 13" x 13" parquet
	Demolish and Install	S.F.	9.75	3.61		13.36	block flooring, 5/16" thick, installed in
	Reinstall	S.F.		2.59		2.59	mastic.
	Clean	S.F.		.38		.38	
	Paint	S.F.	1.41	2.36		3.77	
	Minimum Charge	Job		207		207	

Flooring

Wood Parquet Tile Floor

Wood Parquet Tile Floor	Unit	Material	Labor	Equip.	Total	Specification
Walnut						
9″ x 9″						
Demolish	S.F.		1.02		1.02	Includes material and labor to install
Install	S.F.	5.45	3.32		8.77	prefinished walnut 9″ x 9″ parquet
Demolish and Install	S.F.	5.45	4.34		9.79	flooring in mastic.
Reinstall	S.F.		2.65		2.65	
Clean	S.F.		.38		.38	
Paint	S.F.	1.41	2.36		3.77	
Minimum Charge	Job		207		207	
13″ x 13″						
Demolish	S.F.		1.02		1.02	Includes material and labor to install
Install	S.F.	10.10	2.59		12.69	prefinished walnut 13″ x 13″ parquet
Demolish and Install	S.F.	10.10	3.61		13.71	block flooring, 5/16″ thick, installed in
Reinstall	S.F.		2.59		2.59	mastic.
Clean	S.F.		.38		.38	
Paint	S.F.	1.41	2.36		3.77	
Minimum Charge	Job		207		207	
Acrylic Impregnated						
Oak 12″ x 12″						
Demolish	S.F.		1.02		1.02	Includes material and labor to install
Install	S.F.	8.45	2.96		11.41	red oak 12″ x 12″ acrylic
Demolish and Install	S.F.	8.45	3.98		12.43	impregnated parquet block flooring,
Reinstall	S.F.		2.96		2.96	5/16″ thick, installed in mastic.
Clean	S.F.		.38		.38	
Minimum Charge	Job		207		207	
Cherry 12″ x 12″						
Demolish	S.F.		1.02		1.02	Includes material and labor to install
Install	S.F.	11.95	2.96		14.91	prefinished cherry 12″ x 12″ acrylic
Demolish and Install	S.F.	11.95	3.98		15.93	impregnated parquet block flooring,
Reinstall	S.F.		2.96		2.96	5/16″ thick, installed in mastic.
Clean	S.F.		.38		.38	
Minimum Charge	Job		207		207	
Ash 12″ x 12″						
Demolish	S.F.		1.02		1.02	Includes material and labor to install
Install	S.F.	10.75	2.96		13.71	ash 12″ x 12″ acrylic impregnated
Demolish and Install	S.F.	10.75	3.98		14.73	parquet block flooring, 5/16″ thick in
Reinstall	S.F.		2.96		2.96	mastic.
Clean	S.F.		.38		.38	
Minimum Charge	Job		207		207	
Teak						
Demolish	S.F.		1.02		1.02	Includes material and labor to install
Install	S.F.	9.20	2.59		11.79	prefinished teak parquet block
Demolish and Install	S.F.	9.20	3.61		12.81	flooring, 5/16″ thick, and installed in
Reinstall	S.F.		2.59		2.59	mastic.
Clean	S.F.		.38		.38	
Paint	S.F.	1.41	2.36		3.77	
Minimum Charge	Job		207		207	
Clean and Wax						
Clean	S.F.	.03	.24		.27	Includes labor and material to wash
Minimum Charge	Job		207		207	and wax a hardwood floor.

Flooring

Ceramic Tile Flooring

Ceramic Tile Flooring		Unit	Material	Labor	Equip.	Total	Specification
Economy Grade							
	Demolish	S.F.		1.01		1.01	Cost includes material and labor to
	Install	S.F.	8.70	7.20		15.90	install 4-1/4" x 4-1/4" ceramic tile in
	Demolish and Install	S.F.	8.70	8.21		16.91	mortar bed including grout.
	Clean	S.F.		.58		.58	
	Minimum Charge	Job		184		184	
Average Grade							
	Demolish	S.F.		1.01		1.01	Cost includes material and labor to
	Install	S.F.	11.05	7.35		18.40	install 4-1/4" x 4-1/4" ceramic tile in
	Demolish and Install	S.F.	11.05	8.36		19.41	mortar bed including grout.
	Clean	S.F.		.58		.58	
	Minimum Charge	Job		184		184	
Premium Grade							
	Demolish	S.F.		1.01		1.01	Cost includes material and labor to
	Install	S.F.	13.25	7.35		20.60	install 4-1/4" x 4-1/4" ceramic tile in
	Demolish and Install	S.F.	13.25	8.36		21.61	mortar bed including grout.
	Clean	S.F.		.58		.58	
	Minimum Charge	Job		184		184	
Re-grout							
	Install	S.F.	.15	2.94		3.09	Includes material and labor to regrout
	Minimum Charge	Job		184		184	tile floors.

Hard Tile Flooring

Hard Tile Flooring		Unit	Material	Labor	Equip.	Total	Specification
Thick Set Paver							
Brick							
	Demolish	S.F.		2.13		2.13	Cost includes material and labor to
	Install	S.F.	1.52	17.50		19.02	install 6" x 12" adobe brick paver with
	Demolish and Install	S.F.	1.52	19.63		21.15	1/2" mortar joints.
	Clean	S.F.		.58		.58	
	Minimum Charge	Job		184		184	
Mexican Red							
	Demolish	S.F.		2.13		2.13	Cost includes material and labor to
	Install	S.F.	1.80	7.65		9.45	install 12" x 12" red Mexican paver
	Demolish and Install	S.F.	1.80	9.78		11.58	tile in mortar bed with grout.
	Clean	S.F.		.58		.58	
	Minimum Charge	Job		184		184	
Saltillo							
	Demolish	S.F.		1.01		1.01	Cost includes material and labor to
	Install	S.F.	1.80	7.65		9.45	install 12" x 12"saltillo tile in mortar
	Demolish and Install	S.F.	1.80	8.66		10.46	bed with grout.
	Clean	S.F.		.58		.58	
	Minimum Charge	Job		184		184	
Marble							
Premium Grade							
	Demolish	S.F.		1.01		1.01	Cost includes material and labor to
	Install	S.F.	20.50	16		36.50	install 3/8" x 12" x 12" marble, in
	Demolish and Install	S.F.	20.50	17.01		37.51	mortar bed with grout.
	Clean	S.F.		.58		.58	
	Minimum Charge	Job		184		184	

Flooring

Hard Tile Flooring		Unit	Material	Labor	Equip.	Total	Specification
Terrazzo							
Gray Cement							
	Demolish	S.F.		1.35		1.35	Cost includes material and labor to
	Install	S.F.	3.47	8.90	3.84	16.21	install 1-3/4" terrazzo , #1 and #2
	Demolish and Install	S.F.	3.47	10.25	3.84	17.56	chips in gray Portland cement.
	Clean	S.F.		.58		.58	
	Minimum Charge	Job		335	144	479	
White Cement							
	Demolish	S.F.		1.35		1.35	Cost includes material and labor to
	Install	S.F.	3.86	8.90	3.84	16.60	install 1-3/4" terrazzo, #1 and #2
	Demolish and Install	S.F.	3.86	10.25	3.84	17.95	chips in white Portland cement.
	Clean	S.F.		.58		.58	
	Minimum Charge	Job		335	144	479	
Non-skid Gray							
	Demolish	S.F.		1.35		1.35	Cost includes material and labor to
	Install	S.F.	6.45	11.15	4.80	22.40	install 1-3/4" terrazzo, #1 and #2
	Demolish and Install	S.F.	6.45	12.50	4.80	23.75	chips in gray Portland cement with
	Clean	S.F.		.58		.58	light non-skid abrasive.
	Minimum Charge	Job		335	144	479	
Non-skid White							
	Demolish	S.F.		1.35		1.35	Cost includes material and labor to
	Install	S.F.	6.70	11.15	4.80	22.65	install 1-3/4" terrazzo, #1 and #2
	Demolish and Install	S.F.	6.70	12.50	4.80	24	chips in white Portland cement with
	Clean	S.F.		.58		.58	light non-skid abrasive.
	Minimum Charge	Job		335	144	479	
Gray w / Brass Divider							
	Demolish	S.F.		1.36		1.36	Cost includes material and labor to
	Install	S.F.	9.75	12.15	5.25	27.15	install 1-3/4" terrazzo, #1 and #2
	Demolish and Install	S.F.	9.75	13.51	5.25	28.51	chips in gray Portland cement with
	Clean	S.F.		.58		.58	brass strips 2' O.C. each way.
	Minimum Charge	Job		335	144	479	
Clean							
	Clean	S.F.	.21	.39		.60	Includes labor and material to clean
	Minimum Charge	Job		335	144	479	terrazzo flooring.
Slate							
	Demolish	S.F.		1.22		1.22	Includes material and labor to install
	Install	S.F.	8.25	3.65		11.90	slate tile flooring in thin set with grout.
	Demolish and Install	S.F.	8.25	4.87		13.12	
	Clean	S.F.		.58		.58	
	Minimum Charge	Job		184		184	
Granite							
	Demolish	S.F.		1		1	Includes material and labor to install
	Install	S.F.	22.50	3.68		26.18	granite tile flooring in thin set with
	Demolish and Install	S.F.	22.50	4.68		27.18	grout.
	Reinstall	S.F.		3.68		3.68	
	Clean	S.F.		.58		.58	
	Minimum Charge	Job		184		184	
Re-grout							
	Install	S.F.	.15	2.94		3.09	Includes material and labor to regrout
	Minimum Charge	Job		184		184	tile floors.

Flooring

Sheet Vinyl Per S.F.

	Unit	Material	Labor	Equip.	Total	Specification
Economy Grade						
Demolish	S.F.		.49		.49	Includes material and labor to install
Install	S.F.	2.37	1.15		3.52	resilient sheet vinyl flooring.
Demolish and Install	S.F.	2.37	1.64		4.01	
Clean	S.F.		.38		.38	
Minimum Charge	Job		184		184	
Average Grade						
Demolish	S.F.		.49		.49	Includes material and labor to install
Install	S.F.	3.75	1.15		4.90	resilient sheet vinyl flooring.
Demolish and Install	S.F.	3.75	1.64		5.39	
Clean	S.F.		.38		.38	
Minimum Charge	Job		184		184	
Premium Grade						
Demolish	S.F.		.49		.49	Includes material and labor to install
Install	S.F.	6	1.15		7.15	resilient sheet vinyl flooring.
Demolish and Install	S.F.	6	1.64		7.64	
Clean	S.F.		.38		.38	
Minimum Charge	Job		184		184	
Clean and Wax						
Clean	S.F.	.03	.19		.22	Includes labor and material to wash
Minimum Charge	Job		184		184	and wax a vinyl tile floor.

Sheet Vinyl

	Unit	Material	Labor	Equip.	Total	Specification
Economy Grade						
Demolish	S.Y.		4.39		4.39	Includes material and labor to install
Install	S.Y.	21	10.35		31.35	no wax sheet vinyl flooring.
Demolish and Install	S.Y.	21	14.74		35.74	
Clean	S.Y.		2.66		2.66	
Minimum Charge	Job		184		184	
Average Grade						
Demolish	S.Y.		4.39		4.39	Includes material and labor to install
Install	S.Y.	34	10.35		44.35	no wax sheet vinyl flooring.
Demolish and Install	S.Y.	34	14.74		48.74	
Clean	S.Y.		2.66		2.66	
Minimum Charge	Job		184		184	
Premium Grade						
Demolish	S.Y.		4.39		4.39	Includes material and labor to install
Install	S.Y.	53.50	10.35		63.85	no wax sheet vinyl flooring.
Demolish and Install	S.Y.	53.50	14.74		68.24	
Clean	S.Y.		2.66		2.66	
Minimum Charge	Job		184		184	
Clean and Wax						
Clean	S.F.	.03	.19		.22	Includes labor and material to wash
Minimum Charge	Job		184		184	and wax a vinyl tile floor.

Vinyl Tile

	Unit	Material	Labor	Equip.	Total	Specification
Economy Grade						
Demolish	S.F.		.68		.68	Includes material and labor to install
Install	S.F.	3.58	.74		4.32	no wax 12" x 12" vinyl tile.
Demolish and Install	S.F.	3.58	1.42		5	
Clean	S.F.		.38		.38	
Minimum Charge	Job		184		184	

Flooring

Vinyl Tile

	Unit	Material	Labor	Equip.	Total	Specification
Average Grade						
Demolish	S.F.		.68		.68	Includes material and labor to install
Install	S.F.	6.45	.74		7.19	no wax 12″ x 12″ vinyl tile.
Demolish and Install	S.F.	6.45	1.42		7.87	
Clean	S.F.		.38		.38	
Minimum Charge	Job		184		184	
Premium Grade						
Demolish	S.F.		.68		.68	Includes material and labor to install
Install	S.F.	15.40	.74		16.14	no wax 12″ x 12″ vinyl tile.
Demolish and Install	S.F.	15.40	1.42		16.82	
Clean	S.F.		.38		.38	
Minimum Charge	Job		184		184	
Clean and Wax						
Clean	S.F.	.03	.19		.22	Includes labor and material to wash
Minimum Charge	Job		184		184	and wax a vinyl tile floor.

Carpeting Per S.F.

	Unit	Material	Labor	Equip.	Total	Specification
Economy Grade						
Demolish	S.F.		.08		.08	Includes material and labor to install
Install	S.F.	1.45	.72		2.17	carpet including tack strips and hot
Demolish and Install	S.F.	1.45	.80		2.25	melt tape on seams.
Clean	S.F.		.53		.53	
Minimum Charge	Job		184		184	
Average Grade						
Demolish	S.F.		.08		.08	Includes material and labor to install
Install	S.F.	1.69	.72		2.41	carpet including tack strips and hot
Demolish and Install	S.F.	1.69	.80		2.49	melt tape on seams.
Clean	S.F.		.53		.53	
Minimum Charge	Job		184		184	
Premium Grade						
Demolish	S.F.		.08		.08	Includes material and labor to install
Install	S.F.	2.98	.72		3.70	carpet including tack strips and hot
Demolish and Install	S.F.	2.98	.80		3.78	melt tape on seams.
Clean	S.F.		.53		.53	
Minimum Charge	Job		184		184	
Indoor/Outdoor						
Demolish	S.F.		.08		.08	Includes material and labor to install
Install	S.F.	1.16	.87		2.03	indoor-outdoor carpet.
Demolish and Install	S.F.	1.16	.95		2.11	
Clean	S.F.		.53		.53	
Minimum Charge	Job		184		184	
100% Wool						
Average Grade						
Demolish	S.F.		.08		.08	Includes material and labor to install
Install	S.F.	11	.73		11.73	carpet including tack strips and hot
Demolish and Install	S.F.	11	.81		11.81	melt tape on seams.
Clean	S.F.		.53		.53	
Minimum Charge	Job		184		184	
Premium Grade						
Demolish	S.F.		.08		.08	Includes material and labor to install
Install	S.F.	12.20	.73		12.93	carpet including tack strips and hot
Demolish and Install	S.F.	12.20	.81		13.01	melt tape on seams.
Clean	S.F.		.53		.53	
Minimum Charge	Job		184		184	

Flooring

Carpeting Per S.F.

Carpeting Per S.F.		Unit	Material	Labor	Equip.	Total	Specification
Luxury Grade							
	Demolish	S.F.		.08		.08	Includes material and labor to install
	Install	S.F.	17.10	.73		17.83	carpet including tack strips and hot
	Demolish and Install	S.F.	17.10	.81		17.91	melt tape on seams.
	Clean	S.F.		.53		.53	
	Minimum Charge	Job		184		184	
Berber							
Average Grade							
	Demolish	S.F.		.08		.08	Includes material and labor to install
	Install	S.F.	4.06	.87		4.93	carpet including tack strips and hot
	Demolish and Install	S.F.	4.06	.95		5.01	melt tape on seams.
	Clean	S.F.		.53		.53	
	Minimum Charge	Job		184		184	
Premium Grade							
	Demolish	S.F.		.08		.08	Includes material and labor to install
	Install	S.F.	8	.87		8.87	carpet including tack strips and hot
	Demolish and Install	S.F.	8	.95		8.95	melt tape on seams.
	Clean	S.F.		.53		.53	
	Minimum Charge	Job		184		184	

Carpeting

Carpeting		Unit	Material	Labor	Equip.	Total	Specification
Indoor/Outdoor							
	Demolish	S.Y.		1.13		1.13	Includes material and labor to install
	Install	S.Y.	10.40	7.80		18.20	indoor-outdoor carpet.
	Demolish and Install	S.Y.	10.40	8.93		19.33	
	Reinstall	S.Y.		6.26		6.26	
	Clean	S.Y.		4.79		4.79	
	Minimum Charge	Job		184		184	
Economy Grade							
	Demolish	S.Y.		1.13		1.13	Includes material and labor to install
	Install	S.Y.	13.05	6.45		19.50	carpet including tack strips and hot
	Demolish and Install	S.Y.	13.05	7.58		20.63	melt tape on seams.
	Reinstall	S.Y.		5.16		5.16	
	Clean	S.Y.		4.79		4.79	
	Minimum Charge	Job		184		184	
Average Grade							
	Demolish	S.Y.		1.13		1.13	Includes material and labor to install
	Install	S.Y.	15.25	6.45		21.70	carpet including tack strips and hot
	Demolish and Install	S.Y.	15.25	7.58		22.83	melt tape on seams.
	Reinstall	S.Y.		5.16		5.16	
	Clean	S.Y.		4.79		4.79	
	Minimum Charge	Job		184		184	
Premium Grade							
	Demolish	S.Y.		1.13		1.13	Includes material and labor to install
	Install	S.Y.	27	6.45		33.45	carpet including tack strips and hot
	Demolish and Install	S.Y.	27	7.58		34.58	melt tape on seams.
	Reinstall	S.Y.		5.16		5.16	
	Clean	S.Y.		4.79		4.79	
	Minimum Charge	Job		184		184	

Flooring

Carpeting

	Unit	Material	Labor	Equip.	Total	Specification
100% Wool						
Average Grade						
Demolish	S.Y.		1.13		1.13	Includes material and labor to install
Install	S.Y.	99	6.55		105.55	wool carpet including tack strips and
Demolish and Install	S.Y.	99	7.68		106.68	hot melt tape on seams.
Reinstall	S.Y.		5.25		5.25	
Clean	S.Y.		4.79		4.79	
Minimum Charge	Job		184		184	
Premium Grade						
Demolish	S.Y.		1.13		1.13	Includes material and labor to install
Install	S.Y.	110	6.55		116.55	carpet including tack strips and hot
Demolish and Install	S.Y.	110	7.68		117.68	melt tape on seams.
Reinstall	S.Y.		5.25		5.25	
Clean	S.Y.		4.79		4.79	
Minimum Charge	Job		184		184	
Luxury Grade						
Demolish	S.Y.		1.13		1.13	Includes material and labor to install
Install	S.Y.	154	6.55		160.55	carpet including tack strips and hot
Demolish and Install	S.Y.	154	7.68		161.68	melt tape on seams.
Reinstall	S.Y.		5.25		5.25	
Clean	S.Y.		4.79		4.79	
Minimum Charge	Job		184		184	
Berber						
Average Grade						
Demolish	S.Y.		1.13		1.13	Includes material and labor to install
Install	S.Y.	36.50	7.80		44.30	berber carpet including tack strips and
Demolish and Install	S.Y.	36.50	8.93		45.43	hot melt tape on seams.
Reinstall	S.Y.		6.26		6.26	
Clean	S.Y.		4.79		4.79	
Minimum Charge	Job		184		184	
Premium Grade						
Demolish	S.Y.		1.13		1.13	Includes material and labor to install
Install	S.Y.	71.50	7.80		79.30	carpet including tack strips and hot
Demolish and Install	S.Y.	71.50	8.93		80.43	melt tape on seams.
Reinstall	S.Y.		6.26		6.26	
Clean	S.Y.		4.79		4.79	
Minimum Charge	Job		184		184	

Carpet Pad Per S.F.

	Unit	Material	Labor	Equip.	Total	Specification
Urethane						
Demolish	S.F.		.02		.02	Includes material and labor to install
Install	S.F.	.57	.27		.84	urethane carpet pad.
Demolish and Install	S.F.	.57	.29		.86	
Minimum Charge	Job		184		184	
Foam Rubber Slab						
Demolish	S.F.		.02		.02	Includes material and labor to install
Install	S.F.	.63	.27		.90	carpet pad, 3/8" thick foam rubber.
Demolish and Install	S.F.	.63	.29		.92	
Minimum Charge	Job		184		184	
Waffle						
Demolish	S.F.		.02		.02	Includes material and labor to install
Install	S.F.	.41	.03		.44	rubber waffle carpet pad.
Demolish and Install	S.F.	.41	.05		.46	
Minimum Charge	Job		184		184	

Flooring

Carpet Pad Per S.F.

Carpet Pad Per S.F.	Unit	Material	Labor	Equip.	Total	Specification
Jute						
Demolish	S.F.		.02		.02	Includes material and labor to install
Install	S.F.	.75	.24		.99	jute hair carpet pad.
Demolish and Install	S.F.	.75	.26		1.01	
Minimum Charge	Job		184		184	
Rebound						
Demolish	S.F.		.02		.02	Includes material and labor to install
Install	S.F.	.34	.20		.54	rebound carpet pad.
Demolish and Install	S.F.	.34	.22		.56	
Minimum Charge	Job		184		184	

Carpet Pad

Carpet Pad	Unit	Material	Labor	Equip.	Total	Specification
Urethane						
Demolish	S.Y.		.19		.19	Includes material and labor to install
Install	S.Y.	5.10	2.45		7.55	urethane carpet pad.
Demolish and Install	S.Y.	5.10	2.64		7.74	
Reinstall	S.Y.		1.96		1.96	
Minimum Charge	Job		184		184	
Foam Rubber Slab						
Demolish	S.Y.		.19		.19	Includes material and labor to install
Install	S.Y.	5.65	2.45		8.10	rubber slab carpet pad.
Demolish and Install	S.Y.	5.65	2.64		8.29	
Reinstall	S.Y.		1.96		1.96	
Minimum Charge	Job		184		184	
Waffle						
Demolish	S.Y.		.19		.19	Includes material and labor to install
Install	S.Y.	3.65	.27		3.92	rubber waffle carpet pad.
Demolish and Install	S.Y.	3.65	.46		4.11	
Reinstall	S.Y.		.22		.22	
Minimum Charge	Job		184		184	
Jute						
Demolish	S.Y.		.19		.19	Includes material and labor to install
Install	S.Y.	6.75	2.16		8.91	jute hair carpet pad.
Demolish and Install	S.Y.	6.75	2.35		9.10	
Reinstall	S.Y.		1.73		1.73	
Minimum Charge	Job		184		184	
Rebound						
Demolish	S.Y.		.19		.19	Includes material and labor to install
Install	S.Y.	3.11	1.83		4.94	rebound carpet pad.
Demolish and Install	S.Y.	3.11	2.02		5.13	
Reinstall	S.Y.		1.47		1.47	
Minimum Charge	Job		184		184	

Stair Components

Stair Components	Unit	Material	Labor	Equip.	Total	Specification
Carpeting						
Demolish	Ea.		2.06		2.06	Includes material and labor to install
Install	Riser	54.50	9.65		64.15	carpet and pad on stairs.
Demolish and Install	Riser	54.50	11.71		66.21	
Reinstall	Riser		7.74		7.74	
Clean	Ea.		4.79		4.79	
Minimum Charge	Job		184		184	

Tub/Shower

Stainless Steel Double Sink

Water Closet

Commode

	Unit	Material	Labor	Equip.	Total	Specification
Demolish	Ea.		47.50		47.50	Includes material and labor to install a
Install	Ea.	272	161		433	toilet with valve, seat and cover.
Demolish and Install	Ea.	272	208.50		480.50	
Reinstall	Ea.		129.16		129.16	
Clean	Ea.	.47	15.30		15.77	
Minimum Charge	Job		238		238	

Wall w / Flush Valve

	Unit	Material	Labor	Equip.	Total	Specification
Demolish	Ea.		47.50		47.50	Includes material and labor to install a
Install	Ea.	500	148		648	wall hung toilet with flush valve, seat
Demolish and Install	Ea.	500	195.50		695.50	and cover.
Reinstall	Ea.		118.02		118.02	
Clean	Ea.	.47	15.30		15.77	
Minimum Charge	Job		238		238	

Designer Floor Mount

	Unit	Material	Labor	Equip.	Total	Specification
Demolish	Ea.		47.50		47.50	Includes material and labor to install a
Install	Ea.	970	161		1131	toilet with valve, seat and cover.
Demolish and Install	Ea.	970	208.50		1178.50	
Reinstall	Ea.		129.16		129.16	
Clean	Ea.	.47	15.30		15.77	
Minimum Charge	Job		238		238	

Urinal

	Unit	Material	Labor	Equip.	Total	Specification
Demolish	Ea.		47.50		47.50	Includes material and labor to install a
Install	Ea.	320	285		605	wall hung urinal with flush valve.
Demolish and Install	Ea.	320	332.50		652.50	
Reinstall	Ea.		228.18		228.18	
Clean	Ea.	.47	15.30		15.77	
Minimum Charge	Job		238		238	

Bidet

Vitreous China

	Unit	Material	Labor	Equip.	Total	Specification
Demolish	Ea.		47.50		47.50	Includes material and labor to install a
Install	Ea.	675	171		846	vitreous china bidet complete with
Demolish and Install	Ea.	675	218.50		893.50	trim.
Reinstall	Ea.		136.91		136.91	
Clean	Ea.	.47	15.30		15.77	
Minimum Charge	Job		238		238	

Finish Mechanical

Commode

Commode		Unit	Material	Labor	Equip.	Total	Specification
Chrome Fittings							
	Install	Ea.	189	59.50		248.50	Includes labor and materials to install chrome fittings for a bidet.
Brass Fittings							
	Install	Ea.	208	59.50		267.50	Includes labor and materials to install brass fittings for a bidet.
Seat							
	Demolish	Ea.		19.80		19.80	Includes material and labor to install a toilet seat and cover.
	Install	Ea.	32	19.80		51.80	
	Demolish and Install	Ea.	32	39.60		71.60	
	Reinstall	Ea.		15.84		15.84	
	Clean	Ea.	.24	6.40		6.64	
	Minimum Charge	Job		238		238	
Rough-in							
	Install	Ea.	460	300		760	Includes labor and materials to install water supply pipe with valves and drain, waste and vent pipe with all couplings, hangers and fasteners necessary.

Sink (assembly)

Sink (assembly)		Unit	Material	Labor	Equip.	Total	Specification
Single							
Porcelain							
	Demolish	Ea.		29.50		29.50	Includes material and labor to install a single bowl enamel finished cast iron kitchen sink with faucet and drain.
	Install	Ea.	580	153		733	
	Demolish and Install	Ea.	580	182.50		762.50	
	Reinstall	Ea.		122.24		122.24	
	Clean	Ea.	.31	10.95		11.26	
	Minimum Charge	Job		238		238	
Stainless Steel							
	Demolish	Ea.		29.50		29.50	Includes material and labor to install a single bowl stainless steel kitchen sink with faucet and drain.
	Install	Ea.	710	153		863	
	Demolish and Install	Ea.	710	182.50		892.50	
	Reinstall	Ea.		122.24		122.24	
	Clean	Ea.	.31	10.95		11.26	
	Minimum Charge	Job		238		238	
Double							
Porcelain							
	Demolish	Ea.		34		34	Includes material and labor to install a double bowl enamel finished cast iron kitchen sink with faucet and drain.
	Install	Ea.	1150	178		1328	
	Demolish and Install	Ea.	1150	212		1362	
	Reinstall	Ea.		142.61		142.61	
	Clean	Ea.	.47	15.30		15.77	
	Minimum Charge	Job		238		238	
Stainless Steel							
	Demolish	Ea.		34		34	Includes material and labor to install a double bowl stainless steel kitchen sink with faucet and drain.
	Install	Ea.	455	178		633	
	Demolish and Install	Ea.	455	212		667	
	Reinstall	Ea.		142.61		142.61	
	Clean	Ea.	.47	15.30		15.77	
	Minimum Charge	Job		238		238	
Bar							
	Demolish	Ea.		29.50		29.50	Includes material and labor to install a small single bowl stainless steel bar / vegetable / kitchen sink with faucet and drain.
	Install	Ea.	190	119		309	
	Demolish and Install	Ea.	190	148.50		338.50	
	Reinstall	Ea.		95.04		95.04	
	Clean	Ea.	.31	10.95		11.26	
	Minimum Charge	Job		238		238	

Finish Mechanical

Sink (assembly)

		Unit	Material	Labor	Equip.	Total	Specification
Floor							Includes material and labor to install
	Demolish	Ea.		95		95	an enameled cast iron floor mounted
	Install	Ea.	970	194		1164	corner service sink with faucet and
	Demolish and Install	Ea.	970	289		1259	drain.
	Reinstall	Ea.		155.58		155.58	
	Clean	Ea.	.47	7.65		8.12	
	Minimum Charge	Job		238		238	
Pedestal							Includes material and labor to install a
	Demolish	Ea.		29.50		29.50	vitreous china pedestal lavatory with
	Install	Ea.	430	134		564	faucet set and pop-up drain.
	Demolish and Install	Ea.	430	163.50		593.50	
	Reinstall	Ea.		106.96		106.96	
	Clean	Ea.	.31	10.95		11.26	
	Minimum Charge	Job		238		238	
Vanity Lavatory							Includes material and labor to install a
	Demolish	Ea.		29.50		29.50	vitreous china lavatory with faucet set
	Install	Ea.	294	158		452	and pop-up drain.
	Demolish and Install	Ea.	294	187.50		481.50	
	Reinstall	Ea.		126.77		126.77	
	Clean	Ea.	.31	10.95		11.26	
	Minimum Charge	Job		238		238	
Rough-in							Includes labor and materials to install
	Install	Ea.	515	400		915	copper supply pipe with valves and
							drain, waste and vent pipe with all
							couplings, hangers and fasteners
							necessary.
Laundry							Includes material and labor to install a
	Demolish	Ea.		30.50		30.50	laundry sink (wall mounted or with
	Install	Ea.	164	132		296	legs) including faucet and pop up
	Demolish and Install	Ea.	164	162.50		326.50	drain.
	Clean	Ea.	.31	10.95		11.26	
	Minimum Charge	Job		238		238	

Sink Only

		Unit	Material	Labor	Equip.	Total	Specification
Single							
Porcelain							Includes material and labor to install a
	Demolish	Ea.		29.50		29.50	single bowl enamel finished cast iron
	Install	Ea.	495	170		665	kitchen sink.
	Demolish and Install	Ea.	495	199.50		694.50	
	Reinstall	Ea.		135.77		135.77	
	Clean	Ea.	.31	10.95		11.26	
	Minimum Charge	Job		238		238	
Stainless Steel							Includes material and labor to install a
	Demolish	Ea.		29.50		29.50	single bowl stainless steel kitchen sink.
	Install	Ea.	625	119		744	
	Demolish and Install	Ea.	625	148.50		773.50	
	Reinstall	Ea.		95.04		95.04	
	Clean	Ea.	.31	10.95		11.26	
	Minimum Charge	Job		238		238	

Finish Mechanical

Sink Only

	Unit	Material	Labor	Equip.	Total	Specification
Double						
Porcelain						
Demolish	Ea.		34		34	Includes material and labor to install a
Install	Ea.	221	198		419	double bowl enamel finished cast iron
Demolish and Install	Ea.	221	232		453	kitchen sink.
Reinstall	Ea.		158.40		158.40	
Clean	Ea.	.47	15.30		15.77	
Minimum Charge	Job		238		238	
Stainless Steel						
Demolish	Ea.		34		34	Includes material and labor to install a
Install	Ea.	935	153		1088	double bowl stainless steel kitchen
Demolish and Install	Ea.	935	187		1122	sink.
Reinstall	Ea.		122.63		122.63	
Clean	Ea.	.47	15.30		15.77	
Minimum Charge	Job		238		238	
Bar						
Demolish	Ea.		29.50		29.50	Includes material and labor to install a
Install	Ea.	75.50	119		194.50	small single bowl stainless steel bar /
Demolish and Install	Ea.	75.50	148.50		224	vegetable / kitchen sink.
Reinstall	Ea.		95.04		95.04	
Clean	Ea.	.31	10.95		11.26	
Minimum Charge	Job		238		238	
Floor						
Demolish	Ea.		95		95	Includes material and labor to install
Install	Ea.	835	216		1051	an enameled cast iron floor mounted
Demolish and Install	Ea.	835	311		1146	corner service sink.
Reinstall	Ea.		172.80		172.80	
Clean	Ea.	.47	7.65		8.12	
Minimum Charge	Job		238		238	
Pedestal						
Demolish	Ea.		29.50		29.50	Includes material and labor to install a
Install	Ea.	315	149		464	vitreous china pedestal lavatory.
Demolish and Install	Ea.	315	178.50		493.50	
Reinstall	Ea.		118.80		118.80	
Clean	Ea.	.31	10.95		11.26	
Minimum Charge	Job		238		238	
Vanity Lavatory						
Demolish	Ea.		29.50		29.50	Includes material and labor to install a
Install	Ea.	168	149		317	vitreous china lavatory.
Demolish and Install	Ea.	168	178.50		346.50	
Reinstall	Ea.		118.80		118.80	
Clean	Ea.	.31	10.95		11.26	
Minimum Charge	Job		238		238	
Rough-in						
Install	Ea.	460	370		830	Includes labor and materials to install copper supply pipe with valves and drain, waste and vent pipe with all couplings, hangers and fasteners necessary.
Faucet Sink						
Good Grade						
Demolish	Ea.		24		24	Includes material and labor to install a
Install	Ea.	67.50	33		100.50	sink faucet and fittings.
Demolish and Install	Ea.	67.50	57		124.50	
Reinstall	Ea.		26.24		26.24	
Clean	Ea.	.19	9.60		9.79	
Minimum Charge	Job		238		238	

Finish Mechanical

Sink Only

	Unit	Material	Labor	Equip.	Total	Specification
Better Grade						Includes material and labor to install a sink faucet and fittings.
Demolish	Ea.		24		24	
Install	Ea.	114	33		147	
Demolish and Install	Ea.	114	57		171	
Reinstall	Ea.		26.24		26.24	
Clean	Ea.	.19	9.60		9.79	
Minimum Charge	Job		238		238	
Premium Grade						Includes material and labor to install a sink faucet and fittings.
Demolish	Ea.		24		24	
Install	Ea.	222	41		263	
Demolish and Install	Ea.	222	65		287	
Reinstall	Ea.		32.72		32.72	
Clean	Ea.	.19	9.60		9.79	
Minimum Charge	Job		238		238	
Drain & Basket						Includes material and labor to install a sink drain and basket.
Demolish	Ea.		14.85		14.85	
Install	Ea.	13.35	29.50		42.85	
Demolish and Install	Ea.	13.35	44.35		57.70	
Reinstall	Ea.		23.76		23.76	
Clean	Ea.	.19	9.60		9.79	
Minimum Charge	Job		238		238	

Bathtub

	Unit	Material	Labor	Equip.	Total	Specification
Enameled Steel						Includes labor and material to install a formed steel bath tub with spout, mixing valve, shower head and pop-up drain.
Demolish	Ea.		85.50		85.50	
Install	Ea.	535	156		691	
Demolish and Install	Ea.	535	241.50		776.50	
Reinstall	Ea.		124.46		124.46	
Clean	Ea.	.96	25.50		26.46	
Minimum Charge	Job		238		238	
Cast Iron						Includes material and labor to install a cast iron bath tub with spout, mixing valve, shower head and pop-up drain.
Demolish	Ea.		85.50		85.50	
Install	Ea.	1125	194		1319	
Demolish and Install	Ea.	1125	279.50		1404.50	
Reinstall	Ea.		155.58		155.58	
Clean	Ea.	.96	25.50		26.46	
Minimum Charge	Job		238		238	
Fiberglass						Includes material and labor to install an acrylic soaking tub with spout, mixing valve, shower head and pop-up drain.
Demolish	Ea.		85.50		85.50	
Install	Ea.	1975	156		2131	
Demolish and Install	Ea.	1975	241.50		2216.50	
Reinstall	Ea.		124.46		124.46	
Clean	Ea.	.96	25.50		26.46	
Minimum Charge	Job		238		238	
Institutional						Includes material and labor to install a hospital / institutional type bathtub with spout, mixing valve, shower head and pop-up drain.
Demolish	Ea.		85.50		85.50	
Install	Ea.	1300	285		1585	
Demolish and Install	Ea.	1300	370.50		1670.50	
Reinstall	Ea.		228.18		228.18	
Clean	Ea.	.96	25.50		26.46	
Minimum Charge	Job		238		238	

Finish Mechanical

Bathtub	Unit	Material	Labor	Equip.	Total	Specification
Whirlpool (Acrylic)						
Demolish	Ea.		264		264	Includes material and labor to install a
Install	Ea.	1825	855		2680	molded fiberglass whirlpool tub.
Demolish and Install	Ea.	1825	1119		2944	
Reinstall	Ea.		684.54		684.54	
Clean	Ea.	.96	25.50		26.46	
Minimum Charge	Job		238		238	
Pump / Motor						
Demolish	Ea.		66		66	Includes material and labor to install a
Install	Ea.	246	143		389	whirlpool tub pump / motor.
Demolish and Install	Ea.	246	209		455	
Reinstall	Ea.		114.16		114.16	
Clean	Ea.	.24	19.15		19.39	
Minimum Charge	Job		238		238	
Heater / Motor						
Demolish	Ea.		66		66	Includes material and labor to install a
Install	Ea.	350	211		561	whirlpool tub heater.
Demolish and Install	Ea.	350	277		627	
Reinstall	Ea.		168.96		168.96	
Clean	Ea.	.24	19.15		19.39	
Minimum Charge	Job		238		238	
Thermal Cover						
Demolish	Ea.		10.55		10.55	Includes material and labor to install a
Install	Ea.	228	29.50		257.50	whirlpool tub thermal cover.
Demolish and Install	Ea.	228	40.05		268.05	
Reinstall	Ea.		23.76		23.76	
Clean	Ea.	2.39	19.15		21.54	
Minimum Charge	Job		238		238	
Tub / Shower Combination						
Demolish	Ea.		75.50		75.50	Includes material and labor to install a
Install	Ea.	870	214		1084	fiberglass module tub with shower
Demolish and Install	Ea.	870	289.50		1159.50	surround with spout, mixing valve,
Reinstall	Ea.		171.14		171.14	shower head and pop-up drain.
Clean	Ea.	1.20	38.50		39.70	
Minimum Charge	Job		238		238	
Accessories						
Sliding Door						
Demolish	Ea.		21.50		21.50	Includes material and labor to install a
Install	Ea.	595	96.50		691.50	48" aluminum framed tempered glass
Demolish and Install	Ea.	595	118		713	shower door.
Reinstall	Ea.		77.14		77.14	
Clean	Ea.	1.99	12.75		14.74	
Minimum Charge	Job		238		238	
Shower Head						
Demolish	Ea.		5.95		5.95	Includes material and labor to install a
Install	Ea.	57	19.80		76.80	water saving shower head.
Demolish and Install	Ea.	57	25.75		82.75	
Reinstall	Ea.		15.84		15.84	
Clean	Ea.	.02	3.83		3.85	
Minimum Charge	Job		238		238	
Faucet Set						
Demolish	Ea.		29.50		29.50	Includes material and labor to install a
Install	Ea.	95	59.50		154.50	combination spout / diverter for a
Demolish and Install	Ea.	95	89		184	bathtub.
Reinstall	Ea.		47.52		47.52	
Clean	Ea.	.19	9.60		9.79	
Minimum Charge	Job		238		238	

Finish Mechanical

Bathtub

		Unit	Material	Labor	Equip.	Total	Specification
Shower Rod							Includes material and labor to install a chrome plated shower rod.
	Demolish	Ea.		3.55		3.55	
	Install	Ea.	31	32		63	
	Demolish and Install	Ea.	31	35.55		66.55	
	Reinstall	Ea.		25.50		25.50	
	Clean	Ea.		3.83		3.83	
	Minimum Charge	Job		238		238	
Rough-in							Includes labor and materials to install copper supply pipe with valves and drain, waste and vent pipe with all couplings, hangers and fasteners necessary.
	Install	Ea.	535	415		950	

Shower

		Unit	Material	Labor	Equip.	Total	Specification
Fiberglass							
32" x 32"							Includes material and labor to install a fiberglass shower stall with door, mixing valve and shower head and drain fitting.
	Demolish	Ea.		178		178	
	Install	Ea.	600	156		756	
	Demolish and Install	Ea.	600	334		934	
	Reinstall	Ea.		124.46		124.46	
	Clean	Ea.	.96	25.50		26.46	
	Minimum Charge	Job		238		238	
36" x 36"							Includes material and labor to install a fiberglass shower stall with door, mixing valve and shower head and drain fitting.
	Demolish	Ea.		178		178	
	Install	Ea.	610	156		766	
	Demolish and Install	Ea.	610	334		944	
	Reinstall	Ea.		124.46		124.46	
	Clean	Ea.	.96	25.50		26.46	
	Minimum Charge	Job		238		238	
35" x 60"							Includes material and labor to install a handicap fiberglass shower stall with door & seat, mixing valve and shower head and drain fitting.
	Demolish	Ea.		178		178	
	Install	Ea.	825	214		1039	
	Demolish and Install	Ea.	825	392		1217	
	Reinstall	Ea.		171.14		171.14	
	Clean	Ea.	.96	25.50		26.46	
	Minimum Charge	Job		238		238	
Accessories							
Single Door							Includes material and labor to install a shower door.
	Demolish	Ea.		21.50		21.50	
	Install	Ea.	147	51		198	
	Demolish and Install	Ea.	147	72.50		219.50	
	Reinstall	Ea.		40.71		40.71	
	Clean	Ea.	1.99	12.75		14.74	
	Minimum Charge	Job		238		238	
Shower Head							Includes material and labor to install a water saving shower head.
	Demolish	Ea.		5.95		5.95	
	Install	Ea.	57	19.80		76.80	
	Demolish and Install	Ea.	57	25.75		82.75	
	Reinstall	Ea.		15.84		15.84	
	Clean	Ea.	.02	3.83		3.85	
	Minimum Charge	Job		238		238	

Finish Mechanical

Shower

	Unit	Material	Labor	Equip.	Total	Specification
Faucet Set						
Demolish	Ea.		29.50		29.50	Includes material and labor to install a
Install	Ea.	95	59.50		154.50	combination spout / diverter for a
Demolish and Install	Ea.	95	89		184	bathtub.
Reinstall	Ea.		47.52		47.52	
Clean	Ea.	.19	9.60		9.79	
Minimum Charge	Job		238		238	
Shower Pan						
Demolish	Ea.		22		22	Includes material and labor to install
Install	Ea.	118	59.50		177.50	the base portion of a fiberglass
Demolish and Install	Ea.	118	81.50		199.50	shower unit.
Reinstall	Ea.		47.52		47.52	
Clean	Ea.	.96	25.50		26.46	
Minimum Charge	Job		238		238	
Rough-in						
Install	Ea.	650	415		1065	Includes labor and materials to install copper supply pipe with valves and drain, waste and vent pipe with all couplings, hangers and fasteners necessary.

Ductwork

	Unit	Material	Labor	Equip.	Total	Specification
Return Grill						
Under 10" Wide						
Demolish	Ea.		10.20		10.20	Includes material and labor to install a
Install	Ea.	40	25.50		65.50	10" x 10" air return register.
Demolish and Install	Ea.	40	35.70		75.70	
Reinstall	Ea.		20.36		20.36	
Clean	Ea.	.24	8.50		8.74	
Minimum Charge	Job		229		229	
12" to 20" Wide						
Demolish	Ea.		10.20		10.20	Includes material and labor to install a
Install	Ea.	56.50	27		83.50	16" x 16" air return register.
Demolish and Install	Ea.	56.50	37.20		93.70	
Reinstall	Ea.		21.55		21.55	
Clean	Ea.	.24	8.50		8.74	
Minimum Charge	Job		229		229	
Over 20" Wide						
Demolish	Ea.		15.40		15.40	Includes material and labor to install a
Install	Ea.	104	41.50		145.50	24" x 24" air return register.
Demolish and Install	Ea.	104	56.90		160.90	
Reinstall	Ea.		33.31		33.31	
Clean	Ea.	.24	9.60		9.84	
Minimum Charge	Job		229		229	
Supply Grill						
Baseboard Type						
Demolish	Ea.		7.25		7.25	Includes material and labor to install a
Install	Ea.	21	23		44	14" x 6" baseboard air supply
Demolish and Install	Ea.	21	30.25		51.25	register.
Reinstall	Ea.		18.32		18.32	
Clean	Ea.	.24	8.50		8.74	
Minimum Charge	Job		229		229	

Finish Mechanical

Ductwork

	Unit	Material	Labor	Equip.	Total	Specification
10″ Wide						
Demolish	Ea.		8.50		8.50	Includes material and labor to install a
Install	Ea.	44	23		67	10″ x 6″ air supply register.
Demolish and Install	Ea.	44	31.50		75.50	
Reinstall	Ea.		18.32		18.32	
Clean	Ea.	.24	8.50		8.74	
Minimum Charge	Job		229		229	
12″ to 15″ Wide						
Demolish	Ea.		8.50		8.50	Includes material and labor to install a
Install	Ea.	61	27		88	14″ x 8″ air supply register.
Demolish and Install	Ea.	61	35.50		96.50	
Reinstall	Ea.		21.55		21.55	
Clean	Ea.	.24	8.50		8.74	
Minimum Charge	Job		229		229	
18″ to 24″ Wide						
Demolish	Ea.		10.20		10.20	Includes material and labor to install a
Install	Ea.	84	35		119	24″ x 8″ air supply register.
Demolish and Install	Ea.	84	45.20		129.20	
Reinstall	Ea.		28.18		28.18	
Clean	Ea.	.24	9.60		9.84	
Minimum Charge	Job		229		229	
30″ to 36″ Wide						
Demolish	Ea.		12.70		12.70	Includes material and labor to install a
Install	Ea.	110	32.50		142.50	30″ x 8″ air supply register.
Demolish and Install	Ea.	110	45.20		155.20	
Reinstall	Ea.		26.17		26.17	
Clean	Ea.	.24	19.15		19.39	
Minimum Charge	Job		229		229	

Diffuser

	Unit	Material	Labor	Equip.	Total	Specification
12″ Louver						
Demolish	Ea.		10.20		10.20	Includes material and labor to install a
Install	Ea.	49	32.50		81.50	12″ aluminum louvered diffuser.
Demolish and Install	Ea.	49	42.70		91.70	
Reinstall	Ea.		26.17		26.17	
Clean	Ea.	.24	8.50		8.74	
Minimum Charge	Job		229		229	
14″ to 20″ Louver						
Demolish	Ea.		10.20		10.20	Includes material and labor to install a
Install	Ea.	55	46		101	14″ to 20″ aluminum louvered diffuser.
Demolish and Install	Ea.	55	56.20		111.20	
Reinstall	Ea.		36.64		36.64	
Clean	Ea.	.24	9.60		9.84	
Minimum Charge	Job		229		229	
25″ to 32″ Louver						
Demolish	Ea.		15.40		15.40	Includes material and labor to install a
Install	Ea.	71.50	65.50		137	25″ to 32″ aluminum louvered diffuser.
Demolish and Install	Ea.	71.50	80.90		152.40	
Reinstall	Ea.		52.34		52.34	
Clean	Ea.	.24	12.75		12.99	
Minimum Charge	Job		229		229	
12″ Round						
Demolish	Ea.		14.15		14.15	Includes material and labor to install a
Install	Ea.	46	38		84	12″ diameter aluminum diffuser with a
Demolish and Install	Ea.	46	52.15		98.15	butterfly damper.
Reinstall	Ea.		30.53		30.53	
Clean	Ea.	.24	8.50		8.74	
Minimum Charge	Job		229		229	

Finish Mechanical

Ductwork

Ductwork	Unit	Material	Labor	Equip.	Total	Specification
14″ to 20″ Round						
Demolish	Ea.		18.85		18.85	Includes material and labor to install a
Install	Ea.	158	51		209	20″ diameter aluminum diffuser with a
Demolish and Install	Ea.	158	69.85		227.85	butterfly damper.
Reinstall	Ea.		40.71		40.71	
Clean	Ea.	.24	9.60		9.84	
Minimum Charge	Job		229		229	
Flush-out / Sanitize						
Install	L.F.	.96	3.83		4.79	Includes labor and material costs to
Minimum Charge	Job		229		229	clean ductwork.

Finish Electrical

Lighting Fixture   Duplex Receptacle

Electrical Per S.F.		Unit	Material	Labor	Equip.	Total	Specification
Residential							
Light Fixtures							
	Install	S.F.	.29	.23		.52	Includes labor and material to replace house light fixtures. Apply S.F. cost to floor area including garages but not basements.

Circuits		Unit	Material	Labor	Equip.	Total	Specification
Outlet with Wiring							
	Demolish	Ea.		25		25	Includes material and labor to install general purpose outlet with cover, up to 20 feet of #12/2 wire.
	Install	Ea.	13.70	31		44.70	
	Demolish and Install	Ea.	13.70	56		69.70	
	Reinstall	Ea.		24.85		24.85	
	Clean	Ea.		1.92		1.92	
	Minimum Charge	Job		226		226	
GFCI Outlet w / Wiring							
	Demolish	Ea.		25		25	Cost includes material and labor to install 120V GFCI receptacle and wall plate, with up to 20 feet of #12/2 wire.
	Install	Ea.	53	36.50		89.50	
	Demolish and Install	Ea.	53	61.50		114.50	
	Reinstall	Ea.		29.37		29.37	
	Clean	Ea.		1.92		1.92	
	Minimum Charge	Job		226		226	
Exterior Outlet w / Wiring							
	Demolish	Ea.		25		25	Cost includes material and labor to install 110V waterproof external receptacle and cover plate with up to 20' of #12/2 wire.
	Install	Ea.	42.50	37.50		80	
	Demolish and Install	Ea.	42.50	62.50		105	
	Reinstall	Ea.		30.13		30.13	
	Clean	Ea.		1.92		1.92	
	Minimum Charge	Job		226		226	
240V Outlet w / Wiring							
	Demolish	Ea.		25		25	Cost includes material and labor to install 240V receptacle and cover plate with up to 20' of #12/2 wire.
	Install	Ea.	80.50	70.50		151	
	Demolish and Install	Ea.	80.50	95.50		176	
	Reinstall	Ea.		56.41		56.41	
	Clean	Ea.		1.92		1.92	
	Minimum Charge	Job		226		226	

Finish Electrical

Circuits

	Unit	Material	Labor	Equip.	Total	Specification
TV / Cable Jack w / Wiring						Includes material and labor to install
Demolish	Ea.		25		25	TV/cable outlet box and cover plate
Install	Ea.	22.50	28.50		51	including 20' of wiring.
Demolish and Install	Ea.	22.50	53.50		76	
Reinstall	Ea.		22.60		22.60	
Clean	Ea.		1.92		1.92	
Minimum Charge	Job		226		226	
Phone Jack with Wiring						Includes material and labor to install
Demolish	Ea.		25		25	phone jack and cover plate including
Install	Ea.	13.35	17.40		30.75	up to 20' of telephone cable.
Demolish and Install	Ea.	13.35	42.40		55.75	
Reinstall	Ea.		13.91		13.91	
Clean	Ea.		1.20		1.20	
Minimum Charge	Job		226		226	

Light Switch

	Unit	Material	Labor	Equip.	Total	Specification
Single						
Switch						
Demolish	Ea.		5		5	Includes material and labor to install
Install	Ea.	8.85	21.50		30.35	single switch and wall plate. Wiring is
Demolish and Install	Ea.	8.85	26.50		35.35	not included.
Reinstall	Ea.		17.22		17.22	
Clean	Ea.		1.92		1.92	
Minimum Charge	Job		226		226	
Plate						
Demolish	Ea.		2.51		2.51	Includes material and labor to install a
Install	Ea.	.43	5.65		6.08	one gang brown wall switch plate.
Demolish and Install	Ea.	.43	8.16		8.59	
Reinstall	Ea.		4.52		4.52	
Clean	Ea.	.10	.38		.48	
Minimum Charge	Job		226		226	
Double						
Switch						
Demolish	Ea.		10.05		10.05	Includes material and labor to install
Install	Ea.	9.80	32.50		42.30	double switch and wall plate. Wiring
Demolish and Install	Ea.	9.80	42.55		52.35	is not included.
Reinstall	Ea.		25.83		25.83	
Clean	Ea.	.10	6.15		6.25	
Minimum Charge	Job		226		226	
Plate						
Demolish	Ea.		2.51		2.51	Includes material and labor to install a
Install	Ea.	.91	8.55		9.46	two gang brown wall switch plate.
Demolish and Install	Ea.	.91	11.06		11.97	
Reinstall	Ea.		6.82		6.82	
Clean	Ea.	.10	.38		.48	
Minimum Charge	Job		226		226	
Triple						
Switch						
Demolish	Ea.		15.20		15.20	Includes material and labor to install
Install	Ea.	28	37.50		65.50	triple switch and wall plate. Wiring is
Demolish and Install	Ea.	28	52.70		80.70	not included.
Reinstall	Ea.		30.13		30.13	
Clean	Ea.	.10	9.20		9.30	
Minimum Charge	Job		226		226	

Finish Electrical

Light Switch

	Unit	Material	Labor	Equip.	Total	Specification
Plate						
Demolish	Ea.		2.51		2.51	Includes material and labor to install a
Install	Ea.	1.36	14.15		15.51	three gang brown wall switch plate.
Demolish and Install	Ea.	1.36	16.66		18.02	
Reinstall	Ea.		11.30		11.30	
Clean	Ea.	.10	.38		.48	
Minimum Charge	Job		226		226	
Dimmer						
Switch						
Demolish	Ea.		5		5	Includes material and labor to install
Install	Ea.	26.50	26.50		53	dimmer switch. Wiring is not included.
Demolish and Install	Ea.	26.50	31.50		58	
Reinstall	Ea.		21.27		21.27	
Clean	Ea.		1.92		1.92	
Minimum Charge	Job		226		226	
Plate						
Demolish	Ea.		2.51		2.51	Includes material and labor to install a
Install	Ea.	.43	5.65		6.08	one gang brown wall switch plate.
Demolish and Install	Ea.	.43	8.16		8.59	
Reinstall	Ea.		4.52		4.52	
Clean	Ea.	.10	.38		.48	
Minimum Charge	Job		226		226	
With Wiring						
Single						
Demolish	Ea.		25		25	Includes material and labor to install
Install	Ea.	15.35	26.50		41.85	single switch and plate including up to
Demolish and Install	Ea.	15.35	51.50		66.85	20' of romex cable.
Reinstall	Ea.		21.15		21.15	
Clean	Ea.		1.92		1.92	
Minimum Charge	Job		226		226	
Double						
Demolish	Ea.		25		25	Includes material and labor to install
Install	Ea.	34.50	45		79.50	double switch and plate including up
Demolish and Install	Ea.	34.50	70		104.50	to 20' of romex cable.
Reinstall	Ea.		36.16		36.16	
Clean	Ea.	.10	6.15		6.25	
Minimum Charge	Job		226		226	
Triple						
Demolish	Ea.		37.50		37.50	Includes material and labor to install
Install	Ea.	37	51		88	triple switch and plate including up to
Demolish and Install	Ea.	37	88.50		125.50	20' of romex cable.
Reinstall	Ea.		40.67		40.67	
Clean	Ea.	.10	9.20		9.30	
Minimum Charge	Job		226		226	
Dimmer						
Demolish	Ea.		25		25	Includes material and labor to install
Install	Ea.	33	31		64	dimmer switch and cover plate
Demolish and Install	Ea.	33	56		89	including up to 20' of romex cable.
Reinstall	Ea.		24.85		24.85	
Clean	Ea.		1.92		1.92	
Minimum Charge	Job		226		226	

Finish Electrical

Cover for Outlet / Switch

	Unit	Material	Labor	Equip.	Total	Specification
High Grade						
Demolish	Ea.		2.51		2.51	Includes material and labor to install
Install	Ea.	2.75	5.65		8.40	wall plate, stainless steel, 1 gang.
Demolish and Install	Ea.	2.75	8.16		10.91	
Reinstall	Ea.		4.52		4.52	
Clean	Ea.	.10	.38		.48	
Minimum Charge	Job		226		226	
Deluxe Grade						
Demolish	Ea.		2.51		2.51	Includes material and labor to install
Install	Ea.	5.80	5.65		11.45	wall plate, brushed brass, 1 gang.
Demolish and Install	Ea.	5.80	8.16		13.96	
Reinstall	Ea.		4.52		4.52	
Clean	Ea.	.10	.38		.48	
Minimum Charge	Job		226		226	

Residential Light Fixture

	Unit	Material	Labor	Equip.	Total	Specification
Ceiling						
Good Quality						
Demolish	Ea.		10.45		10.45	Includes material and labor to install
Install	Ea.	40.50	11.30		51.80	standard quality incandescent ceiling
Demolish and Install	Ea.	40.50	21.75		62.25	light fixture. Wiring is not included.
Reinstall	Ea.		9.04		9.04	
Clean	Ea.	.12	25.50		25.62	
Minimum Charge	Job		226		226	
Better Quality						
Demolish	Ea.		10.45		10.45	Includes material and labor to install
Install	Ea.	102	24		126	custom quality incandescent ceiling
Demolish and Install	Ea.	102	34.45		136.45	light fixture. Wiring is not included.
Reinstall	Ea.		19.03		19.03	
Clean	Ea.	.12	25.50		25.62	
Minimum Charge	Job		226		226	
Premium Quality						
Demolish	Ea.		10.45		10.45	Includes material and labor to install
Install	Ea.	299	24		323	deluxe quality incandescent ceiling
Demolish and Install	Ea.	299	34.45		333.45	light fixture. Wiring is not included.
Reinstall	Ea.		19.03		19.03	
Clean	Ea.	.12	25.50		25.62	
Minimum Charge	Job		226		226	
Recessed Ceiling						
Demolish	Ea.		21		21	Includes material and labor to install
Install	Ea.	51	15.05		66.05	standard quality recessed eyeball
Demolish and Install	Ea.	51	36.05		87.05	spotlight with housing. Wiring is not
Reinstall	Ea.		12.05		12.05	included.
Clean	Ea.	.04	3.19		3.23	
Minimum Charge	Job		226		226	
Recessed Eyeball						
Demolish	Ea.		21		21	Includes material and labor to install
Install	Ea.	76.50	16.15		92.65	custom quality recessed eyeball
Demolish and Install	Ea.	76.50	37.15		113.65	spotlight with housing. Wiring is not
Reinstall	Ea.		12.91		12.91	included.
Clean	Ea.	.04	3.19		3.23	
Minimum Charge	Job		226		226	

Finish Electrical

Residential Light Fixture

	Unit	Material	Labor	Equip.	Total	Specification
Recessed Shower Type						
Demolish	Ea.		21		21	Includes material and labor to install
Install	Ea.	63.50	15.05		78.55	deluxe quality recessed eyeball
Demolish and Install	Ea.	63.50	36.05		99.55	spotlight with housing. Wiring is not
Reinstall	Ea.		12.05		12.05	included.
Clean	Ea.	.04	3.19		3.23	
Minimum Charge	Job		226		226	
Run Wiring						
Install	Ea.	22.50	18.10		40.60	Includes labor and material to install a
Minimum Charge	Job		226		226	electric fixture utility box with non-metallic cable.
Fluorescent						
Good Quality						
Demolish	Ea.		23		23	Includes material and labor to install
Install	Ea.	49	64.50		113.50	standard quality 12" wide by 48" long
Demolish and Install	Ea.	49	87.50		136.50	decorative surface mounted fluorescent
Reinstall	Ea.		51.66		51.66	fixture w/acrylic diffuser.
Clean	Ea.	.04	3.19		3.23	
Minimum Charge	Job		226		226	
Better Quality						
Demolish	Ea.		23		23	Includes material and labor to install
Install	Ea.	100	73		173	an interior fluorescent lighting fixture.
Demolish and Install	Ea.	100	96		196	
Reinstall	Ea.		58.32		58.32	
Clean	Ea.	.04	3.19		3.23	
Minimum Charge	Job		226		226	
Premium Quality						
Demolish	Ea.		23		23	Includes material and labor to install
Install	Ea.	104	85.50		189.50	deluxe quality 24" wide by 48" long
Demolish and Install	Ea.	104	108.50		212.50	decorative surface mounted fluorescent
Reinstall	Ea.		68.23		68.23	fixture w/acrylic diffuser.
Clean	Ea.	.04	3.19		3.23	
Minimum Charge	Job		226		226	
Run Wiring						
Install	Ea.	22.50	18.10		40.60	Includes labor and material to install a
Minimum Charge	Job		226		226	electric fixture utility box with non-metallic cable.
Exterior						
Good Quality						
Demolish	Ea.		20		20	Includes material and labor to install
Install	Ea.	46	28.50		74.50	standard quality incandescent outdoor
Demolish and Install	Ea.	46	48.50		94.50	light fixture. Wiring is not included.
Reinstall	Ea.		22.60		22.60	
Clean	Ea.	.24	12.75		12.99	
Minimum Charge	Job		226		226	
Better Quality						
Demolish	Ea.		20		20	Includes material and labor to install
Install	Ea.	116	28.50		144.50	custom quality incandescent outdoor
Demolish and Install	Ea.	116	48.50		164.50	light fixture. Wiring is not included.
Reinstall	Ea.		22.60		22.60	
Clean	Ea.	.24	12.75		12.99	
Minimum Charge	Job		226		226	
Premium Quality						
Demolish	Ea.		20		20	Includes material and labor to install
Install	Ea.	175	113		288	deluxe quality incandescent outdoor
Demolish and Install	Ea.	175	133		308	light fixture. Wiring is not included.
Reinstall	Ea.		90.40		90.40	
Clean	Ea.	.24	12.75		12.99	
Minimum Charge	Job		226		226	

Finish Electrical

Residential Light Fixture

Residential Light Fixture	Unit	Material	Labor	Equip.	Total	Specification
Outdoor w / Pole						Includes material and labor to install post lantern type incandescent outdoor light fixture. Wiring is not included.
Demolish	Ea.		20		20	
Install	Ea.	129	113		242	
Demolish and Install	Ea.	129	133		262	
Reinstall	Ea.		90.40		90.40	
Clean	Ea.	.24	12.75		12.99	
Minimum Charge	Job		226		226	
Run Wiring						Includes labor and material to install a electric fixture utility box with non-metallic cable.
Install	Ea.	22.50	18.10		40.60	
Minimum Charge	Job		226		226	
Track Lighting						Includes material and labor to install track lighting.
Demolish	L.F.		7		7	
Install	L.F.	17.80	18.85		36.65	
Demolish and Install	L.F.	17.80	25.85		43.65	
Reinstall	L.F.		15.07		15.07	
Clean	L.F.	.24	6.15		6.39	
Minimum Charge	Job		226		226	

Commercial Light Fixture

Commercial Light Fixture	Unit	Material	Labor	Equip.	Total	Specification
Fluorescent						
2 Bulb, 2'						Includes material and labor to install a 2' long surface mounted fluorescent light fixture with two 40 watt bulbs.
Demolish	Ea.		20		20	
Install	Ea.	38	56.50		94.50	
Demolish and Install	Ea.	38	76.50		114.50	
Reinstall	Ea.		45.20		45.20	
Clean	Ea.	1.20	22		23.20	
Minimum Charge	Job		226		226	
2 Bulb, 4'						Includes material and labor to install a 4' long surface mounted fluorescent light fixture with two 40 watt bulbs.
Demolish	Ea.		20		20	
Install	Ea.	69	64.50		133.50	
Demolish and Install	Ea.	69	84.50		153.50	
Reinstall	Ea.		51.66		51.66	
Clean	Ea.	1.20	22		23.20	
Minimum Charge	Job		226		226	
3 Bulb, 4'						Includes material and labor to install a 4' long pendant mounted fluorescent light fixture with three 34 watt bulbs.
Demolish	Ea.		20		20	
Install	Ea.	103	64.50		167.50	
Demolish and Install	Ea.	103	84.50		187.50	
Reinstall	Ea.		51.66		51.66	
Clean	Ea.	1.20	22		23.20	
Minimum Charge	Job		226		226	
4 Bulb, 4'						Includes material and labor to install a 4' long pendant mounted fluorescent light fixture with four 34 watt bulbs.
Demolish	Ea.		20		20	
Install	Ea.	94.50	69.50		164	
Demolish and Install	Ea.	94.50	89.50		184	
Reinstall	Ea.		55.63		55.63	
Clean	Ea.	1.20	22		23.20	
Minimum Charge	Job		226		226	
2 Bulb, 8'						Includes material and labor to install a 8' long surface mounted fluorescent light fixture with two 110 watt bulbs.
Demolish	Ea.		25		25	
Install	Ea.	106	85.50		191.50	
Demolish and Install	Ea.	106	110.50		216.50	
Reinstall	Ea.		68.23		68.23	
Clean	Ea.	1.20	22		23.20	
Minimum Charge	Job		226		226	

Finish Electrical

Commercial Light Fixture

	Unit	Material	Labor	Equip.	Total	Specification
Run Wiring						
Install	Ea.	22.50	18.10		40.60	Includes labor and material to install a
Minimum Charge	Job		226		226	electric fixture utility box with
						non-metallic cable.
Ceiling, Recessed						
Eyeball Type						
Demolish	Ea.		21		21	Includes material and labor to install
Install	Ea.	76.50	16.15		92.65	custom quality recessed eyeball
Demolish and Install	Ea.	76.50	37.15		113.65	spotlight with housing. Wiring is not
Reinstall	Ea.		12.91		12.91	included.
Clean	Ea.	.04	3.19		3.23	
Minimum Charge	Job		226		226	
Shower Type						
Demolish	Ea.		21		21	Includes material and labor to install
Install	Ea.	63.50	15.05		78.55	deluxe quality recessed eyeball
Demolish and Install	Ea.	63.50	36.05		99.55	spotlight with housing. Wiring is not
Reinstall	Ea.		12.05		12.05	included.
Clean	Ea.	.04	3.19		3.23	
Minimum Charge	Job		226		226	
Run Wiring						
Install	Ea.	22.50	18.10		40.60	Includes labor and material to install a
Minimum Charge	Job		226		226	electric fixture utility box with
						non-metallic cable.
Ceiling Grid Type						
2 Tube						
Demolish	Ea.		29.50		29.50	Cost includes material and labor to
Install	Ea.	64	85.50		149.50	install 2 lamp fluorescent light fixture
Demolish and Install	Ea.	64	115		179	in 2' x 4' ceiling grid system including
Reinstall	Ea.		68.23		68.23	lens and tubes.
Clean	Ea.	1.20	22		23.20	
Minimum Charge	Job		226		226	
4 Tube						
Demolish	Ea.		33.50		33.50	Cost includes material and labor to
Install	Ea.	73.50	96		169.50	install 4 lamp fluorescent light fixture
Demolish and Install	Ea.	73.50	129.50		203	in 2' x 4' ceiling grid system including
Reinstall	Ea.		76.94		76.94	lens and tubes.
Clean	Ea.	1.20	22		23.20	
Minimum Charge	Job		226		226	
Acrylic Diffuser						
Demolish	Ea.		5.25		5.25	Includes material and labor to install
Install	Ea.	56	13.70		69.70	fluorescent light fixture w/acrylic
Demolish and Install	Ea.	56	18.95		74.95	diffuser.
Reinstall	Ea.		10.96		10.96	
Clean	Ea.	.77	3.83		4.60	
Minimum Charge	Job		226		226	
Louver Diffuser						
Demolish	Ea.		6.30		6.30	Includes material and labor to install
Install	Ea.	62.50	13.70		76.20	fluorescent light fixture w/louver
Demolish and Install	Ea.	62.50	20		82.50	diffuser.
Reinstall	Ea.		10.96		10.96	
Clean	Ea.	.77	3.83		4.60	
Minimum Charge	Job		226		226	
Run Wiring						
Install	Ea.	22.50	18.10		40.60	Includes labor and material to install a
Minimum Charge	Job		226		226	electric fixture utility box with
						non-metallic cable.

Finish Electrical

Commercial Light Fixture

	Unit	Material	Labor	Equip.	Total	Specification
Track Lighting						
Demolish	L.F.		7		7	Includes material and labor to install
Install	L.F.	17.80	18.85		36.65	track lighting.
Demolish and Install	L.F.	17.80	25.85		43.65	
Reinstall	L.F.		15.07		15.07	
Clean	L.F.	.24	6.15		6.39	
Minimum Charge	Job		226		226	
Emergency						
Demolish	Ea.		36		36	Includes material and labor to install
Install	Ea.	136	113		249	battery-powered emergency lighting
Demolish and Install	Ea.	136	149		285	unit with two (2) lights, including
Reinstall	Ea.		90.40		90.40	wiring.
Clean	Ea.	.59	22		22.59	
Minimum Charge	Job		226		226	
Run Wiring						
Install	Ea.	22.50	18.10		40.60	Includes labor and material to install a
Minimum Charge	Job		226		226	electric fixture utility box with non-metallic cable.

Fan

	Unit	Material	Labor	Equip.	Total	Specification
Ceiling Paddle						
Good Quality						
Demolish	Ea.		28		28	Includes material and labor to install
Install	Ea.	102	45		147	standard ceiling fan.
Demolish and Install	Ea.	102	73		175	
Reinstall	Ea.		36.16		36.16	
Clean	Ea.	.47	19.15		19.62	
Minimum Charge	Job		226		226	
Better Quality						
Demolish	Ea.		28		28	Includes material and labor to install
Install	Ea.	154	45		199	better ceiling fan.
Demolish and Install	Ea.	154	73		227	
Reinstall	Ea.		36.16		36.16	
Clean	Ea.	.47	19.15		19.62	
Minimum Charge	Job		226		226	
Premium Quality						
Demolish	Ea.		28		28	Includes material and labor to install
Install	Ea.	365	56.50		421.50	deluxe ceiling fan.
Demolish and Install	Ea.	365	84.50		449.50	
Reinstall	Ea.		45.20		45.20	
Clean	Ea.	.47	19.15		19.62	
Minimum Charge	Job		226		226	
Light Kit						
Install	Ea.	42.50	56.50		99	Includes labor and material to install a
Minimum Charge	Job		226		226	ceiling fan light kit.
Bathroom Exhaust						
Ceiling Mounted						
Demolish	Ea.		23		23	Cost includes material and labor to
Install	Ea.	60.50	45		105.50	install 60 CFM ceiling mounted
Demolish and Install	Ea.	60.50	68		128.50	bathroom exhaust fan, up to 10' of
Reinstall	Ea.		36.05		36.05	wiring with one wall switch.
Clean	Ea.	.24	7.65		7.89	
Minimum Charge	Job		226		226	

Finish Electrical

Fan

	Unit	Material	Labor	Equip.	Total	Specification
Wall Mounted						
Demolish	Ea.		23		23	Cost includes material and labor to
Install	Ea.	76	45		121	install 110 CFM wall mounted
Demolish and Install	Ea.	76	68		144	bathroom exhaust fan, up to 10' of
Reinstall	Ea.		36.05		36.05	wiring with one wall switch.
Clean	Ea.	.24	7.65		7.89	
Minimum Charge	Job		226		226	
Lighted						
Demolish	Ea.		23		23	Cost includes material and labor to
Install	Ea.	56	45		101	install 50 CFM ceiling mounted lighted
Demolish and Install	Ea.	56	68		124	exhaust fan, up to 10' of wiring with
Reinstall	Ea.		36.05		36.05	one wall switch..
Clean	Ea.	.24	7.65		7.89	
Minimum Charge	Job		226		226	
Blower Heater w / Light						
Demolish	Ea.		23		23	Includes material and labor to install
Install	Ea.	111	75		186	ceiling blower type ventilator with
Demolish and Install	Ea.	111	98		209	switch, light and snap-on grill. Includes
Reinstall	Ea.		60.09		60.09	1300 watt/120 volt heater.
Clean	Ea.	.24	7.65		7.89	
Minimum Charge	Job		226		226	
Fan Heater w / Light						
Demolish	Ea.		23		23	Includes material and labor to install
Install	Ea.	153	75		228	circular ceiling fan heater unit, 1500
Demolish and Install	Ea.	153	98		251	watt, surface mounted.
Reinstall	Ea.		60.09		60.09	
Clean	Ea.	.24	7.65		7.89	
Minimum Charge	Job		226		226	
Whole House Exhaust						
36" Ceiling Mounted						
Install	Ea.	990	113		1103	Includes material and labor to install a
Clean	Ea.	.08	5.60		5.68	whole house exhaust fan.
Minimum Charge	Job		226		226	
Kitchen Exhaust						
Standard Model						
Install	Ea.	82	30		112	Includes labor and materials to install
Clean	Ea.	.08	5.60		5.68	a bathroom or kitchen vent fan.
Minimum Charge	Job		226		226	
Low Noise Model						
Install	Ea.	102	30		132	Includes labor and materials to install
Clean	Ea.	.08	5.60		5.68	a bathroom or kitchen vent fan, low
Minimum Charge	Job		226		226	noise model.

Low Voltage Systems

	Unit	Material	Labor	Equip.	Total	Specification
Smoke Detector						
Pre-wired						
Demolish	Ea.		10.45		10.45	Includes material and labor to install
Install	Ea.	22	85		107	AC type smoke detector including
Demolish and Install	Ea.	22	95.45		117.45	wiring.
Reinstall	Ea.		67.84		67.84	
Clean	Ea.	.10	9.60		9.70	
Minimum Charge	Job		226		226	

Low Voltage Systems		Unit	Material	Labor	Equip.	Total	Specification
Run Wiring							
	Install	Ea.	22.50	18.10		40.60	Includes labor and material to install a
	Minimum Charge	Job		226		226	electric fixture utility box with
							non-metallic cable.
Door Bell / Chimes							
Good Quality							
	Demolish	Ea.		31.50		31.50	Includes material and labor to install
	Install	Ea.	66	113		179	surface mounted 2 note door bell.
	Demolish and Install	Ea.	66	144.50		210.50	Wiring is not included.
	Reinstall	Ea.		90.40		90.40	
	Clean	Ea.	.24	9.60		9.84	
	Minimum Charge	Job		226		226	
Better Quality							
	Demolish	Ea.		31.50		31.50	Includes material and labor to install
	Install	Ea.	90	113		203	standard quality surface mounted 2
	Demolish and Install	Ea.	90	144.50		234.50	note door bell. Wiring is not included.
	Reinstall	Ea.		90.40		90.40	
	Clean	Ea.	.24	9.60		9.84	
	Minimum Charge	Job		226		226	
Premium Quality							
	Demolish	Ea.		31.50		31.50	Includes material and labor to install
	Install	Ea.	102	113		215	deluxe quality surface mounted 2 note
	Demolish and Install	Ea.	102	144.50		246.50	door bell. Wiring is not included.
	Reinstall	Ea.		90.40		90.40	
	Clean	Ea.	.24	9.60		9.84	
	Minimum Charge	Job		226		226	
Run Wiring							
	Install	Ea.	22.50	18.10		40.60	Includes labor and material to install a
	Minimum Charge	Job		226		226	electric fixture utility box with
							non-metallic cable.
Intercom System							
Intercom (master)							
	Demolish	Ea.		83.50		83.50	Includes material and labor to install
	Install	Ea.	635	226		861	master intercom station with AM/FM
	Demolish and Install	Ea.	635	309.50		944.50	music and room monitoring. Wiring is
	Reinstall	Ea.		180.80		180.80	not included.
	Clean	Ea.	.24	25.50		25.74	
	Minimum Charge	Job		226		226	
Intercom (remote)							
	Demolish	Ea.		50		50	Includes material and labor to install
	Install	Ea.	57	56.50		113.50	remote station for master intercom
	Demolish and Install	Ea.	57	106.50		163.50	system. Wiring is not included.
	Reinstall	Ea.		45.20		45.20	
	Clean	Ea.	.24	9.60		9.84	
	Minimum Charge	Job		226		226	
Security System							
Alarm Panel							
	Demolish	Ea.		100		100	Includes material and labor to install a
	Install	Ea.	163	226		389	6 zone burglar alarm panel.
	Demolish and Install	Ea.	163	326		489	
	Reinstall	Ea.		180.80		180.80	
	Clean	Ea.	.24	9.60		9.84	
	Minimum Charge	Job		226		226	

Finish Electrical

Low Voltage Systems	Unit	Material	Labor	Equip.	Total	Specification
Motion Detector						
Demolish	Ea.		72		72	Includes material and labor to install a
Install	Ea.	248	197		445	ultrasonic motion detector for a
Demolish and Install	Ea.	248	269		517	security system.
Reinstall	Ea.		157.22		157.22	
Clean	Ea.	.24	9.60		9.84	
Minimum Charge	Job		226		226	
Door Switch						
Demolish	Ea.		31.50		31.50	Includes material and labor to install a
Install	Ea.	150	85.50		235.50	door / window contact for a security
Demolish and Install	Ea.	150	117		267	system.
Reinstall	Ea.		68.23		68.23	
Clean	Ea.	.24	3.06		3.30	
Minimum Charge	Job		226		226	
Window Switch						
Demolish	Ea.		31.50		31.50	Includes material and labor to install a
Install	Ea.	150	85.50		235.50	door / window contact for a security
Demolish and Install	Ea.	150	117		267	system.
Reinstall	Ea.		68.23		68.23	
Clean	Ea.	.24	3.06		3.30	
Minimum Charge	Job		226		226	
Satellite System						
Dish						
Demolish	Ea.		140		140	Includes material, labor and
Install	Ea.	1275	375		1650	equipment to install 10' mesh dish.
Demolish and Install	Ea.	1275	515		1790	
Reinstall	Ea.		301.33		301.33	
Clean	Ea.	4.77	38.50		43.27	
Minimum Charge	Job		226		226	
Motor						
Demolish	Ea.		70		70	Includes material and labor to install a
Install	Ea.	395	188		583	television satellite dish motor unit.
Demolish and Install	Ea.	395	258		653	
Reinstall	Ea.		150.67		150.67	
Clean	Ea.	.24	9.60		9.84	
Minimum Charge	Job		226		226	
Television Antenna						
40' Pole						
Demolish	Ea.		78.50		78.50	Includes material and labor to install
Install	Ea.	29.50	141		170.50	stand-alone 1"-2" metal pole, 10' long.
Demolish and Install	Ea.	29.50	219.50		249	Cost does not include antenna.
Reinstall	Ea.		113		113	
Clean	Ea.	.96	38.50		39.46	
Paint	Ea.	7.80	44.50		52.30	
Minimum Charge	Job		226		226	
Rotor Unit						
Demolish	Ea.		63		63	Includes material and labor to install a
Install	Ea.	82.50	56.50		139	television antenna rotor.
Demolish and Install	Ea.	82.50	119.50		202	
Reinstall	Ea.		45.20		45.20	
Clean	Ea.	.96	38.50		39.46	
Minimum Charge	Job		226		226	
Single Booster						
Demolish	Ea.		63		63	Includes material and labor to install
Install	Ea.	40	56.50		96.50	standard grade VHF television signal
Demolish and Install	Ea.	40	119.50		159.50	booster unit and all hardware required
Reinstall	Ea.		45.20		45.20	for connection to TV cable.
Clean	Ea.	.04	4.79		4.83	
Minimum Charge	Job		226		226	

Gazebo	Gutter	Shutter

Window Treatment		Unit	Material	Labor	Equip.	Total	Specification
Drapery							
Good Grade							
	Install	L.F.	45.50	6.15		51.65	Includes material and labor to install
	Reinstall	L.F.		4.90		4.90	good quality drapery.
	Clean	L.F.	2.79	.15		2.94	
	Minimum Charge	Job		153		153	
Premium Grade							
	Install	L.F.	80.50	6.15		86.65	Includes material and labor to install
	Reinstall	L.F.		4.90		4.90	premium quality drapery.
	Clean	L.F.	2.79	.17		2.96	
	Minimum Charge	Job		153		153	
Lining							
	Install	L.F.	19.90	6.15		26.05	Includes material and labor to install
	Reinstall	L.F.		4.90		4.90	drapery lining.
	Clean	L.F.	1.40	.09		1.49	
	Minimum Charge	Job		153		153	
Valance Board							
	Demolish	L.F.		1.70		1.70	Includes material and labor to install a
	Install	L.F.	4.74	12.25		16.99	drapery valance board.
	Demolish and Install	L.F.	4.74	13.95		18.69	
	Reinstall	L.F.		9.80		9.80	
	Clean	L.F.	1.40	.31		1.71	
	Minimum Charge	Job		153		153	
Rod							
	Demolish	L.F.		4.26		4.26	Includes material and labor to install
	Install	L.F.	6.35	7		13.35	standard traverse drapery hardware.
	Demolish and Install	L.F.	6.35	11.26		17.61	
	Reinstall	L.F.		5.62		5.62	
	Clean	L.F.	.09	.28		.37	
	Paint	L.F.	.07	.68		.75	
	Minimum Charge	Job		153		153	
Blinds							
Mini-type							
	Demolish	S.F.		.90		.90	Includes material and labor to install
	Install	S.F.	6.05	.70		6.75	horizontal 1″ slat blinds.
	Demolish and Install	S.F.	6.05	1.60		7.65	
	Reinstall	S.F.		.56		.56	
	Clean	S.F.	.53	.03		.56	
	Minimum Charge	Job		153		153	

Improvements / Appliances / Treatments

Window Treatment		Unit	Material	Labor	Equip.	Total	Specification
Vertical Type							
	Demolish	S.F.		.90		.90	Includes material and labor to install
	Install	S.F.	10.90	.90		11.80	vertical 3″ - 5″ cloth or PVC blinds.
	Demolish and Install	S.F.	10.90	1.80		12.70	
	Reinstall	S.F.		.72		.72	
	Clean	S.F.	.28	.03		.31	
	Minimum Charge	Job		153		153	
Vertical Type per L.F.							
	Demolish	L.F.		1.42		1.42	Includes material and labor to install
	Install	L.F.	65.50	4.09		69.59	vertical 3″ - 5″ cloth or PVC blinds x
	Demolish and Install	L.F.	65.50	5.51		71.01	72″ long.
	Reinstall	L.F.		3.27		3.27	
	Clean	L.F.	1.98	.21		2.19	
	Minimum Charge	Job		153		153	
Venetian Type							
	Demolish	S.F.		.90		.90	Includes material and labor to install
	Install	S.F.	9.40	.70		10.10	horizontal 2″ slat blinds.
	Demolish and Install	S.F.	9.40	1.60		11	
	Reinstall	S.F.		.56		.56	
	Clean	S.F.	.28	.03		.31	
	Minimum Charge	Job		153		153	
Wood Shutter							
27″ x 36″, 4 Panel							
	Demolish	Ea.		29		29	Includes material and labor to install
	Install	Pr.	99	24.50		123.50	moveable louver, up to 33″ x 36″, 4
	Demolish and Install	Pr.	99	53.50		152.50	panel shutter.
	Reinstall	Pr.		19.50		19.50	
	Clean	Ea.	.09	9.35		9.44	
	Paint	Ea.	1.25	25.50		26.75	
	Minimum Charge	Job		207		207	
33″ x 36″, 4 Panel							
	Demolish	Ea.		29		29	Includes material and labor to install
	Install	Pr.	99	24.50		123.50	moveable louver, up to 33″ x 36″, 4
	Demolish and Install	Pr.	99	53.50		152.50	panel shutter.
	Reinstall	Pr.		19.50		19.50	
	Clean	Ea.	.09	9.35		9.44	
	Paint	Ea.	1.31	27.50		28.81	
	Minimum Charge	Job		207		207	
39″ x 36″, 4 Panel							
	Demolish	Ea.		29		29	Includes material and labor to install
	Install	Pr.	108	24.50		132.50	moveable louver, up to 47″ x 36″, 4
	Demolish and Install	Pr.	108	53.50		161.50	panel shutter.
	Reinstall	Pr.		19.50		19.50	
	Clean	Ea.	.09	9.35		9.44	
	Paint	Ea.	1.31	27.50		28.81	
	Minimum Charge	Job		207		207	
47″ x 36″, 4 Panel							
	Demolish	Ea.		29		29	Includes material and labor to install
	Install	Pr.	108	24.50		132.50	moveable louver, up to 47″ x 36″, 4
	Demolish and Install	Pr.	108	53.50		161.50	panel shutter.
	Reinstall	Pr.		19.50		19.50	
	Clean	Ea.	.09	9.35		9.44	
	Paint	Ea.	1.36	29.50		30.86	
	Minimum Charge	Job		207		207	

Stairs

Stairs		Unit	Material	Labor	Equip.	Total	Specification
Concrete Steps							
Precast							
	Demolish	Ea.		59	41	100	Includes material and labor to install
	Install	Flight	470	143	39.50	652.50	precast concrete front entrance stairs,
	Demolish and Install	Flight	470	202	80.50	752.50	4' wide, with 48" platform and 2
	Clean	Ea.		4.26		4.26	risers.
	Paint	Ea.	4.03	44.50		48.53	
	Minimum Charge	Job		370		370	
Metal							
Concrete Filled							
	Demolish	Ea.		17		17	Includes material and labor to install
	Install	Riser	580	69	4.46	653.46	steel, cement filled metal pan stairs
	Demolish and Install	Riser	580	86	4.46	670.46	with picket rail.
	Clean	Ea.	.15	2.63		2.78	
	Paint	Ea.	.69	2.63		3.32	
	Minimum Charge	Job		255		255	
Landing							
	Demolish	S.F.		4.26		4.26	Includes material and labor to install
	Install	S.F.	121	8.10	.52	129.62	pre-erected conventional steel pan
	Demolish and Install	S.F.	121	12.36	.52	133.88	landing.
	Clean	S.F.	.15	.55		.70	
	Paint	S.F.	.24	.76		1	
	Minimum Charge	Job		255		255	
Railing							
	Demolish	L.F.		2.35		2.35	Includes material and labor to install
	Install	L.F.	15.95	11.75	.76	28.46	primed steel pipe.
	Demolish and Install	L.F.	15.95	14.10	.76	30.81	
	Clean	L.F.	.96	1.92		2.88	
	Paint	L.F.	.75	5.90		6.65	
	Minimum Charge	Job		255		255	

Elevator

Elevator		Unit	Material	Labor	Equip.	Total	Specification
2 Stop Residential							
	Install	Ea.	12100	6225		18325	Includes labor, material and
	Clean	Ea.	1.09	19.15		20.24	equipment to install 2 stop elevator for
	Minimum Charge	Job		620		620	residential use.
2 Stop Commercial							
	Install	Ea.	50500	12400		62900	Includes labor, material and
	Clean	Ea.	1.09	19.15		20.24	equipment to install 2 stop elevator for
	Minimum Charge	Job		620		620	apartment or commercial building with
							2,000 lb/13 passenger capacity.
3 Stop Commercial							
	Install	Ea.	64500	19100		83600	Includes labor, material and
	Clean	Ea.	1.09	19.15		20.24	equipment to install 3 stop elevator for
	Minimum Charge	Job		620		620	apartment or commercial building with
							2,000 lb/13 passenger capacity.
4 Stop Commercial							
	Install	Ea.	77500	25900		103400	Includes labor, material and
	Clean	Ea.	1.09	19.15		20.24	equipment to install 4 stop elevator for
	Minimum Charge	Job		620		620	apartment or commercial building with
							2,000 lb/13 passenger capacity.

Improvements / Appliances / Treatments

Elevator

	Unit	Material	Labor	Equip.	Total	Specification
5 Stop Commercial						
Install	Ea.	91500	32700		124200	Includes labor, material and
Clean	Ea.	1.09	19.15		20.24	equipment to install 5 stop elevator for
Minimum Charge	Job		620		620	apartment or commercial building with 2,000 lb/13 passenger capacity.

Rangetop

	Unit	Material	Labor	Equip.	Total	Specification
4-burner						
Demolish	Ea.		31		31	Cost includes material and labor to
Install	Ea.	305	75.50		380.50	install 4-burner electric surface unit.
Demolish and Install	Ea.	305	106.50		411.50	
Reinstall	Ea.		60.27		60.27	
Clean	Ea.	.08	28		28.08	
Minimum Charge	Job		76.50		76.50	
6-burner						
Demolish	Ea.		31		31	Includes material and labor to install a
Install	Ea.	2300	90.50		2390.50	6-burner cooktop unit.
Demolish and Install	Ea.	2300	121.50		2421.50	
Reinstall	Ea.		72.32		72.32	
Clean	Ea.	.08	28		28.08	
Minimum Charge	Job		76.50		76.50	
Premium Brand w / Grill						
Demolish	Ea.		31		31	Includes material and labor to install
Install	Ea.	1000	90.50		1090.50	electric downdraft cooktop with grill.
Demolish and Install	Ea.	1000	121.50		1121.50	
Reinstall	Ea.		72.32		72.32	
Clean	Ea.	.08	28		28.08	
Minimum Charge	Job		76.50		76.50	

Rangehood

	Unit	Material	Labor	Equip.	Total	Specification
Vented						
30"						
Demolish	Ea.		28.50		28.50	Includes material and labor to install a
Install	Ea.	63.50	90.50		154	vented range hood.
Demolish and Install	Ea.	63.50	119		182.50	
Reinstall	Ea.		72.32		72.32	
Clean	Ea.	.08	8.05		8.13	
Minimum Charge	Job		76.50		76.50	
36"						
Demolish	Ea.		28.50		28.50	Includes material and labor to install a
Install	Ea.	153	90.50		243.50	vented range hood.
Demolish and Install	Ea.	153	119		272	
Reinstall	Ea.		72.32		72.32	
Clean	Ea.	.08	8.05		8.13	
Minimum Charge	Job		76.50		76.50	
42"						
Demolish	Ea.		28.50		28.50	Includes material and labor to install a
Install	Ea.	199	105		304	vented range hood.
Demolish and Install	Ea.	199	133.50		332.50	
Reinstall	Ea.		84.38		84.38	
Clean	Ea.	.08	8.05		8.13	
Minimum Charge	Job		76.50		76.50	

Rangehood

Rangehood	Unit	Material	Labor	Equip.	Total	Specification
Ventless						
30″						
Demolish	Ea.		28.50		28.50	Includes material and labor to install a
Install	Ea.	81	56.50		137.50	ventless range hood.
Demolish and Install	Ea.	81	85		166	
Reinstall	Ea.		45.20		45.20	
Clean	Ea.	.08	8.05		8.13	
Minimum Charge	Job		76.50		76.50	
36″						
Demolish	Ea.		28.50		28.50	Includes material and labor to install a
Install	Ea.	136	90.50		226.50	ventless range hood.
Demolish and Install	Ea.	136	119		255	
Reinstall	Ea.		72.32		72.32	
Clean	Ea.	.08	8.05		8.13	
Minimum Charge	Job		76.50		76.50	
42″						
Demolish	Ea.		28.50		28.50	Includes material and labor to install a
Install	Ea.	218	75.50		293.50	ventless range hood.
Demolish and Install	Ea.	218	104		322	
Reinstall	Ea.		60.27		60.27	
Clean	Ea.	.08	8.05		8.13	
Minimum Charge	Job		76.50		76.50	

Oven

Oven	Unit	Material	Labor	Equip.	Total	Specification
Free Standing						
Demolish	Ea.		31		31	Cost includes material and labor to
Install	Ea.	570	61.50		631.50	install 30″ free standing electric range
Demolish and Install	Ea.	570	92.50		662.50	with self-cleaning oven.
Reinstall	Ea.		49.02		49.02	
Clean	Ea.	.08	28		28.08	
Minimum Charge	Job		76.50		76.50	
Single Wall Oven						
Demolish	Ea.		31		31	Includes material and labor to install a
Install	Ea.	605	113		718	built-in oven.
Demolish and Install	Ea.	605	144		749	
Reinstall	Ea.		90.40		90.40	
Clean	Ea.	.08	28		28.08	
Minimum Charge	Job		76.50		76.50	
Double Wall Oven						
Demolish	Ea.		31		31	Includes material and labor to install a
Install	Ea.	1475	207		1682	conventional double oven.
Demolish and Install	Ea.	1475	238		1713	
Reinstall	Ea.		165.76		165.76	
Clean	Ea.	.08	28		28.08	
Minimum Charge	Job		76.50		76.50	
Drop-in Type w / Range						
Demolish	Ea.		31		31	Includes material and labor to install a
Install	Ea.	715	75.50		790.50	built-in cooking range with oven.
Demolish and Install	Ea.	715	106.50		821.50	
Reinstall	Ea.		60.27		60.27	
Clean	Ea.	.08	28		28.08	
Minimum Charge	Job		76.50		76.50	

Oven	Unit	Material	Labor	Equip.	Total	Specification
Hi/Lo w / Range, Microwave						
Demolish	Ea.		31		31	Includes material and labor to install a
Install	Ea.	2025	415		2440	double oven, one conventional, one
Demolish and Install	Ea.	2025	446		2471	microwave.
Reinstall	Ea.		331.52		331.52	
Clean	Ea.	.08	28		28.08	
Minimum Charge	Job		76.50		76.50	
Hi/Lo w/ Range / Double Oven						
Demolish	Ea.		31		31	Includes material and labor to install a
Install	Ea.	1475	207		1682	conventional double oven.
Demolish and Install	Ea.	1475	238		1713	
Reinstall	Ea.		165.76		165.76	
Clean	Ea.	.08	28		28.08	
Minimum Charge	Job		76.50		76.50	
Countertop Microwave						
Demolish	Ea.		10.65		10.65	Includes material and labor to install a
Install	Ea.	144	38.50		182.50	1.0 cubic foot microwave oven.
Demolish and Install	Ea.	144	49.15		193.15	
Reinstall	Ea.		30.64		30.64	
Clean	Ea.	.08	14.05		14.13	
Minimum Charge	Job		76.50		76.50	
Cabinet / Wall Mounted Microwave						
Demolish	Ea.		21.50		21.50	Includes material and labor to install a
Install	Ea.	770	113		883	space saver microwave oven.
Demolish and Install	Ea.	770	134.50		904.50	
Reinstall	Ea.		90.40		90.40	
Clean	Ea.	.08	14.05		14.13	
Minimum Charge	Job		76.50		76.50	

Dryer	Unit	Material	Labor	Equip.	Total	Specification
Basic Grade						
Demolish	Ea.		14.20		14.20	Includes material and labor to install
Install	Ea.	385	241		626	electric or gas dryer. Vent kit not
Demolish and Install	Ea.	385	255.20		640.20	included.
Reinstall	Ea.		192.55		192.55	
Clean	Ea.	.08	28		28.08	
Minimum Charge	Job		76.50		76.50	
Good Grade						
Demolish	Ea.		14.20		14.20	Includes material and labor to install
Install	Ea.	480	241		721	electric or gas dryer. Vent kit not
Demolish and Install	Ea.	480	255.20		735.20	included.
Reinstall	Ea.		192.55		192.55	
Clean	Ea.	.08	28		28.08	
Minimum Charge	Job		76.50		76.50	
Premium Grade						
Demolish	Ea.		14.20		14.20	Includes material and labor to install
Install	Ea.	1575	360		1935	electric or gas dryer. Vent kit not
Demolish and Install	Ea.	1575	374.20		1949.20	included.
Reinstall	Ea.		288.83		288.83	
Clean	Ea.	.08	28		28.08	
Minimum Charge	Job		76.50		76.50	

Improvements / Appliances / Treatments

Dryer

	Unit	Material	Labor	Equip.	Total	Specification
Washer / Dryer Combination Unit						
Demolish	Ea.		14.20		14.20	Includes material and labor to install
Install	Ea.	1075	61.50		1136.50	electric washer/dryer combination
Demolish and Install	Ea.	1075	75.70		1150.70	unit, 27" wide, stackable or unitized.
Reinstall	Ea.		49.02		49.02	
Clean	Ea.	.08	28		28.08	
Minimum Charge	Job		76.50		76.50	

Washer

	Unit	Material	Labor	Equip.	Total	Specification
Basic Grade						
Demolish	Ea.		14.20		14.20	Includes material and labor to install
Install	Ea.	455	158		613	washing machine. New hoses not
Demolish and Install	Ea.	455	172.20		627.20	included.
Reinstall	Ea.		126.72		126.72	
Clean	Ea.	.08	28		28.08	
Minimum Charge	Job		76.50		76.50	
Good Grade						
Demolish	Ea.		14.20		14.20	Includes material and labor to install
Install	Ea.	750	238		988	washing machine. New hoses not
Demolish and Install	Ea.	750	252.20		1002.20	included.
Reinstall	Ea.		190.08		190.08	
Clean	Ea.	.08	28		28.08	
Minimum Charge	Job		76.50		76.50	
Premium Grade						
Demolish	Ea.		14.20		14.20	Includes material and labor to install
Install	Ea.	1650	475		2125	washing machine with digital
Demolish and Install	Ea.	1650	489.20		2139.20	computer readouts and large capacity.
Reinstall	Ea.		380.16		380.16	New hoses not included.
Clean	Ea.	.08	28		28.08	
Minimum Charge	Job		76.50		76.50	
Washer / Dryer Combination Unit						
Demolish	Ea.		14.20		14.20	Includes material and labor to install
Install	Ea.	1075	61.50		1136.50	electric washer/dryer combination
Demolish and Install	Ea.	1075	75.70		1150.70	unit, 27" wide, stackable or unitized.
Reinstall	Ea.		49.02		49.02	
Clean	Ea.	.08	28		28.08	
Minimum Charge	Job		76.50		76.50	

Refrigerator

	Unit	Material	Labor	Equip.	Total	Specification
12 Cubic Foot						
Demolish	Ea.		42.50		42.50	Includes material and labor to install a
Install	Ea.	470	61.50		531.50	refrigerator.
Demolish and Install	Ea.	470	104		574	
Reinstall	Ea.		49.02		49.02	
Clean	Ea.	.08	28		28.08	
Minimum Charge	Job		76.50		76.50	
16 Cubic Foot						
Demolish	Ea.		42.50		42.50	Includes material and labor to install a
Install	Ea.	565	68		633	refrigerator.
Demolish and Install	Ea.	565	110.50		675.50	
Reinstall	Ea.		54.47		54.47	
Clean	Ea.	.08	28		28.08	
Minimum Charge	Job		76.50		76.50	

Improvements / Appliances / Treatments

Refrigerator

Refrigerator	Unit	Material	Labor	Equip.	Total	Specification
18 Cubic Foot						
Demolish	Ea.		42.50		42.50	Includes material and labor to install a
Install	Ea.	690	76.50		766.50	refrigerator.
Demolish and Install	Ea.	690	119		809	
Reinstall	Ea.		61.28		61.28	
Clean	Ea.	.08	28		28.08	
Minimum Charge	Job		76.50		76.50	
21 Cubic Foot						
Demolish	Ea.		42.50		42.50	Includes material and labor to install a
Install	Ea.	1050	87.50		1137.50	refrigerator.
Demolish and Install	Ea.	1050	130		1180	
Reinstall	Ea.		70.03		70.03	
Clean	Ea.	.08	28		28.08	
Minimum Charge	Job		76.50		76.50	
24 Cubic Foot						
Demolish	Ea.		42.50		42.50	Includes material and labor to install a
Install	Ea.	1400	87.50		1487.50	refrigerator.
Demolish and Install	Ea.	1400	130		1530	
Reinstall	Ea.		70.03		70.03	
Clean	Ea.	.08	28		28.08	
Minimum Charge	Job		76.50		76.50	
27 Cubic Foot						
Demolish	Ea.		42.50		42.50	Includes material and labor to install a
Install	Ea.	2850	61.50		2911.50	refrigerator.
Demolish and Install	Ea.	2850	104		2954	
Reinstall	Ea.		49.02		49.02	
Clean	Ea.	.08	28		28.08	
Minimum Charge	Job		76.50		76.50	
Ice Maker						
Install	Ea.	68	59.50		127.50	Includes labor and material to install
Minimum Charge	Job		76.50		76.50	an automatic ice maker in a refrigerator.

Freezer

Freezer	Unit	Material	Labor	Equip.	Total	Specification
15 Cubic Foot						
Demolish	Ea.		42.50		42.50	Cost includes material and labor to
Install	Ea.	635	61.50		696.50	install 15 cubic foot freezer.
Demolish and Install	Ea.	635	104		739	
Reinstall	Ea.		49.02		49.02	
Clean	Ea.	.08	28		28.08	
Minimum Charge	Job		76.50		76.50	
18 Cubic Foot						
Demolish	Ea.		42.50		42.50	Cost includes material and labor to
Install	Ea.	840	61.50		901.50	install 18 cubic foot freezer.
Demolish and Install	Ea.	840	104		944	
Reinstall	Ea.		49.02		49.02	
Clean	Ea.	.08	28		28.08	
Minimum Charge	Job		76.50		76.50	
21 Cubic Foot						
Demolish	Ea.		42.50		42.50	Includes material and labor to install a
Install	Ea.	735	61.50		796.50	15 to 23 cubic foot deep freezer.
Demolish and Install	Ea.	735	104		839	
Reinstall	Ea.		49.02		49.02	
Clean	Ea.	.08	28		28.08	
Minimum Charge	Job		76.50		76.50	

Improvements / Appliances / Treatments

Freezer

	Unit	Material	Labor	Equip.	Total	Specification
24 Cubic Foot						
Demolish	Ea.		42.50		42.50	Includes material and labor to install a
Install	Ea.	820	123		943	24 cubic foot deep freezer.
Demolish and Install	Ea.	820	165.50		985.50	
Reinstall	Ea.		98.05		98.05	
Clean	Ea.	.08	28		28.08	
Minimum Charge	Job		76.50		76.50	
Chest-type						
Demolish	Ea.		42.50		42.50	Cost includes material and labor to
Install	Ea.	635	61.50		696.50	install 15 cubic foot freezer.
Demolish and Install	Ea.	635	104		739	
Clean	Ea.	.08	28		28.08	
Minimum Charge	Job		76.50		76.50	

Dishwasher

	Unit	Material	Labor	Equip.	Total	Specification
4 Cycle						
Demolish	Ea.		34		34	Includes material and labor to install
Install	Ea.	360	147		507	good grade automatic dishwasher.
Demolish and Install	Ea.	360	181		541	
Reinstall	Ea.		117.64		117.64	
Clean	Ea.	.08	28		28.08	
Minimum Charge	Job		76.50		76.50	

Garbage Disposal

	Unit	Material	Labor	Equip.	Total	Specification
In Sink Unit						
Demolish	Ea.		33		33	Cost includes material and labor to
Install	Ea.	169	59		228	install 1/2 HP custom disposal unit.
Demolish and Install	Ea.	169	92		261	
Reinstall	Ea.		47.06		47.06	
Clean	Ea.	.03	8.05		8.08	
Minimum Charge	Job		76.50		76.50	

Trash Compactor

	Unit	Material	Labor	Equip.	Total	Specification
4 to 1 Compaction						
Demolish	Ea.		31.50		31.50	Includes material and labor to install a
Install	Ea.	845	83		928	trash compactor.
Demolish and Install	Ea.	845	114.50		959.50	
Reinstall	Ea.		66.30		66.30	
Clean	Ea.	.08	19.15		19.23	
Minimum Charge	Job		76.50		76.50	

Kitchenette Unit

	Unit	Material	Labor	Equip.	Total	Specification
Range, Refrigerator and Sink						
Demolish	Ea.		126		126	Includes material and labor to install
Install	Ea.	4850	490		5340	range/refrigerator/sink unit, 72"
Demolish and Install	Ea.	4850	616		5466	wide, base unit only.
Reinstall	Ea.		392.13		392.13	
Clean	Ea.	1.20	14.05		15.25	
Minimum Charge	Job		76.50		76.50	

Bath Accessories	Unit	Material	Labor	Equip.	Total	Specification
Towel Bar						
Demolish	Ea.		7.10		7.10	Includes material and labor to install
Install	Ea.	60.50	17.25		77.75	towel bar up to 24″ long.
Demolish and Install	Ea.	60.50	24.35		84.85	
Reinstall	Ea.		13.81		13.81	
Clean	Ea.		3.83		3.83	
Minimum Charge	Job		207		207	
Toothbrush Holder						
Demolish	Ea.		7.10		7.10	Includes material and labor to install a
Install	Ea.	15.20	20.50		35.70	surface mounted tumbler and
Demolish and Install	Ea.	15.20	27.60		42.80	toothbrush holder.
Reinstall	Ea.		16.58		16.58	
Clean	Ea.		3.83		3.83	
Minimum Charge	Job		207		207	
Grab Rail						
Demolish	Ea.		10.65		10.65	Includes material and labor to install a
Install	Ea.	33	18		51	24″ long grab bar. Blocking is not
Demolish and Install	Ea.	33	28.65		61.65	included.
Reinstall	Ea.		14.41		14.41	
Clean	Ea.	.47	6.40		6.87	
Minimum Charge	Job		207		207	
Soap Dish						
Demolish	Ea.		7.10		7.10	Includes material and labor to install a
Install	Ea.	6.15	20.50		26.65	surface mounted soap dish.
Demolish and Install	Ea.	6.15	27.60		33.75	
Reinstall	Ea.		16.58		16.58	
Clean	Ea.		3.83		3.83	
Minimum Charge	Job		207		207	
Toilet Paper Roller						
Demolish	Ea.		7.10		7.10	Includes material and labor to install a
Install	Ea.	18.75	13.80		32.55	surface mounted toilet tissue dispenser.
Demolish and Install	Ea.	18.75	20.90		39.65	
Reinstall	Ea.		11.05		11.05	
Clean	Ea.	.47	9.60		10.07	
Minimum Charge	Job		207		207	
Dispenser						
Soap						
Demolish	Ea.		9.45		9.45	Includes material and labor to install a
Install	Ea.	46	20.50		66.50	surface mounted soap dispenser.
Demolish and Install	Ea.	46	29.95		75.95	
Reinstall	Ea.		16.58		16.58	
Clean	Ea.	.47	9.60		10.07	
Minimum Charge	Job		207		207	
Towel						
Demolish	Ea.		10.65		10.65	Includes material and labor to install a
Install	Ea.	47	26		73	surface mounted towel dispenser.
Demolish and Install	Ea.	47	36.65		83.65	
Reinstall	Ea.		20.72		20.72	
Clean	Ea.	.47	12.75		13.22	
Minimum Charge	Job		207		207	
Seat Cover						
Demolish	Ea.		7.10		7.10	Includes material and labor to install a
Install	Ea.	35	27.50		62.50	surface mounted toilet seat cover
Demolish and Install	Ea.	35	34.60		69.60	dispenser.
Reinstall	Ea.		22.10		22.10	
Clean	Ea.	.47	9.60		10.07	
Minimum Charge	Job		207		207	

Improvements / Appliances / Treatments

Bath Accessories		Unit	Material	Labor	Equip.	Total	Specification
Sanitary Napkin							
	Demolish	Ea.		17.90		17.90	Includes material and labor to install a
	Install	Ea.	34	43.50		77.50	surface mounted sanitary napkin
	Demolish and Install	Ea.	34	61.40		95.40	dispenser.
	Reinstall	Ea.		34.90		34.90	
	Clean	Ea.	.24	12.75		12.99	
	Minimum Charge	Job		207		207	
Partition							
Urinal							
	Demolish	Ea.		21.50		21.50	Includes material and labor to install a
	Install	Ea.	251	104		355	urinal screen.
	Demolish and Install	Ea.	251	125.50		376.50	
	Reinstall	Ea.		82.88		82.88	
	Clean	Ea.	.72	8.50		9.22	
	Minimum Charge	Job		207		207	
Toilet							
	Demolish	Ea.		63		63	Includes material and labor to install
	Install	Ea.	675	166		841	baked enamel standard size partition,
	Demolish and Install	Ea.	675	229		904	floor or ceiling mounted with one wall
	Reinstall	Ea.		132.61		132.61	and one door.
	Clean	Ea.	4.77	19.15		23.92	
	Minimum Charge	Job		207		207	
Handicap							
	Demolish	Ea.		63		63	Includes material and labor to install
	Install	Ea.	1000	166		1166	baked enamel handicap partition,
	Demolish and Install	Ea.	1000	229		1229	floor or ceiling mounted with one wall
	Reinstall	Ea.		132.61		132.61	and one door.
	Clean	Ea.	4.77	19.15		23.92	
	Minimum Charge	Job		207		207	

Fire Prevention / Protection		Unit	Material	Labor	Equip.	Total	Specification
Fire Extinguisher							
5# Carbon Dioxide							
	Install	Ea.	189			189	Includes labor and material to install one wall mounted 5 lb. carbon dioxide factory charged unit, complete with hose, horn and wall mounting bracket.
10# Carbon Dioxide							
	Install	Ea.	273			273	Includes labor and material to install one wall mounted 10 lb. carbon dioxide factory charged unit, complete with hose, horn and wall mounting bracket.
15# Carbon Dioxide							
	Install	Ea.	345			345	Includes labor and material to install one wall mounted 15 lb. carbon dioxide factory charged unit, complete with hose, horn and wall mounting bracket.

Improvements / Appliances / Treatments

Fire Prevention / Protection		Unit	Material	Labor	Equip.	Total	Specification
5# Dry Chemical							
	Install	Ea.	51.50			51.50	Includes labor and material to install one wall mounted 5 lb. dry chemical factory charged unit, complete with hose, horn and wall mounting bracket.
20# Dry Chemical							
	Install	Ea.	139			139	Includes labor and material to install one wall mounted 20 lb. dry chemical factory charged unit, complete with hose, horn and wall mounting bracket.

Gutters		Unit	Material	Labor	Equip.	Total	Specification
Galvanized							
	Demolish	L.F.		1.42		1.42	Cost includes material and labor to install 5" galvanized steel gutter with enamel finish, fittings, hangers, and corners.
	Install	L.F.	2.22	3.82		6.04	
	Demolish and Install	L.F.	2.22	5.24		7.46	
	Reinstall	L.F.		3.05		3.05	
	Clean	L.F.		.41		.41	
	Paint	L.F.	.21	1.09		1.30	
	Minimum Charge	Job		229		229	
Aluminum							
	Demolish	L.F.		1.42		1.42	Cost includes material and labor to install 5" aluminum gutter with enamel finish, fittings, hangers, and corners.
	Install	L.F.	2.94	3.82		6.76	
	Demolish and Install	L.F.	2.94	5.24		8.18	
	Reinstall	L.F.		3.05		3.05	
	Clean	L.F.		.41		.41	
	Paint	L.F.	.21	1.09		1.30	
	Minimum Charge	Job		229		229	
Copper							
	Demolish	L.F.		1.42		1.42	Cost includes material and labor to install 5" half-round copper gutter with fittings, hangers, and corners.
	Install	L.F.	9.90	3.82		13.72	
	Demolish and Install	L.F.	9.90	5.24		15.14	
	Reinstall	L.F.		3.05		3.05	
	Clean	L.F.		.41		.41	
	Minimum Charge	Job		229		229	
Plastic							
	Demolish	L.F.		1.42		1.42	Cost includes material and labor to install 4" white vinyl gutter fittings, hangers, and corners.
	Install	L.F.	1.19	3.77		4.96	
	Demolish and Install	L.F.	1.19	5.19		6.38	
	Reinstall	L.F.		3.01		3.01	
	Clean	L.F.		.41		.41	
	Paint	L.F.	.21	1.09		1.30	
	Minimum Charge	Job		229		229	

Downspouts		Unit	Material	Labor	Equip.	Total	Specification
Galvanized							
	Demolish	L.F.		.97		.97	Cost includes material and labor to install 4" diameter downspout with enamel finish.
	Install	L.F.	2.79	3.16		5.95	
	Demolish and Install	L.F.	2.79	4.13		6.92	
	Reinstall	L.F.		2.53		2.53	
	Clean	L.F.		.41		.41	
	Paint	L.F.	.21	1.09		1.30	
	Minimum Charge	Job		229		229	

Improvements / Appliances / Treatments

Downspouts

	Unit	Material	Labor	Equip.	Total	Specification
Aluminum						
Demolish	L.F.		.97		.97	Includes material and labor to install
Install	L.F.	3.03	3.27		6.30	aluminum enameled downspout.
Demolish and Install	L.F.	3.03	4.24		7.27	
Reinstall	L.F.		2.62		2.62	
Clean	L.F.		.41		.41	
Paint	L.F.	.21	1.09		1.30	
Minimum Charge	Job		229		229	
Copper						
Demolish	L.F.		.97		.97	Includes material and labor to install
Install	L.F.	8.90	2.41		11.31	round copper downspout.
Demolish and Install	L.F.	8.90	3.38		12.28	
Reinstall	L.F.		1.93		1.93	
Clean	L.F.		.41		.41	
Paint	L.F.	.21	1.09		1.30	
Minimum Charge	Job		229		229	
Plastic						
Demolish	L.F.		.97		.97	Cost includes material and labor to
Install	L.F.	2.29	2.18		4.47	install 2″ x 3″ vinyl rectangular
Demolish and Install	L.F.	2.29	3.15		5.44	downspouts.
Reinstall	L.F.		1.74		1.74	
Clean	L.F.		.41		.41	
Paint	L.F.	.21	1.09		1.30	
Minimum Charge	Job		229		229	

Shutters

	Unit	Material	Labor	Equip.	Total	Specification
Exterior						
25″ High						
Demolish	Ea.		10.65		10.65	Includes material and labor to install
Install	Pr.	121	41.50		162.50	pair of exterior shutters 25″ x 16″,
Demolish and Install	Pr.	121	52.15		173.15	unpainted, installed as fixed shutters
Reinstall	Pr.		41.44		41.44	on concrete or wood frame.
Clean	Ea.	.09	9.35		9.44	
Paint	Ea.	1.66	19.10		20.76	
Minimum Charge	Job		207		207	
39″ High						
Demolish	Ea.		10.65		10.65	Includes material and labor to install
Install	Pr.	130	41.50		171.50	pair of shutters 39″ x 16″, unpainted,
Demolish and Install	Pr.	130	52.15		182.15	installed as fixed shutters on concrete
Reinstall	Pr.		41.44		41.44	or wood frame.
Clean	Ea.	.09	9.35		9.44	
Paint	Ea.	2.57	25.50		28.07	
Minimum Charge	Job		207		207	
51″ High						
Demolish	Ea.		10.65		10.65	Includes material and labor to install
Install	Pr.	144	41.50		185.50	pair of shutters 51″ x 16″, unpainted,
Demolish and Install	Pr.	144	52.15		196.15	installed as fixed shutters on concrete
Reinstall	Pr.		41.44		41.44	or wood frame.
Clean	Ea.	.09	9.35		9.44	
Paint	Ea.	3.36	26.50		29.86	
Minimum Charge	Job		207		207	

Shutters	Unit	Material	Labor	Equip.	Total	Specification
59" High						
Demolish	Ea.		10.65		10.65	Includes material and labor to install
Install	Pr.	204	41.50		245.50	pair of shutters 59" x 16", unpainted,
Demolish and Install	Pr.	204	52.15		256.15	installed as fixed shutters on concrete
Reinstall	Pr.		41.44		41.44	or wood frame.
Clean	Ea.	.09	9.35		9.44	
Paint	Ea.	3.87	29.50		33.37	
Minimum Charge	Job		207		207	
67" High						
Demolish	Ea.		10.65		10.65	Includes material and labor to install
Install	Pr.	205	46		251	pair of shutters 67" x 16", unpainted,
Demolish and Install	Pr.	205	56.65		261.65	installed as fixed shutters on concrete
Reinstall	Pr.		46.04		46.04	or wood frame.
Clean	Ea.	.09	9.35		9.44	
Paint	Ea.	4.42	33		37.42	
Minimum Charge	Job		207		207	
Interior Wood						
23" x 24", 2 Panel						
Demolish	Ea.		10.65		10.65	Cost includes material and labor to
Install	Ea.	86	24.50		110.50	install 23" x 24", 4 panel interior
Demolish and Install	Ea.	86	35.15		121.15	moveable pine shutter, 1-1/4" louver,
Reinstall	Ea.		19.50		19.50	knobs and hooks and hinges.
Clean	Ea.	.09	9.35		9.44	
Paint	Ea.	1.25	25.50		26.75	
Minimum Charge	Job		207		207	
27" x 24", 4 Panel						
Demolish	Ea.		10.65		10.65	Cost includes material and labor to
Install	Ea.	86	24.50		110.50	install 27" x 24", 4 panel interior
Demolish and Install	Ea.	86	35.15		121.15	moveable pine shutter, 1-1/4" louver,
Reinstall	Ea.		19.50		19.50	knobs and hooks and hinges.
Clean	Ea.	.09	9.35		9.44	
Paint	Ea.	1.25	25.50		26.75	
Minimum Charge	Job		207		207	
31" x 24", 4 Panel						
Demolish	Ea.		10.65		10.65	Cost includes material and labor to
Install	Ea.	94.50	24.50		119	install 31" x 24", 4 panel interior
Demolish and Install	Ea.	94.50	35.15		129.65	moveable pine shutter, 1-1/4" louver,
Reinstall	Ea.		19.50		19.50	knobs and hooks and hinges.
Clean	Ea.	.09	9.35		9.44	
Paint	Ea.	1.25	25.50		26.75	
Minimum Charge	Job		207		207	
35" x 24", 4 Panel						
Demolish	Ea.		10.65		10.65	Cost includes material and labor to
Install	Ea.	101	24.50		125.50	install 35" x 24", 4 panel interior
Demolish and Install	Ea.	101	35.15		136.15	moveable pine shutter, 1-1/4" louver,
Reinstall	Ea.		19.50		19.50	knobs and hooks and hinges.
Clean	Ea.	.09	9.35		9.44	
Paint	Ea.	1.25	25.50		26.75	
Minimum Charge	Job		207		207	
39" x 24", 4 Panel						
Demolish	Ea.		10.65		10.65	Cost includes material and labor to
Install	Ea.	112	24.50		136.50	install 39" x 24", 4 panel interior
Demolish and Install	Ea.	112	35.15		147.15	moveable pine shutter, 1-1/4" louver,
Reinstall	Ea.		19.50		19.50	knobs and hooks and hinges.
Clean	Ea.	.09	9.35		9.44	
Paint	Ea.	1.25	25.50		26.75	
Minimum Charge	Job		207		207	

Improvements / Appliances / Treatments

Shutters

	Unit	Material	Labor	Equip.	Total	Specification
47" x 24", 4 Panel						
Demolish	Ea.		10.65		10.65	Cost includes material and labor to
Install	Ea.	128	24.50		152.50	install 47" x 24", 4 panel interior
Demolish and Install	Ea.	128	35.15		163.15	moveable pine shutter, 1-1/4" louver,
Reinstall	Ea.		19.50		19.50	knobs and hooks and hinges.
Clean	Ea.	.09	9.35		9.44	
Paint	Ea.	1.31	27.50		28.81	
Minimum Charge	Job		207		207	

Awning

	Unit	Material	Labor	Equip.	Total	Specification
Standard Aluminum						
36" Wide x 30" Deep						
Demolish	Ea.		10.65		10.65	Includes material and labor to install
Install	Ea.	206	34.50		240.50	one aluminum awning with
Demolish and Install	Ea.	206	45.15		251.15	weather-resistant finish.
Reinstall	Ea.		27.63		27.63	
Clean	Ea.		12.75		12.75	
Minimum Charge	Job		207		207	
48" Wide x 30" Deep						
Demolish	Ea.		10.65		10.65	Includes material and labor to install
Install	Ea.	231	41.50		272.50	one aluminum awning with
Demolish and Install	Ea.	231	52.15		283.15	weather-resistant finish.
Reinstall	Ea.		33.15		33.15	
Clean	Ea.		12.75		12.75	
Minimum Charge	Job		207		207	
60" Wide x 30" Deep						
Demolish	Ea.		21.50		21.50	Includes material and labor to install
Install	Ea.	270	46		316	one aluminum awning with
Demolish and Install	Ea.	270	67.50		337.50	weather-resistant finish.
Reinstall	Ea.		36.84		36.84	
Clean	Ea.		12.75		12.75	
Minimum Charge	Job		207		207	
72" Wide x 30" Deep						
Demolish	Ea.		21.50		21.50	Includes material and labor to install
Install	Ea.	305	52		357	one aluminum awning with
Demolish and Install	Ea.	305	73.50		378.50	weather-resistant finish.
Reinstall	Ea.		41.44		41.44	
Clean	Ea.		12.75		12.75	
Minimum Charge	Job		207		207	
Roll-up Type						
Demolish	S.F.		.77		.77	Includes material and labor to install
Install	S.F.	11.35	4.14		15.49	an aluminum roll-up awning.
Demolish and Install	S.F.	11.35	4.91		16.26	
Reinstall	S.F.		3.32		3.32	
Clean	S.F.	.04	.64		.68	
Minimum Charge	Job		207		207	
Canvas						
30" Wide						
Demolish	Ea.		6.40		6.40	Includes material and labor to install a
Install	Ea.	202	34.50		236.50	canvas window awning.
Demolish and Install	Ea.	202	40.90		242.90	
Reinstall	Ea.		27.63		27.63	
Clean	Ea.		3.83		3.83	
Minimum Charge	Job		207		207	

Improvements / Appliances / Treatments

Awning	Unit	Material	Labor	Equip.	Total	Specification
36" Wide						
Demolish	Ea.		6.40		6.40	Includes material and labor to install a
Install	Ea.	221	41.50		262.50	canvas window awning.
Demolish and Install	Ea.	221	47.90		268.90	
Reinstall	Ea.		33.15		33.15	
Clean	Ea.		4.20		4.20	
Minimum Charge	Job		207		207	
42" Wide						
Demolish	Ea.		6.40		6.40	Includes material and labor to install a
Install	Ea.	233	52		285	canvas window awning.
Demolish and Install	Ea.	233	58.40		291.40	
Reinstall	Ea.		41.44		41.44	
Clean	Ea.		4.98		4.98	
Minimum Charge	Job		207		207	
48" Wide						
Demolish	Ea.		6.40		6.40	Includes material and labor to install a
Install	Ea.	246	59		305	canvas window awning.
Demolish and Install	Ea.	246	65.40		311.40	
Reinstall	Ea.		47.36		47.36	
Clean	Ea.		5.80		5.80	
Minimum Charge	Job		207		207	
Cloth Canopy Cover						
8' x 10'						
Demolish	Ea.		350		350	Includes material and labor to install
Install	Ea.	425	207		632	one 8' x 10' cloth canopy patio cover
Demolish and Install	Ea.	425	557		982	with front bar and tension support
Reinstall	Ea.		165.76		165.76	rafters and 9" valance.
Clean	Ea.	3.83	51		54.83	
Minimum Charge	Job		415		415	
8' x 15'						
Demolish	Ea.		350		350	Includes material and labor to install
Install	Ea.	580	207		787	one 8' x 15' cloth canopy patio cover
Demolish and Install	Ea.	580	557		1137	with front bar and tension support
Reinstall	Ea.		165.76		165.76	rafters and 9" valance.
Clean	Ea.	3.83	76.50		80.33	
Minimum Charge	Job		415		415	

Vent	Unit	Material	Labor	Equip.	Total	Specification
Small Roof Turbine						
Demolish	Ea.		10.65		10.65	Includes material and labor to install
Install	Ea.	55	41		96	spinner ventilator, wind driven,
Demolish and Install	Ea.	55	51.65		106.65	galvanized, 4" neck diam, 180 CFM.
Reinstall	Ea.		32.96		32.96	
Clean	Ea.		6.80		6.80	
Minimum Charge	Job		238		238	
Large Roof Turbine						
Demolish	Ea.		8.50		8.50	Includes material and labor to install
Install	Ea.	64	59		123	spinner ventilator, wind driven,
Demolish and Install	Ea.	64	67.50		131.50	galvanized, 8" neck diam, 360 CFM.
Reinstall	Ea.		47.09		47.09	
Clean	Ea.		7.65		7.65	
Minimum Charge	Job		238		238	

Improvements / Appliances / Treatments

Vent

Vent		Unit	Material	Labor	Equip.	Total	Specification
Gable Louvered							
	Demolish	Ea.		21.50		21.50	Includes material and labor to install a
	Install	Ea.	42	13.80		55.80	vinyl gable end vent.
	Demolish and Install	Ea.	42	35.30		77.30	
	Reinstall	Ea.		11.05		11.05	
	Clean	Ea.		4.09		4.09	
	Paint	Ea.	1.05	5.45		6.50	
	Minimum Charge	Job		207		207	
Ridge Vent							
	Demolish	L.F.		1.10		1.10	Includes material and labor to install a
	Install	L.F.	3.25	2.95		6.20	mill finish aluminum ridge vent strip.
	Demolish and Install	L.F.	3.25	4.05		7.30	
	Minimum Charge	Job		207		207	
Foundation							
	Demolish	Ea.		7.60		7.60	Includes material and labor to install
	Install	Ea.	27	13.55		40.55	galvanized foundation block vent.
	Demolish and Install	Ea.	27	21.15		48.15	
	Reinstall	Ea.		10.86		10.86	
	Clean	Ea.	.24	7.65		7.89	
	Minimum Charge	Job		207		207	
Frieze							
	Demolish	L.F.		.76		.76	Includes material and labor to install
	Install	L.F.	1.21	.94		2.15	pine frieze board.
	Demolish and Install	L.F.	1.21	1.70		2.91	
	Reinstall	L.F.		.75		.75	
	Clean	L.F.	.06	.26		.32	
	Minimum Charge	Job		207		207	
Water Heater Cap							
	Demolish	Ea.		16.50		16.50	Includes material and labor to install a
	Install	Ea.	32.50	57.50		90	galvanized steel water heater cap.
	Demolish and Install	Ea.	32.50	74		106.50	
	Reinstall	Ea.		45.80		45.80	
	Clean	Ea.	1.67	19.15		20.82	

Cupolas

Cupolas		Unit	Material	Labor	Equip.	Total	Specification
22" x 22"							
	Demolish	Ea.		201		201	Includes material and labor to install a
	Install	Ea.	330	104		434	cedar cupola with aluminum roof
	Demolish and Install	Ea.	330	305		635	covering.
	Reinstall	Ea.		82.88		82.88	
	Minimum Charge	Job		207		207	
29" x 29"							
	Demolish	Ea.		201		201	Includes material and labor to install a
	Install	Ea.	445	104		549	cedar cupola with aluminum roof
	Demolish and Install	Ea.	445	305		750	covering.
	Reinstall	Ea.		82.88		82.88	
	Minimum Charge	Job		207		207	
35" x 35"							
	Demolish	Ea.		201		201	Includes material and labor to install a
	Install	Ea.	750	138		888	cedar cupola with aluminum roof
	Demolish and Install	Ea.	750	339		1089	covering.
	Reinstall	Ea.		110.51		110.51	
	Minimum Charge	Job		207		207	

Improvements / Appliances / Treatments

Cupolas

Cupolas	Unit	Material	Labor	Equip.	Total	Specification
47" x 47"						Includes material and labor to install a cedar cupola with aluminum roof covering.
Demolish	Ea.		201		201	
Install	Ea.	1325	207		1532	
Demolish and Install	Ea.	1325	408		1733	
Reinstall	Ea.		165.76		165.76	
Minimum Charge	Job		207		207	
Weather Vane						Includes minimum labor and equipment to install residential type weathervane.
Install	Ea.	166	52		218	
Minimum Charge	Job		207		207	

Aluminum Carport

Aluminum Carport	Unit	Material	Labor	Equip.	Total	Specification
20' x 20' Complete						Includes material, labor and equipment to install an aluminum carport. Foundations are not included.
Demolish	Ea.		213		213	
Install	Ea.	8475	685	145	9305	
Demolish and Install	Ea.	8475	898	145	9518	
Reinstall	Ea.		549.60	116.35	665.95	
Clean	Ea.	.25	76.50		76.75	
Minimum Charge	Job		415		415	
24' x 24' Complete						Includes material, labor and equipment to install an aluminum carport. Foundations are not included.
Demolish	Ea.		213		213	
Install	Ea.	11600	915	194	12709	
Demolish and Install	Ea.	11600	1128	194	12922	
Reinstall	Ea.		732.80	155.14	887.94	
Clean	Ea.	.25	153		153.25	
Minimum Charge	Job		415		415	
Metal Support Posts						Includes material and labor to install metal support posts for a carport.
Demolish	Ea.		2.84		2.84	
Install	Ea.	18.80	52		70.80	
Demolish and Install	Ea.	18.80	54.84		73.64	
Reinstall	Ea.		41.44		41.44	
Clean	Ea.	.25	3.19		3.44	
Paint	Ea.	.21	7.10		7.31	
Minimum Charge	Job		415		415	

Storage Shed

Storage Shed	Unit	Material	Labor	Equip.	Total	Specification
Aluminum						
Pre-fab (8' x 10')						Includes material and labor to install an aluminum storage shed.
Demolish	Ea.		62		62	
Install	Ea.	1875	600		2475	
Demolish and Install	Ea.	1875	662		2537	
Clean	Ea.	1.60	38.50		40.10	
Minimum Charge	Ea.		510		510	
Pre-fab (10' x 12')						Includes material and labor to install an aluminum storage shed.
Demolish	Ea.		117		117	
Install	Ea.	2375	600		2975	
Demolish and Install	Ea.	2375	717		3092	
Clean	Ea.	1.60	42.50		44.10	
Minimum Charge	Ea.		510		510	

Improvements / Appliances / Treatments

Storage Shed

	Unit	Material	Labor	Equip.	Total	Specification
Wood						
Pre-fab (8' x 10')						
Demolish	Ea.		62		62	Includes material and labor to install a
Install	Ea.	1925	600		2525	pre-fabricated wood storage shed.
Demolish and Install	Ea.	1925	662		2587	
Clean	Ea.	1.60	38.50		40.10	
Minimum Charge	Ea.		510		510	
Pre-fab (10' x 12')						
Demolish	Ea.		117		117	Includes material and labor to install a
Install	Ea.	2425	600		3025	pre-fabricated wood storage shed.
Demolish and Install	Ea.	2425	717		3142	
Clean	Ea.	1.60	42.50		44.10	
Minimum Charge	Ea.		510		510	

Gazebo

	Unit	Material	Labor	Equip.	Total	Specification
Good Grade						
Demolish	S.F.		3.40		3.40	Includes material and labor to install a
Install	S.F.	50.50	31		81.50	gazebo.
Demolish and Install	S.F.	50.50	34.40		84.90	
Reinstall	S.F.		24.86		24.86	
Clean	S.F.	.19	2.04		2.23	
Minimum Charge	Job		207		207	
Custom Grade						
Demolish	S.F.		3.40		3.40	Includes material and labor to install a
Install	S.F.	73	31		104	gazebo.
Demolish and Install	S.F.	73	34.40		107.40	
Reinstall	S.F.		24.86		24.86	
Clean	S.F.	.19	2.04		2.23	
Minimum Charge	Job		207		207	
Bench Seating						
Demolish	L.F.		5.65		5.65	Includes material and labor to install
Install	L.F.	1.76	20.50		22.26	pressure treated bench seating.
Demolish and Install	L.F.	1.76	26.15		27.91	
Reinstall	L.F.		16.58		16.58	
Clean	L.F.	.19	1.53		1.72	
Paint	L.F.	.63	2.84		3.47	
Minimum Charge	Job		207		207	
Re-screen						
Install	S.F.	1.74	1.66		3.40	Includes labor and material to
Minimum Charge	Job		207		207	re-screen wood frame.

Pool

	Unit	Material	Labor	Equip.	Total	Specification
Screen Enclosure						
Re-screen						
Install	SF Wall		5.10		5.10	Includes material and labor to install a
Minimum Charge	Job		207		207	screen enclosure for a pool.
Screen Door						
Demolish	Ea.		8.20		8.20	Includes material and labor to install
Install	Ea.	285	69		354	wood screen door with aluminum cloth
Demolish and Install	Ea.	285	77.20		362.20	screen. Frame and hardware not
Reinstall	Ea.		55.25		55.25	included.
Clean	Ea.	.18	11.25		11.43	
Paint	Ea.	5.05	14.20		19.25	
Minimum Charge	Job		207		207	

Improvements / Appliances / Treatments

Pool	Unit	Material	Labor	Equip.	Total	Specification
Heater / Motor						
Demolish	Ea.		42		42	Includes material and labor to install
Install	Ea.	2475	530		3005	swimming pool heater, not incl. base
Demolish and Install	Ea.	2475	572		3047	or pad, elec., 12 kW, 4,800 gal
Reinstall	Ea.		423.71		423.71	pool, incl. pump.
Clean	Ea.	4.77	38.50		43.27	
Minimum Charge	Job		242		242	
Filter System						
Demolish	Ea.		68		68	Includes material, labor and
Install	Total	1700	380		2080	equipment to install sand filter system
Demolish and Install	Total	1700	448		2148	tank including hook-up to existing
Reinstall	Total		304.13		304.13	equipment. Pump and motor not
Minimum Charge	Job		238		238	included.
Pump / Motor						
Demolish	Ea.		42		42	Includes material and labor to install a
Install	Ea.	570	95		665	22 GPM pump.
Demolish and Install	Ea.	570	137		707	
Reinstall	Ea.		76.03		76.03	
Clean	Ea.	4.77	38.50		43.27	
Minimum Charge	Job		242		242	
Pump Water						
Install	Day		425	91	516	Includes labor and equipment to pump
Minimum Charge	Job		191		191	water from a swimming pool.
Replaster						
Install	SF Surf	1.40	9.85		11.25	Includes labor and material to
Minimum Charge	Job		191		191	replaster gunite pool with a surface
						area of 500 to 600 S.F.
Solar Panels						
Demolish	S.F.		1.76		1.76	Includes material and labor to install
Install	S.F.	34	3.13		37.13	solar panel.
Demolish and Install	S.F.	34	4.89		38.89	
Reinstall	S.F.		2.50		2.50	
Minimum Charge	Ea.		510		510	

Close Out

Construction Clean-up	Unit	Material	Labor	Equip.	Total	Specification
Final						
Clean	S.F.		.27		.27	Includes labor for final site/job
Minimum Charge	Job		153		153	clean-up including detail cleaning.

Location Factors

osts shown in *RSMeans Residential Cost Data* are based on tional averages for materials and installation. To adjust these costs a specific location, simply multiply the base cost by the factor for

that city. The data is arranged alphabetically by state and postal zip code numbers. For a city not listed, use the factor for a nearby city with similar economic characteristics.

STATE	CITY	Residential
ALABAMA		
350-352	Birmingham	.86
354	Tuscaloosa	.77
355	Jasper	.72
356	Decatur	.77
357-358	Huntsville	.83
359	Gadsden	.74
360-361	Montgomery	.75
362	Anniston	.77
363	Dothan	.75
364	Evergreen	.73
365-366	Mobile	.82
367	Selma	.73
368	Phenix City	.73
369	Butler	.73
ALASKA		
995-996	Anchorage	1.23
997	Fairbanks	1.25
998	Juneau	1.22
999	Ketchikan	1.27
ARIZONA		
850,853	Phoenix	.86
851,852	Mesa/Tempe	.84
855	Globe	.76
856-857	Tucson	.83
859	Show Low	.77
860	Flagstaff	.85
863	Prescott	.76
864	Kingman	.83
865	Chambers	.76
ARKANSAS		
716	Pine Bluff	.78
717	Camden	.69
718	Texarkana	.73
719	Hot Springs	.69
720-722	Little Rock	.81
723	West Memphis	.78
724	Jonesboro	.76
725	Batesville	.73
726	Harrison	.74
727	Fayetteville	.70
728	Russellville	.76
729	Fort Smith	.81
CALIFORNIA		
900-902	Los Angeles	1.08
903-905	Inglewood	1.06
906-908	Long Beach	1.05
910-912	Pasadena	1.04
913-916	Van Nuys	1.07
917-918	Alhambra	1.08
919-921	San Diego	1.03
922	Palm Springs	1.04
923-924	San Bernardino	1.05
925	Riverside	1.06
926-927	Santa Ana	1.06
928	Anaheim	1.06
930	Oxnard	1.07
931	Santa Barbara	1.06
932-933	Bakersfield	1.05
934	San Luis Obispo	1.07
935	Mojave	1.04
936-938	Fresno	1.11
939	Salinas	1.15
940-941	San Francisco	1.26
942,956-958	Sacramento	1.14
943	Palo Alto	1.19
944	San Mateo	1.24
945	Vallejo	1.18
946	Oakland	1.24
947	Berkeley	1.26
948	Richmond	1.25
949	San Rafael	1.23
950	Santa Cruz	1.17
951	San Jose	1.22
952	Stockton	1.12
953	Modesto	1.11

STATE	CITY	Residential
CALIFORNIA (CONT'D)		
954	Santa Rosa	1.20
955	Eureka	1.12
959	Marysville	1.12
960	Redding	1.12
961	Susanville	1.11
COLORADO		
800-802	Denver	.91
803	Boulder	.91
804	Golden	.89
805	Fort Collins	.88
806	Greeley	.87
807	Fort Morgan	.91
808-809	Colorado Springs	.88
810	Pueblo	.89
811	Alamosa	.85
812	Salida	.88
813	Durango	.89
814	Montrose	.87
815	Grand Junction	.92
816	Glenwood Springs	.89
CONNECTICUT		
060	New Britain	1.10
061	Hartford	1.09
062	Willimantic	1.10
063	New London	1.09
064	Meriden	1.10
065	New Haven	1.10
066	Bridgeport	1.11
067	Waterbury	1.10
068	Norwalk	1.11
069	Stamford	1.11
D.C.		
200-205	Washington	.95
DELAWARE		
197	Newark	1.02
198	Wilmington	1.03
199	Dover	1.02
FLORIDA		
320,322	Jacksonville	.83
321	Daytona Beach	.88
323	Tallahassee	.79
324	Panama City	.78
325	Pensacola	.82
326,344	Gainesville	.82
327-328,347	Orlando	.88
329	Melbourne	.88
330-332,340	Miami	.87
333	Fort Lauderdale	.87
334,349	West Palm Beach	.87
335-336,346	Tampa	.91
337	St. Petersburg	.81
338	Lakeland	.89
339,341	Fort Myers	.87
342	Sarasota	.90
GEORGIA		
300-303,399	Atlanta	.88
304	Statesboro	.71
305	Gainesville	.78
306	Athens	.76
307	Dalton	.76
308-309	Augusta	.82
310-312	Macon	.79
313-314	Savannah	.80
315	Waycross	.80
316	Valdosta	.75
317,398	Albany	.77
318-319	Columbus	.80
HAWAII		
967	Hilo	1.18
968	Honolulu	1.20

291

Location Factors

STATE	CITY	Residential
STATES & POSS.		
969	Guam	.93
IDAHO		
832	Pocatello	.84
833	Twin Falls	.70
834	Idaho Falls	.72
835	Lewiston	.92
836-837	Boise	.84
838	Coeur d'Alene	.90
ILLINOIS		
600-603	North Suburban	1.19
604	Joliet	1.21
605	South Suburban	1.19
606-608	Chicago	1.22
609	Kankakee	1.12
610-611	Rockford	1.12
612	Rock Island	.97
613	La Salle	1.10
614	Galesburg	1.02
615-616	Peoria	1.05
617	Bloomington	1.04
618-619	Champaign	1.05
620-622	East St. Louis	1.02
623	Quincy	1.02
624	Effingham	1.03
625	Decatur	1.04
626-627	Springfield	1.04
628	Centralia	1.03
629	Carbondale	.99
INDIANA		
460	Anderson	.92
461-462	Indianapolis	.94
463-464	Gary	1.05
465-466	South Bend	.90
467-468	Fort Wayne	.90
469	Kokomo	.91
470	Lawrenceburg	.87
471	New Albany	.87
472	Columbus	.92
473	Muncie	.92
474	Bloomington	.95
475	Washington	.91
476-477	Evansville	.91
478	Terre Haute	.91
479	Lafayette	.93
IOWA		
500-503,509	Des Moines	.91
504	Mason City	.78
505	Fort Dodge	.77
506-507	Waterloo	.84
508	Creston	.86
510-511	Sioux City	.85
512	Sibley	.74
513	Spencer	.76
514	Carroll	.81
515	Council Bluffs	.87
516	Shenandoah	.82
520	Dubuque	.86
521	Decorah	.78
522-524	Cedar Rapids	.93
525	Ottumwa	.83
526	Burlington	.89
527-528	Davenport	.95
KANSAS		
660-662	Kansas City	.98
664-666	Topeka	.77
667	Fort Scott	.88
668	Emporia	.83
669	Belleville	.80
670-672	Wichita	.77
673	Independence	.87
674	Salina	.80
675	Hutchinson	.79
676	Hays	.81
677	Colby	.83
678	Dodge City	.81
679	Liberal	.80
KENTUCKY		
400-402	Louisville	.91
403-405	Lexington	.90

STATE	CITY	Residential
KENTUCKY (CONT'D)		
406	Frankfort	.89
407-409	Corbin	.82
410	Covington	.95
411-412	Ashland	.94
413-414	Campton	.89
415-416	Pikeville	.93
417-418	Hazard	.88
420	Paducah	.89
421-422	Bowling Green	.89
423	Owensboro	.91
424	Henderson	.91
425-426	Somerset	.84
427	Elizabethtown	.87
LOUISIANA		
700-701	New Orleans	.87
703	Thibodaux	.82
704	Hammond	.76
705	Lafayette	.82
706	Lake Charles	.83
707-708	Baton Rouge	.83
710-711	Shreveport	.75
712	Monroe	.72
713-714	Alexandria	.72
MAINE		
039	Kittery	.90
040-041	Portland	.90
042	Lewiston	.89
043	Augusta	.92
044	Bangor	.88
045	Bath	.90
046	Machias	.91
047	Houlton	.91
048	Rockland	.91
049	Waterville	.91
MARYLAND		
206	Waldorf	.90
207-208	College Park	.89
209	Silver Spring	.89
210-212	Baltimore	.90
214	Annapolis	.89
215	Cumberland	.87
216	Easton	.84
217	Hagerstown	.88
218	Salisbury	.83
219	Elkton	.90
MASSACHUSETTS		
010-011	Springfield	1.05
012	Pittsfield	1.04
013	Greenfield	1.03
014	Fitchburg	1.13
015-016	Worcester	1.14
017	Framingham	1.15
018	Lowell	1.15
019	Lawrence	1.16
020-022, 024	Boston	1.22
023	Brockton	1.15
025	Buzzards Bay	1.13
026	Hyannis	1.12
027	New Bedford	1.14
MICHIGAN		
480,483	Royal Oak	1.03
481	Ann Arbor	1.03
482	Detroit	1.06
484-485	Flint	.97
486	Saginaw	.93
487	Bay City	.94
488-489	Lansing	.95
490	Battle Creek	.93
491	Kalamazoo	.93
492	Jackson	.93
493,495	Grand Rapids	.89
494	Muskegon	.90
496	Traverse City	.84
497	Gaylord	.81
498-499	Iron mountain	.91
MINNESOTA		
550-551	Saint Paul	1.13
553-555	Minneapolis	1.15
556-558	Duluth	1.08

292

Location Factors

STATE	CITY	Residential
MINNESOTA (CONT'D)		
559	Rochester	1.06
560	Mankato	1.01
561	Windom	.94
562	Willmar	.99
563	St. Cloud	1.08
564	Brainerd	.99
565	Detroit Lakes	.97
566	Bemidji	.96
567	Thief River Falls	.96
MISSISSIPPI		
386	Clarksdale	.76
387	Greenville	.82
388	Tupelo	.77
389	Greenwood	.78
390-392	Jackson	.82
393	Meridian	.81
394	Laurel	.78
395	Biloxi	.80
396	Mccomb	.75
397	Columbus	.77
MISSOURI		
630-631	St. Louis	1.02
633	Bowling Green	.95
634	Hannibal	.91
635	Kirksville	.88
636	Flat River	.95
637	Cape Girardeau	.89
638	Sikeston	.86
639	Poplar Bluff	.86
640-641	Kansas City	1.04
644-645	St. Joseph	.95
646	Chillicothe	.88
647	Harrisonville	1.00
648	Joplin	.86
650-651	Jefferson City	.92
652	Columbia	.92
653	Sedalia	.92
654-655	Rolla	.94
656-658	Springfield	.87
MONTANA		
590-591	Billings	.87
592	Wolf Point	.82
593	Miles City	.84
594	Great Falls	.89
595	Havre	.82
596	Helena	.86
597	Butte	.85
598	Missoula	.85
599	Kalispell	.82
NEBRASKA		
680-681	Omaha	.91
683-685	Lincoln	.84
686	Columbus	.84
687	Norfolk	.89
688	Grand Island	.89
689	Hastings	.90
690	Mccook	.82
691	North Platte	.89
692	Valentine	.82
693	Alliance	.82
NEVADA		
889-891	Las Vegas	1.03
893	Ely	.99
894-895	Reno	.94
897	Carson City	.93
898	Elko	.92
NEW HAMPSHIRE		
030	Nashua	.94
031	Manchester	.94
032-033	Concord	.93
034	Keene	.72
035	Littleton	.78
036	Charleston	.72
037	Claremont	.72
038	Portsmouth	.95

STATE	CITY	Residential
NEW JERSEY		
070-071	Newark	1.13
072	Elizabeth	1.15
073	Jersey City	1.12
074-075	Paterson	1.13
076	Hackensack	1.12
077	Long Branch	1.12
078	Dover	1.12
079	Summit	1.13
080,083	Vineland	1.10
081	Camden	1.11
082,084	Atlantic City	1.13
085-086	Trenton	1.12
087	Point Pleasant	1.11
088-089	New Brunswick	1.13
NEW MEXICO		
870-872	Albuquerque	.82
873	Gallup	.82
874	Farmington	.82
875	Santa Fe	.83
877	Las Vegas	.82
878	Socorro	.82
879	Truth/Consequences	.81
880	Las Cruces	.81
881	Clovis	.82
882	Roswell	.82
883	Carrizozo	.82
884	Tucumcari	.83
NEW YORK		
100-102	New York	1.37
103	Staten Island	1.31
104	Bronx	1.32
105	Mount Vernon	1.14
106	White Plains	1.16
107	Yonkers	1.17
108	New Rochelle	1.17
109	Suffern	1.12
110	Queens	1.32
111	Long Island City	1.35
112	Brooklyn	1.36
113	Flushing	1.34
114	Jamaica	1.34
115,117,118	Hicksville	1.21
116	Far Rockaway	1.33
119	Riverhead	1.22
120-122	Albany	.95
123	Schenectady	.97
124	Kingston	1.05
125-126	Poughkeepsie	1.17
127	Monticello	1.06
128	Glens Falls	.90
129	Plattsburgh	.94
130-132	Syracuse	.97
133-135	Utica	.93
136	Watertown	.93
137-139	Binghamton	.94
140-142	Buffalo	1.05
143	Niagara Falls	1.04
144-146	Rochester	.96
147	Jamestown	.89
148-149	Elmira	.91
NORTH CAROLINA		
270,272-274	Greensboro	.80
271	Winston-Salem	.80
275-276	Raleigh	.81
277	Durham	.80
278	Rocky Mount	.74
279	Elizabeth City	.73
280	Gastonia	.81
281-282	Charlotte	.81
283	Fayetteville	.80
284	Wilmington	.82
285	Kinston	.75
286	Hickory	.76
287-288	Asheville	.79
289	Murphy	.70
NORTH DAKOTA		
580-581	Fargo	.78
582	Grand Forks	.73
583	Devils Lake	.76
584	Jamestown	.71
585	Bismarck	.76

Location Factors

STATE	CITY	Residential
NORTH DAKOTA (CONT'D)		
586	Dickinson	.74
587	Minot	.81
588	Williston	.74
OHIO		
430-432	Columbus	.95
433	Marion	.91
434-436	Toledo	.99
437-438	Zanesville	.90
439	Steubenville	.94
440	Lorain	.96
441	Cleveland	1.00
442-443	Akron	.98
444-445	Youngstown	.95
446-447	Canton	.93
448-449	Mansfield	.92
450	Hamilton	.92
451-452	Cincinnati	.92
453-454	Dayton	.92
455	Springfield	.93
456	Chillicothe	.97
457	Athens	.91
458	Lima	.91
OKLAHOMA		
730-731	Oklahoma City	.77
734	Ardmore	.76
735	Lawton	.78
736	Clinton	.75
737	Enid	.75
738	Woodward	.74
739	Guymon	.65
740-741	Tulsa	.75
743	Miami	.85
744	Muskogee	.69
745	Mcalester	.72
746	Ponca City	.75
747	Durant	.75
748	Shawnee	.74
749	Poteau	.76
OREGON		
970-972	Portland	.98
973	Salem	.96
974	Eugene	.97
975	Medford	.96
976	Klamath Falls	.97
977	Bend	.98
978	Pendleton	.96
979	Vale	.95
PENNSYLVANIA		
150-152	Pittsburgh	1.00
153	Washington	.95
154	Uniontown	.93
155	Bedford	.90
156	Greensburg	.96
157	Indiana	.93
158	Dubois	.91
159	Johnstown	.91
160	Butler	.93
161	New Castle	.92
162	Kittanning	.94
163	Oil City	.90
164-165	Erie	.94
166	Altoona	.88
167	Bradford	.90
168	State College	.91
169	Wellsboro	.91
170-171	Harrisburg	.95
172	Chambersburg	.89
173-174	York	.92
175-176	Lancaster	.92
177	Williamsport	.84
178	Sunbury	.93
179	Pottsville	.93
180	Lehigh Valley	1.02
181	Allentown	1.04
182	Hazleton	.93
183	Stroudsburg	.92
184-185	Scranton	.97
186-187	Wilkes-Barre	.94
188	Montrose	.92
189	Doylestown	1.06

STATE	CITY	Residential
PENNSYLVANIA (CONT'D)		
190-191	Philadelphia	1.16
193	Westchester	1.11
194	Norristown	1.11
195-196	Reading	.97
PUERTO RICO		
009	San Juan	.73
RHODE ISLAND		
028	Newport	1.07
029	Providence	1.07
SOUTH CAROLINA		
290-292	Columbia	.81
293	Spartanburg	.81
294	Charleston	.84
295	Florence	.77
296	Greenville	.80
297	Rock Hill	.79
298	Aiken	1.00
299	Beaufort	.79
SOUTH DAKOTA		
570-571	Sioux Falls	.76
572	Watertown	.73
573	Mitchell	.74
574	Aberdeen	.75
575	Pierre	.74
576	Mobridge	.73
577	Rapid City	.76
TENNESSEE		
370-372	Nashville	.83
373-374	Chattanooga	.82
375,380-381	Memphis	.83
376	Johnson City	.71
377-379	Knoxville	.75
382	Mckenzie	.74
383	Jackson	.78
384	Columbia	.78
385	Cookeville	.72
TEXAS		
750	Mckinney	.72
751	Waxahackie	.78
752-753	Dallas	.83
754	Greenville	.69
755	Texarkana	.73
756	Longview	.67
757	Tyler	.74
758	Palestine	.76
759	Lufkin	.78
760-761	Fort Worth	.82
762	Denton	.74
763	Wichita Falls	.77
764	Eastland	.74
765	Temple	.73
766-767	Waco	.76
768	Brownwood	.71
769	San Angelo	.72
770-772	Houston	.83
773	Huntsville	.76
774	Wharton	.72
775	Galveston	.81
776-777	Beaumont	.81
778	Bryan	.73
779	Victoria	.71
780	Laredo	.72
781-782	San Antonio	.79
783-784	Corpus Christi	.77
785	Mc Allen	.74
786-787	Austin	.77
788	Del Rio	.71
789	Giddings	.77
790-791	Amarillo	.79
792	Childress	.79
793-794	Lubbock	.78
795-796	Abilene	.75
797	Midland	.75
798-799,885	El Paso	.74
UTAH		
840-841	Salt Lake City	.80
842,844	Ogden	.79
843	Logan	.80

Location Factors

STATE	CITY	Residential
UTAH (CONT'D)		
845	Price	.78
846-847	Provo	.80
VERMONT		
050	White River Jct.	.74
051	Bellows Falls	.81
052	Bennington	.80
053	Brattleboro	.80
054	Burlington	.79
056	Montpelier	.79
057	Rutland	.79
058	St. Johnsbury	.76
059	Guildhall	.75
VIRGINIA		
220-221	Fairfax	1.02
222	Arlington	1.03
223	Alexandria	1.07
224-225	Fredericksburg	.92
226	Winchester	.88
227	Culpeper	.97
228	Harrisonburg	.86
229	Charlottesville	.88
230-232	Richmond	.94
233-235	Norfolk	.97
236	Newport News	.96
237	Portsmouth	.90
238	Petersburg	.93
239	Farmville	.85
240-241	Roanoke	.93
242	Bristol	.82
243	Pulaski	.80
244	Staunton	.87
245	Lynchburg	.92
246	Grundy	.80
WASHINGTON		
980-981,987	Seattle	1.02
982	Everett	1.02
983-984	Tacoma	1.00
985	Olympia	.98
986	Vancouver	.95
988	Wenatchee	.92
989	Yakima	.97
990-992	Spokane	.97
993	Richland	.96
994	Clarkston	.92
WEST VIRGINIA		
247-248	Bluefield	.91
249	Lewisburg	.91
250-253	Charleston	.96
254	Martinsburg	.87
255-257	Huntington	.97
258-259	Beckley	.91
260	Wheeling	.93
261	Parkersburg	.92
262	Buckhannon	.92
263-264	Clarksburg	.92
265	Morgantown	.93
266	Gassaway	.92
267	Romney	.90
268	Petersburg	.91
WISCONSIN		
530,532	Milwaukee	1.08
531	Kenosha	1.03
534	Racine	1.01
535	Beloit	.98
537	Madison	.98
538	Lancaster	.96
539	Portage	.96
540	New Richmond	.99
541-543	Green Bay	1.00
544	Wausau	.95
545	Rhinelander	.95
546	La Crosse	.95
547	Eau Claire	.98
548	Superior	.97
549	Oshkosh	.91
WYOMING		
820	Cheyenne	.79
821	Yellowstone Nat. Pk.	.73
822	Wheatland	.73

STATE	CITY	Residential
WYOMING (CONT'D)		
823	Rawlins	.73
824	Worland	.73
825	Riverton	.73
826	Casper	.73
827	Newcastle	.73
828	Sheridan	.77
829-831	Rock Springs	.77
CANADIAN FACTORS (reflect Canadian currency)		
ALBERTA		
	Calgary	1.16
	Edmonton	1.14
	Fort McMurray	1.16
	Lethbridge	1.13
	Lloydminster	1.08
	Medicine Hat	1.08
	Red Deer	1.08
BRITISH COLUMBIA		
	Kamloops	1.07
	Prince George	1.06
	Vancouver	1.09
	Victoria	1.04
MANITOBA		
	Brandon	1.04
	Portage la Prairie	1.03
	Winnipeg	1.03
NEW BRUNSWICK		
	Bathurst	.96
	Dalhousie	.96
	Fredericton	1.02
	Moncton	.96
	Newcastle	.96
	St. John	1.02
NEWFOUNDLAND		
	Corner Brook	.97
	St Johns	1.00
NORTHWEST TERRITORIES		
	Yellowknife	1.10
NOVA SCOTIA		
	Bridgewater	.99
	Dartmouth	1.00
	Halifax	1.01
	New Glasgow	.99
	Sydney	.98
	Truro	.99
	Yarmouth	.99
ONTARIO		
	Barrie	1.15
	Brantford	1.16
	Cornwall	1.15
	Hamilton	1.14
	Kingston	1.15
	Kitchener	1.08
	London	1.12
	North Bay	1.13
	Oshawa	1.14
	Ottawa	1.13
	Owen Sound	1.14
	Peterborough	1.14
	Sarnia	1.16
	Sault Ste Marie	1.08
	St. Catharines	1.09
	Sudbury	1.07
	Thunder Bay	1.11
	Timmins	1.13
	Toronto	1.16
	Windsor	1.10
PRINCE EDWARD ISLAND		
	Charlottetown	.93
	Summerside	.93
QUEBEC		
	Cap-de-la-Madeleine	1.14
	Charlesbourg	1.14
	Chicoutimi	1.14
	Gatineau	1.13
	Granby	1.14

Location Factors

STATE	CITY	Residential
QUEBEC (CONT'D)		
	Hull	1.13
	Joliette	1.14
	Laval	1.14
	Montreal	1.16
	Quebec	1.15
	Rimouski	1.14
	Rouyn-Noranda	1.13
	Saint Hyacinthe	1.14
	Sherbrooke	1.14
	Sorel	1.14
	St Jerome	1.13
	Trois Rivieres	1.14
SASKATCHEWAN		
	Moose Jaw	.96
	Prince Albert	.95
	Regina	1.06
	Saskatoon	1.05
YUKON		
	Whitehorse	.96

Abbreviations

A	Area
ASTM	American Society for Testing and Materials
B.F.	Board feet
Carp.	Carpenter
C.F.	Cubic feet
CWJ	Composite wood joist
C.Y.	Cubic yard
Ea.	Each
Equip.	Equipment
Exp.	Exposure
Ext.	Exterior
F	Fahrenheit
Ft.	Foot, feet
Gal.	Gallon
Hr.	Hour
in.	Inch, inches
Inst.	Installation
Int.	Interior
Lb.	Pound
L.F.	Linear feet
LVL	Laminated veneer lumber
Mat.	Material
Max.	Maximum
MBF	Thousand board feet
MBM	Thousand feet board measure
MSF	Thousand square feet
Min.	Minimum
O.C.	On center
O&P	Overhead and profit
OWJ	Open web wood joist
Oz.	Ounce
Pr.	Pair
Quan.	Quantity
S.F.	Square foot
Sq.	Square, 100 square feet
S.Y.	Square yard
V.L.F.	Vertical linear feet
'	Foot, feet
"	Inch, inches
°	Degrees

Index

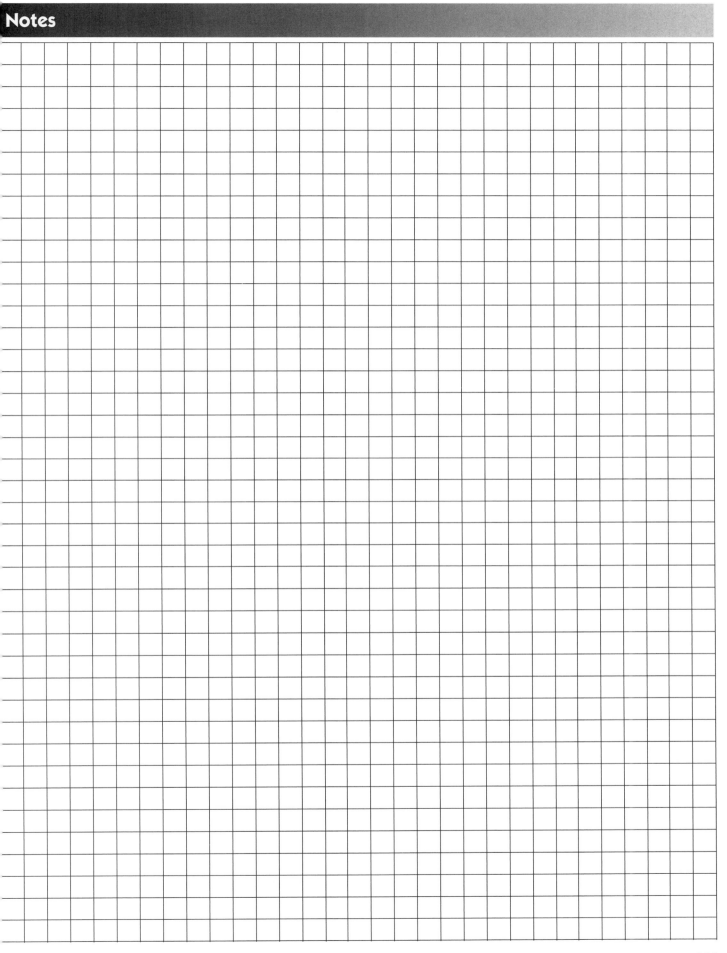

For more information visit the RSMeans website at **www.rsmeans.com**

Unit prices according to the latest MasterForm

RSMeans Building Construction Cost Data 2012

Offers you unchallenged unit price reliability in an easy-to-use format. Whether used for verifying complete, finished estimates or for periodic checks, it supplies more cost facts better and faster than any comparable source. Over 23,000 unit prices have been updated for 2012. The City Cost Indexes and Location Factors cover over 930 areas, for indexing to any project location in North America. Order and get *RSMeans Quarterly Update Service* FREE. You'll have year-long access to the RSMeans Estimating **HOTLINE** FREE with your subscription. Expert assistance when using RSMeans data is just a phone call away.

$177.95 per copy | Available Sept. 2011 | Catalog no. 60012

RSMeans Green Building Cost Data 2012

Estimate, plan, and budget the costs of green building for both new commercia construction and renovation work with this first edition of RSMeans Green Building Cost Data. More than 9,000 unit costs for a wide array of green building products plus assemblies costs Easily identified cross references to LEED and Green Globes building ratins systems criteria.

$147.95 per copy | Available Nov. 2011 | Catalog no. 60552

RSMeans Mechanical Cost Data 2012

Total unit and systems price guidance for mechanical construction. . . materials, parts, fittings, and complete labor cost information. Includes prices for piping, heating, air conditioning, ventilation, and all related construction.

Plus new 2012 unit costs for:

- Thousands of installed HVAC/ controls assemblies components

- "On-site" Location Factors for over 930 cities and towns in the U.S. and Canada

- Crews, labor, and equipment

$174.95 per copy | Available Oct. 2011 | Catalog no. 60022

RSMeans Facilities Construction Cost Data 2012

For the maintenance and construction commercial, industrial, municipal, and institutional properties. Costs are show for new and remodeling construction ar are broken down into materials, labor, equipment, and overhead and profit. Special emphasis is given to sections on mechanical, electrical, furnishings, site work, building maintenance, finish work, and demolition.

More than 47,000 unit costs, plus assemblies costs and a comprehensive Reference Section are included.

$453.95 per copy | Available Nov. 2011 | Catalog no. 60202

RSMeans Square Foot Costs 2012

Accurate and Easy To Use

- **Updated price information** based on nationwide figures from suppliers, estimators, labor experts, and contractors

- "How-to-Use" sections, with **clear examples** of commercial, residential, industrial, and institutional structures

- Realistic graphics, offering true-to-life illustrations of building projects

- Extensive information on using square foot cost data, including sample estimates and alternate pricing methods

$187.95 per copy | Available Oct. 2011 | Catalog no. 60052

RSMeans Commercial Renovation Cost Data 2012

Commercial/Multifamily Residential

Use this valuable tool to estimate commercial and multifamily residentia renovation and remodeling.

Includes: New costs for hundreds of unique methods, materials, and conditions that only come up in repair and remodeling, PLUS:

- Unit costs for more than 17,000 construction components
- Installed costs for more than 2,000 assemblies
- More than 930 "on-site" localization factors for the U.S. and Canada

$144.95 per copy | Available Oct. 2011 | Catalog no. 60042

RSMeans Electrical Cost Data 2012

Pricing information for every part of electrical cost planning. More than 13,000 unit and systems costs with design tables; clear specifications and drawings; engineering guides; illustrated estimating procedures; complete labor-hour and materials costs for better scheduling and procurement; and the latest electrical products and construction methods.

- A variety of special electrical systems including cathodic protection
- Costs for maintenance, demolition, HVAC/mechanical, specialties, equipment, and more

79.95 per copy | Available Oct. 2011 | Catalog no. 60032

RSMeans Electrical Change Order Cost Data 2012

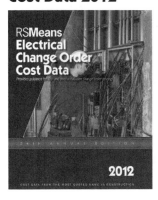

RSMeans Electrical Change Order Cost Data provides you with electrical unit prices exclusively for pricing change orders—based on the recent, direct experience of contractors and suppliers. Analyze and check your own change order estimates against the experience others have had doing the same work. It also covers productivity analysis and change order cost justifications. With useful information for calculating the effects of change orders and dealing with their administration.

$174.95 per copy | Available Dec. 2011 | Catalog no. 60232

RSMeans Assemblies Cost Data 2012

RSMeans Assemblies Cost Data takes the guesswork out of preliminary or conceptual estimates. Now you don't have to try to calculate the assembled cost by working up individual component costs. We've done all the work for you.

Presents detailed illustrations, descriptions, specifications, and costs for every conceivable building assembly—over 350 types in all—arranged in the easy-to-use UNIFORMAT II system. Each illustrated "assembled" cost includes omplete grouping of materials and associated installation costs, cluding the installing contractor's overhead and profit.

90.95 per copy | Available Sept. 2011 | Catalog no. 60062

RSMeans Open Shop Building Construction Cost Data 2012

The latest costs for accurate budgeting and estimating of new commercial and residential construction. . . renovation work. . . change orders. . . cost engineering.

RSMeans Open Shop "BCCD" will assist you to:

- Develop benchmark prices for change orders
- Plug gaps in preliminary estimates and budgets
- Estimate complex projects
- Substantiate invoices on contracts
- Price ADA-related renovations

$152.95 per copy | Available Dec. 2011 | Catalog no. 60152

RSMeans Residential Cost Data 2012

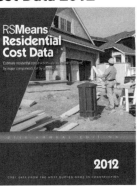

Contains square foot costs for 28 basic home models with the look of today, plus hundreds of custom additions and modifications you can quote right off the page. Includes costs for more than 700 residential systems. Complete with blank estimating forms, sample estimates, and step-by-step instructions.

Now contains line items for cultured stone and brick, PVC trim lumber, and TPO roofing.

27.95 per copy | Available Oct. 2011 | Catalog no. 60172

RSMeans Site Work & Landscape Cost Data 2012

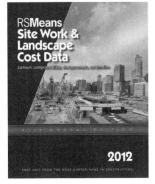

Includes unit and assemblies costs for earthwork, sewerage, piped utilities, site improvements, drainage, paving, trees and shrubs, street openings/repairs, underground tanks, and more. Contains 78 types of assemblies costs for accurate conceptual estimates.

Includes:

- Estimating for infrastructure improvements
- Environmentally-oriented construction
- ADA-mandated handicapped access
- Hazardous waste line items

$172.95 per copy | Available Dec. 2011 | Catalog no. 60282

Annual Cost Guides

For more information visit the RSMeans website at **www.rsmeans.com**

Unit prices according to the latest MasterForma

RSMeans Facilities Maintenance & Repair Cost Data 2012

RSMeans Facilities Maintenance & Repair Cost Data gives you a complete system to manage and plan your facility repair and maintenance costs and budget efficiently. Guidelines for auditing a facility and developing an annual maintenance plan. Budgeting is included, along with reference tables on cost and management, and information on frequency and productivity of maintenance operations.

The only nationally recognized source of maintenance and repair costs. Developed in cooperation with the Civil Engineering Research Laboratory (CERL) of the Army Corps of Engineers.

$399.95 per copy | Available Nov. 2011 | Catalog no. 60302

RSMeans Concrete & Masonry Cost Data 2012

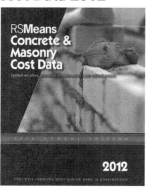

Provides you with cost facts for virtually all concrete/masonry estimating needs, from complicated formwork to various sizes and face finishes of brick and block—all in great detail. The comprehensive Unit Price Section contains more than 8,000 selected entries. Also contains an Assemblies [Cost] Section, and a detailed Reference Section that supplements the cost data.

$162.95 per copy | Available Dec. 2011 | Catalog no. 60112

RSMeans Construction Cost Indexes 2012

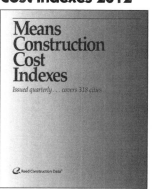

What materials and labor costs will change unexpectedly this year? By how much?

• Breakdowns for 318 major cities

• National averages for 30 key cities

• Expanded five major city indexes

• Historical construction cost indexes

$362.00 per year (subscription) | Catalog no. 50142
$90.50 individual quarters | Catalog no. 60142 A,B,C,D

RSMeans Light Commercial Cost Data 2012

Specifically addresses the light commercial market, which is a specialized niche in the construction industry. Aids you, the owner/designer contractor, in preparing all types of estimates—from budgets to detailed bids. Includes new advances in method and materials.

Assemblies Section allows you to evaluate alternatives in the early stage of design/planning.

Over 13,000 unit costs ensure that you have the prices you need. . . when you need them.

$132.95 per copy | Available Nov. 2011 | Catalog no. 60182

RSMeans Labor Rates for the Construction Industry 2012

Complete information for estimating labor costs, making comparisons, and negotiating wage rates by trade for mor than 300 U.S. and Canadian cities. With 46 construction trades listed by local union number in each city, and historical wage rates included for comparison. Each city chart lists the county and is alphabetically arranged with handy visual flip tabs for quick reference.

$395.95 per copy | Available Dec. 2011 | Catalog no. 60122

RSMeans Interior Cost Data 2012

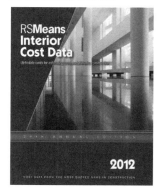

Provides you with prices and guidance needed to make accurate interior work estimates. Contains costs on materials, equipment, hardware, custom installations, furnishings, and labor costs. . . for new and remodel commercial and industrial interior construction, including updated information on office furnishings, and reference information.

$182.95 per copy | Available Nov. 2011 | Catalog no. 60092

Annual Cost Guides

r more information visit the RSMeans website at **www.rsmeans.com**

Unit prices according to the latest MasterFormat!

SMeans Heavy Construction ost Data 2012

A comprehensive guide to heavy construction costs. Includes costs for highly specialized projects such as tunnels, dams, highways, airports, and waterways. Information on labor rates, equipment, and materials costs is included. Features unit price costs, systems costs, and numerous reference tables for costs and design.

77.95 per copy | Available Dec. 2011 | Catalog no. 60162

RSMeans Plumbing Cost Data 2012

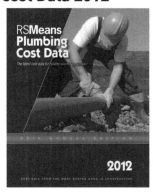

Comprehensive unit prices and assemblies for plumbing, irrigation systems, commercial and residential fire protection, point-of-use water heaters, and the latest approved materials. This publication and its companion, *RSMeans Mechanical Cost Data*, provide full-range cost estimating coverage for all the mechanical trades.

Now contains updated costs for potable water and radiant heat systems and high efficiency fixtures.

$179.95 per copy | Available Oct. 2011 | Catalog no. 60212

2012 RSMeans Seminar Schedule

ote: call for exact dates and details.

ocation	Dates	Location	Dates
s Vegas, NV	March	Las Vegas, NV	October
ashington, DC	April	Orlando, FL	November
n Francisco, CA	June	San Diego, CA	December
ashington, DC	September		
allas, TX	September		

1-800-334-3509, ext. 925115

2012 Regional Seminar Schedule

ote: call for exact dates and details.

ocation	Dates	Location	Dates
attle, WA	January and August	Columbus, GA	June
allas/Ft. Worth, TX	January	El Segundo, CA	August
ustin, TX	February	Jacksonville FL	September
klahoma City, OK	February	Birmingham, AL	October
nchorage, AK	March and September	St. Louis, MO	October
oenix, AZ	March	Houston, TX	October
n Bernardino, CA	April	Portland, OR	November
iea, HI	April	Baltimore, MD	November
ansas City, MO	April	San Antonio, TX	December
oronto	May	Raleigh, NC	December
enver, CO	May		
ethesda, MD	June		

1-800-334-3509, ext. 925115

Registration Information

Register early... Save up to $100! Register 30 days before the start date of a seminar and save $100 off your total fee. *Note: This discount can be applied only once per order. It cannot be applied to team discount registrations or any other special offer.*

How to register Register by phone today! The RSMeans toll-free number for making reservations is **1-800-334-3509, ext. 925115.**

Individual seminar registration fee - $935. *Means CostWorks®* **training registration fee - $375.** To register by mail, complete the registration form and return, with your full fee, to: RSMeans Seminars, 700 Longwater Drive, Norwell, MA 02061.

Government pricing All federal government employees save off the regular seminar price. Other promotional discounts cannot be combined with the government discount.

Team discount program for two to four seminar registrations. Call for pricing: 1-800-334-3509, ext. 925115

Multiple course discounts When signing up for two or more courses, call for pricing.

Refund policy Cancellations will be accepted up to ten business days prior to the seminar start. There are no refunds for cancellations received later than ten working days prior to the first day of the seminar. A $150 processing fee will be applied for all cancellations. Written notice of cancellation is required. Substitutions can be made at any time before the session starts. **No-shows are subject to the full seminar fee.**

AACE approved courses Many seminars described and offered here have been approved for 14 hours (1.4 recertification credits) of credit by the AACE

International Certification Board toward meeting the continuing education requirements for recertification as a Certified Cost Engineer/Certified Cost Consultant.

AIA Continuing Education We are registered with the AIA Continuing Education System (AIA/CES) and are committed to developing quality learning activities in accordance with the CES criteria. Many seminars meet the AIA/CE criteria for Quality Level 2. AIA members may receive (14) learning units (LUs) for each two-day RSMeans course.

Daily course schedule The first day of each seminar session begins at 8:30 a.m. and ends at 4:30 p.m. The second day begins at 8:00 a.m. and ends at 4:00 p.m. Participants are urged to bring a hand-held calculator, since many actual problems will be worked out in each session.

Continental breakfast Your registration includes the cost of a continental breakfast, and a morning and afternoon refreshment break. These informal segments allow you to discuss topics of mutual interest with other seminar attendees. (You are free to make your own lunch and dinner arrangements.)

Hotel/transportation arrangements RSMeans arranges to hold a block of rooms at most host hotels. To take advantage of special group rates when making your reservation, be sure to mention that you are attending the RSMean seminar. You are, of course, free to stay at the lodging place of your choice. (**Hote reservations and transportation arrangements should be made directly by semina attendees.**)

Important Class sizes are limited, so please register as soon as possible.

Note: Pricing subject to change.

Registration Form

ADDS-100

Call 1-800-334-3509, ext. 925115 to register or FAX this form 1-800-632-6732. Visit our website: www.rsmeans.com

Please register the following people for the RSMeans construction seminars as shown here. We understand that we must make our own hotel reservations if overnight stays are necessary.

☐ Full payment of $_____ enclosed.

☐ Bill me.

Please print name of registrant(s).

(To appear on certificate of completion)

_____

_____

_____

_____

P.O. #: _____
    GOVERNMENT AGENCIES MUST SUPPLY PURCHASE ORDER NUMBER OR
    TRAINING FORM.

Firm name_____

Address_____

City/State/Zip_____

Telephone no._____ Fax no._____

E-mail address_____

Charge registration(s) to: ☐ MasterCard ☐ VISA ☐ American Express

Account no._____ Exp. date_____

Cardholder's signature_____

Seminar name_____

Seminar City _____

Please mail check to: RSMeans Seminars, 700 Longwater Drive, Norwell, MA 02061 USA

Professional Development

Means CostWorks.com Training

Construction estimating is vital to the decision-making process in each state of every project. Means CostWorks.com works the way you do. It's systematic, flexible and intuitive. In this one day class you will see how you can estimate any phase of any project faster and better.

Some of what you'll learn:
* Customizing Means CostWorks.com
* Making the most of RSMeans "Circle Reference" numbers
* How to integrate your cost data
* Generate reports, exporting estimates to MS Excel, sharing, collaborating and more

Who should attend: architects & engineers, facility managers, contractors, construction estimators, and anyone using this powerful web-based tool.

Facilities Construction Estimating

In this *two-day* course, professionals working in facilities management can get help with their daily challenges to establish budgets for all phases of a project.

Some of what you'll learn:
* Determining the full scope of a project
* Identifying the scope of risks and opportunities
* Creative solutions to estimating issues
* Organizing estimates for presentation and discussion
* Special techniques for repair/remodel and maintenance projects
* Negotiating project change orders

Who should attend: facility managers, engineers, contractors, facility tradespeople, planners, and project managers.

Scheduling with Microsoft Project

Two days of hands-on training gives you a look at the basics of putting it all together with MS Project to create a complete project schedule. Learn to work better and faster, manage changes and updates, enhance tracking, generate actionable reports, and boost control of your time and budget.

Some of what you'll learn:
* Defining task/activity relationships: link tasks, establish predecessor/successor relationships and create logs
* Baseline scheduling: the essential what/when
* Using MS Project to determine the critical path
* Integrate RSMeans data with MS Project
* The dollar-loaded schedule: enhance the reliability of this "must-know" technique for scheduling public projects.

Who should attend: Contractors' project-management teams, architects and engineers, project owners and their representatives, and those interested in improving their project planning and scheduling and management skills.

Site Work & Heavy Construction Estimating

This *two-day* course teaches attendees how to estimate earthwork, site utilities, foundations, and site improvements, using the assemblies and the unit price methods.

Some of what you'll learn:
* Basic site work and heavy construction estimating skills
* Estimating foundations, utilities, earthwork, and site improvements
* Correct equipment usage, quality control, and site investigation for estimating purposes

Who should attend: project managers, design engineers, estimators, and contractors doing site work and heavy construction.

Practical Project Management for Construction Professionals

In this *two-day* course, acquire the essential knowledge and develop the skills to effectively and efficiently execute the day-to-day responsibilities of the construction project manager.

Covers:
* General conditions of the construction contract
* Contract modifications: change orders and construction change directives
* Negotiations with subcontractors and vendors
* Effective writing: notification and communications
* Dispute resolution: claims and liens

Who should attend: architects, engineers, owner's representatives, project managers.

Mechanical & Electrical Estimating

This *two-day* course teaches attendees how to prepare more accurate and complete mechanical/electrical estimates, avoiding the pitfalls of omission and double-counting, while understanding the composition and rationale within the RSMeans mechanical/electrical database.

Some of what you'll learn:
* The unique way mechanical and electrical systems are interrelated
* M&E estimates—conceptual, planning, budgeting, and bidding stages
* Order of magnitude, square foot, assemblies, and unit price estimating
* Comparative cost analysis of equipment and design alternatives

Who should attend: architects, engineers, facilities managers, mechanical and electrical contractors, and others who need a highly reliable method for developing, understanding, and evaluating mechanical and electrical contracts.

Professional Development

Unit Price Estimating

This interactive *two-day* seminar teaches attendees how to interpret project information and process it into final, detailed estimates with the greatest accuracy level.

The most important credential an estimator can take to the job is the ability to visualize construction and estimate accurately.

Some of what you'll learn:
- Interpreting the design in terms of cost
- The most detailed, time-tested methodology for accurate pricing
- Key cost drivers—material, labor, equipment, staging, and subcontracts
- Understanding direct and indirect costs for accurate job cost accounting and change order management

Who should attend: Corporate and government estimators and purchasers, architects, engineers, and others who need to produce accurate project estimates.

RSMeans CostWorks® CD Training

This one-day course helps users become more familiar with the functionality of *RSMeans CostWork*s program. Each menu, icon, screen, and function found in the program is explained in depth. Time is devoted to hands-on estimating exercises.

Some of what you'll learn:
- Searching the database using all navigation methods
- Exporting RSMeans data to your preferred spreadsheet format
- Viewing crews, assembly components, and much more
- Automatically regionalizing the database

You are required to bring your own laptop computer for this course.

When you register for this course you will receive an outline for your laptop requirements.

Also offering web training for CostWorks CD!

Facilities Maintenance & Repair Estimating

This *two-day* course teaches attendees how to plan, budget, and estimate the cost of ongoing and preventive maintenance and repair for existing buildings and grounds.

Some of what you'll learn:
- The most financially favorable maintenance, repair, and replacement scheduling and estimating
- Auditing and value engineering facilities
- Preventive planning and facilities upgrading
- Determining both in-house and contract-out service costs
- Annual, asset-protecting M&R plan

Who should attend: Facility managers, maintenance supervisors, buildings and grounds superintendents, plant managers, planners, estimators, and others involved in facilities planning and budgeting.

Square Foot Estimating using Means CostWorks

This *two day* class uses the leading industry data and a powerf[u] software package to develop highly accurate conceptual estima[te] for your construction projects. All attendees must bring a lapt[op] computer loaded with the current year *Square Foot Model Cos[t]* and the *Assemblies Cost Data* CostWorks titles.

Some of what you'll learn:
- Introduction to conceptual estimating
- Types of conceptual estimates
- Helpful hints
- Order of magnitude estimating
- Square foot estimating
- Assemblies estimating

Who should attend: architects, engineers, contractors, construction estimators, owner's representatives, and anyone looking for an electronic method for performing square foot estimating.

Assessing Scope of Work for Facility Construction Estimating

This *two-day* practical training program addresses the vital importance of understanding the SCOPE of projects in order to produce accurate cost estimates for facility repair and remodeling.

Some of what you'll learn:
- Discussions of site visits, plans/specs, record drawings of facilities, and site-specific lists
- Review of CSI divisions, including means, methods, materials and the challenges of scoping each topic
- Exercises in SCOPE identification and SCOPE writing for accurate estimating of projects
- Hands-on exercises that require SCOPE, take-off, and pricing

Who should attend: corporate and government estimators, planners, facility managers, and others who need to produce accurate project estimates.

Reference Books

Value Engineering: Practical Applications

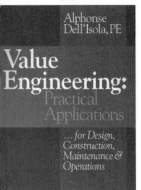

For Design, Construction, Maintenance & Operations
by Alphonse Dell'Isola, PE

A tool for immediate application—for engineers, architects, facility managers, owners, and contractors. Includes making the case for VE—the management briefing; integrating VE into planning, budgeting, and design; conducting life cycle costing; using VE methodology in design review and consultant selection; case studies; VE workbook; and a life cycle costing program on disk.

$9.95 per copy | Over 450 pages, illustrated, softcover | Catalog no. 67319A

Facilities Operations & Engineering Reference

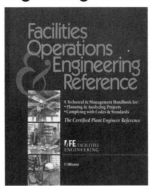

by the Association for Facilities Engineering and RSMeans

An all-in-one technical reference for planning and managing facility projects and solving day-to-day operations problems. Selected as the official certified plant engineer reference, this handbook covers financial analysis, maintenance, HVAC and energy efficiency, and more.

$109.95 per copy | Over 700 pages, illustrated, hardcover | Catalog no. 67318

The Building Professional's Guide to Contract Documents

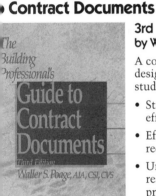

3rd Edition
by Waller S. Poage, AIA, CSI, CVS

A comprehensive reference for owners, design professionals, contractors, and students

- Structure your documents for maximum efficiency.
- Effectively communicate construction requirements.
- Understand the roles and responsibilities of construction professionals.
- Improve methods of project delivery.

$4.95 per copy | 400 pages Diagrams and construction forms, hardcover Catalog no. 67261A

Complete Book of Framing

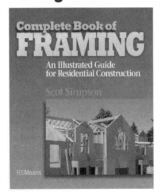

by Scot Simpson

This straightforward, easy-to-learn method will help framers, carpenters, and handy homeowners build their skills in rough carpentry and framing. Shows how to frame all the parts of a house: floors, walls, roofs, door & window openings, and stairs—with hundreds of color photographs and drawings that show every detail.

The book gives beginners all the basics they need to go from zero framing knowledge to a journeyman level.

$29.95 per copy | 336 pages, softcover | Catalog no. 67353

Cost Planning & Estimating for Facilities Maintenance

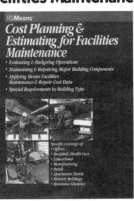

In this unique book, a team of facilities management authorities shares their expertise on:

- Evaluating and budgeting maintenance operations
- Maintaining and repairing key building components
- Applying *RSMeans Facilities Maintenance & Repair Cost Data* to your estimating

Covers special maintenance requirements of the ten major building types

$9.95 per copy | Over 475 pages, hardcover | Catalog no. 67314

Life Cycle Costing for Facilities

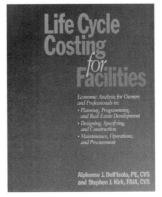

by Alphonse Dell'Isola and Dr. Steven Kirk

Guidance for achieving higher quality design and construction projects at lower costs! Cost-cutting efforts often sacrifice quality to yield the cheapest product. Life cycle costing enables building designers and owners to achieve both. The authors of this book show how LCC can work for a variety of projects — from roads to HVAC upgrades to different types of buildings.

$99.95 per copy | 396 pages, hardcover | Catalog no. 67341

Reference Books

Interior Home Improvement Costs

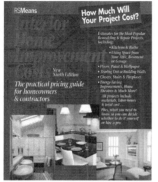

9th Edition

Updated estimates for the most popular remodeling and repair projects—from small, do-it-yourself jobs to major renovations and new construction. Includes: kitchens & baths; new living space from your attic, basement, or garage; new floors, paint, and wallpaper; tearing out or building new walls; closets, stairs, and fireplaces; new energy-saving improvements, home theaters, and more!

$24.95 per copy | 250 pages, illustrated, softcover | Catalog no. 67308E

Exterior Home Improvement Costs

9th Edition

Updated estimates for the most popular remodeling and repair projects—from small, do-it-yourself jobs, to major renovations and new construction. Includes: curb appeal projects—landscaping, patios, porches, driveways, and walkways; new windov and doors; decks, greenhouses, and sunrooms; room additions and garages; roofing, siding, and painting; "green" improvements to save energy & water.

$24.95 per copy | Over 275 pages, illustrated, softcover | Catalog no. 67309E

Builder's Essentials: Plan Reading & Material Takeoff

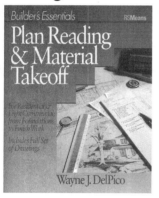

For Residential and Light Commercial Construction
by Wayne J. DelPico

A valuable tool for understanding plans and specs, and accurately calculating material quantities. Step-by-step instructions and takeoff procedures based on a full set of working drawings.

$35.95 per copy | Over 420 pages, softcover | Catalog no. 67307

Means Unit Price Estimating Methods

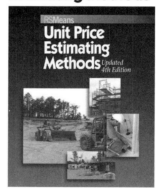

New 4th Edition

This new edition includes up-to-date cost data and estimating examples, updated to reflect changes to the CSI numbering system and new features of RSMeans cost data. It describes the most productive, universally accepted ways to estimate, and uses checklists and forms to illustrate shortcuts and timesavers. A model estimate demonstrates procedures. A new chapter explores computer estimating alternatives.

$59.95 per copy | Over 350 pages, illustrated, softcover | Catalog no. 67303B

Concrete Repair and Maintenance Illustrated

by Peter Emmons

Hundreds of illustrations show users how to analyze, repair, clean, and maintain concrete structures for optimal performance and cost effectiveness. From parking garages to roads and bridges to structural concrete, this comprehensive book describes the causes, effects, and remedies for concrete wear and failure. Invaluable for planning jobs, selecting materials, and training employees, this book is a must-have for concrete specialists, general contractors, facility managers, civil and structural engineers, and architects.

$69.95 per copy | 300 pages, illustrated, softcover | Catalog no. 67146

Total Productive Facilities Management

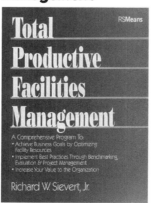

by Richard W. Sievert, Jr.

Today, facilities are viewed as strategic resources. . . elevating the facility manager to the role of asset manager supporting the organization's overall business goals. Now, Richard Sievert Jr., in this well-articulated guidebook, sets forth a new operational standard fo the facility manager's emerging role. . . a comprehensive program for managing facilities as a true profit center.

$79.95 per copy | 275 pages, softcover | Catalog no. 67321

Reference Books

eans Illustrated Construction ctionary

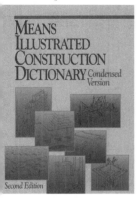

Condensed, 2nd Edition

The best portable dictionary for office or field use—an essential tool for contractors, architects, insurance and real estate personnel, facility managers, homeowners, and anyone who needs quick, clear definitions for construction terms. The second edition has been further enhanced with updates and hundreds of new terms and illustrations . . . in keeping with the most recent developments in the construction industry.

Now with a quick-reference Spanish section. Includes tools and equipment, materials, tasks, and more!

.95 per copy | Over 500 pages, softcover | Catalog no. 67282A

cilities Planning & elocation

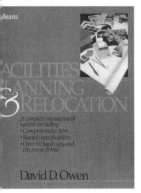

by David D. Owen

A complete system for planning space needs and managing relocations. Includes step-by-step manual, over 50 forms, and extensive reference section on materials and furnishings.

New lower price and user-friendly format.

.95 per copy | Over 450 pages, softcover | Catalog no. 67301

ectrical Estimating ethods

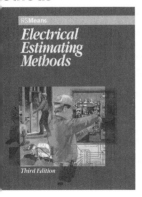

3rd Edition

Expanded edition includes sample estimates and cost information in keeping with the latest version of the CSI MasterFormat and UNIFORMAT II. Complete coverage of fiber optic and uninterruptible power supply electrical systems, broken down by components, and explained in detail. Includes a new chapter on computerized estimating methods. A practical companion to *RSMeans Electrical Cost Data.*

.95 per copy | Over 325 pages, hardcover | Catalog no. 67230B

Square Foot & UNIFORMAT Assemblies Estimating Methods

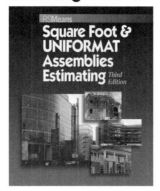

3rd Edition

Develop realistic square foot and assemblies costs for budgeting and construction funding. The new edition features updated guidance on square foot and assemblies estimating using UNIFORMAT II. An essential reference for anyone who performs conceptual estimates.

$69.95 per copy | Over 300 pages, illustrated, softcover | Catalog no. 67145B

Mechanical Estimating Methods

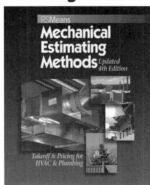

4th Edition

Completely updated, this guide assists you in making a review of plans, specs, and bid packages, with suggestions for takeoff procedures, listings, substitutions, and pre-bid scheduling for all components of HVAC. Includes suggestions for budgeting labor and equipment usage. Compares materials and construction methods to allow you to select the best option.

$64.95 per copy | Over 350 pages, illustrated, softcover | Catalog no. 67294B

Residential & Light Commercial Construction Standards

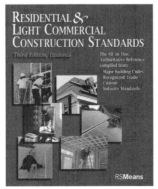

3rd Edition, Updated by RSMeans and contributing authors

This book provides authoritative requirements and recommendations compiled from leading professional associations, industry publications, and building code organizations. This all-in-one reference helps establish a standard for workmanship, quickly resolve disputes, and avoid defect claims. Updated third edition includes new coverage of green building, seismic, hurricane, and mold-resistant construction.

$59.95 | Over 550 pages, illustrated, softcover | Catalog no. 67322B

Reference Books

Construction Business Management

by Nick Ganaway

Only 43% of construction firms stay in business after four years. Make sure your company thrives with valuable guidance from a pro with 25 years of success as a commercial contractor. Find out what it takes to build all aspects of a business that is profitable, enjoyable, and enduring. With a bonus chapter on retail construction.

$49.95 per copy | 200 pages, softcover | Catalog no. 67352

The Practice of Cost Segregation Analysis

by Bruce A. Desrosiers and Wayne J. DelPico

This expert guide walks you through the practice of cost segregation analysis, which enables property owners to defer taxes and benefit from "accelerated cost recovery" through depreciation deductions on assets that are properly identified and classified.

With a glossary of terms, sample cost segregation estimates for various building types, key information resources, and updates via a dedicated website, this book is a critical resource for anyone involved in cost segregation analysis.

$99.95 per copy | Over 225 pages | Catalog no. 67345

How to Estimate with Means Data & CostWorks

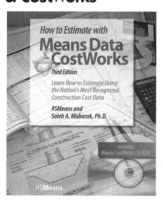

New 3rd Edition
by RSMeans and Saleh A. Mubarak, Ph.D.

New 3rd Edition—fully updated with new chapters, plus new CD with updated *CostWorks* cost data and MasterFormat organization. Includes all major construction items—with more than 300 exercises and two sets of plans that show how to estimate for a broad range of construction items and systems—including general conditions and equipment costs.

$59.95 per copy | 272 pages, softcover | Includes CostWorks CD
Catalog no. 67324B

Project Scheduling & Management for Construction

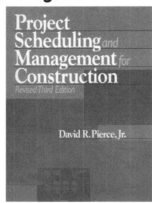

3rd Edition
by David R. Pierce, Jr.

A comprehensive yet easy-to-follow guide to construction project scheduling and control—from vital project management principles through the latest scheduling, tracking, and controlling techniques. The author is a leading authority on scheduling, with years of field and teaching experience at leading academic institutions. Spend a few hours with this book and come away with a solid understanding of this essential management topic.

$64.95 per copy | Over 300 pages, illustrated, hardcover | Catalog no. 67247B

Preventive Maintenance for Multi-Family Housing

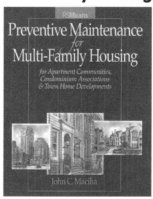

by John C. Maciha

Prepared by one of the nation's leading experts on multi-family housing.

This complete PM system for apartment and condominium communities features expert guidance, checklists for buildings and grounds maintenance tasks and their frequencies, a reusable wall chart to track maintenance, and a dedicated website featuring customizable electronic forms. A must-have for anyone involved with multi-family housing maintenance and upkeep.

$89.95 per copy | 225 pages | Catalog no. 67346

Job Order Contracting Expediting Construction Project Delivery

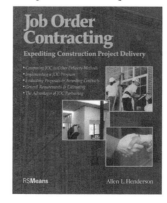

by Allen Henderson

Expert guidance to help you implemen JOC—fast becoming the preferred project delivery method for repair and renovation, minor new construction, a maintenance projects in the public sec and in many states and municipalities. The author, a leading JOC expert and practitioner, shows how to:

- Establish a JOC program
- Evaluate proposals and award contrac
- Handle general requirements and estimating
- Partner for maximum benefits

$89.95 per copy | 192 pages, illustrated, hardcover | Catalog no. 67348

Reference Books

For more information visit the RSMeans website at **www.rsmeans.com**

Unit prices according to the latest MasterFormat!

Estimating Building Costs

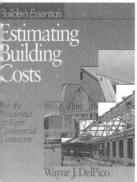

For the Residential & Light Commercial Contractor
by Wayne J. DelPico

Step-by-step estimating methods for residential and light commercial contractors. Includes a detailed look at every construction specialty—explaining all the components, takeoff units, and labor needed for well-organized, complete estimates. Covers correctly interpreting plans and specifications, and developing accurate and complete labor and material costs.

$..95 per copy | Over 400 pages, illustrated, softcover | Catalog no. 67343

Building & Renovating Schools

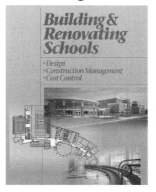

This all-inclusive guide covers every step of the school construction process—from initial planning, needs assessment, and design, right through moving into the new facility. A must-have resource for anyone concerned with new school construction or renovation. With square foot cost models for elementary, middle, and high school facilities, and real-life case studies of recently completed school projects.

The contributors to this book—architects, construction project managers, contractors, and estimators who specialize in school construction—provide start-to-finish, expert guidance on the process.

$99.95 per copy | Over 425 pages, hardcover | Catalog no. 67342

The Homeowner's Guide to Mold

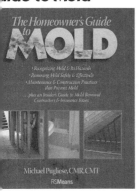

By Michael Pugliese

Expert guidance to protect your health and your home.

Mold, whether caused by leaks, humidity or flooding, is a real health and financial issue—for homeowners and contractors.

This full-color book explains:

- Construction and maintenance practices to prevent mold
- How to inspect for and remove mold
- Mold remediation procedures and costs
- What to do after a flood
- How to deal with insurance companies

$..95 per copy | 144 pages, softcover | Catalog no. 67344

Universal Design Ideas for Style, Comfort & Safety

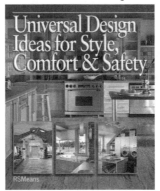

by RSMeans and Lexicon Consulting, Inc.

Incorporating universal design when building or remodeling helps people of any age and physical ability more fully and safely enjoy their living spaces. This book shows how universal design can be artfully blended into the most attractive homes. It discusses specialized products like adjustable countertops and chair lifts, as well as simple ways to enhance a home's safety and comfort. With color photos and expert guidance, every area of the home is covered. Includes budget estimates that give an idea how much projects will cost.

$21.95 | 160 pages, illustrated, softcover | Catalog no. 67354

Landscape Estimating Methods

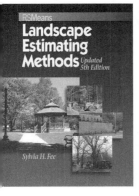

5th Edition

Answers questions about preparing competitive landscape construction estimates, with up-to-date cost estimates and the new MasterFormat classification system. Expanded and revised to address the latest materials and methods, including new coverage on approaches to green building. Includes:

- Step-by-step explanation of the estimating process
- Sample forms and worksheets that save time and prevent errors

$..95 per copy | Over 350 pages, softcover | Catalog no. 67295C

Plumbing Estimating Methods

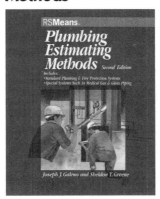

3rd Edition
by Joseph Galeno and Sheldon Greene

Updated and revised! This practical guide walks you through a plumbing estimate, from basic materials and installation methods through change order analysis. *Plumbing Estimating Methods* covers residential, commercial, industrial, and medical systems, and features sample takeoff and estimate forms and detailed illustrations of systems and components.

$59.95 per copy | 330+ pages, softcover | Catalog no. 67283B

Reference Books

For more information visit the RSMeans website at **www.rsmeans.com**

Unit prices according to the latest MasterForma

Understanding & Negotiating Construction Contracts

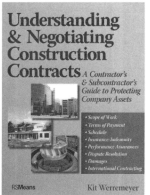

by Kit Werremeyer

Take advantage of the author's 30 years' experience in small-to-large (including international) construction projects. Learn how to identify, understand, and evaluate high risk terms and conditions typically found in all construction contracts—then negotiate to lower or eliminate the risk, improve terms of payment, and reduce exposure to claims and disputes. The author avoids "legalese" and gives real-life examples from actual projects.

$69.95 per copy | 300 pages, softcover | Catalog no. 67350

How Your House Works

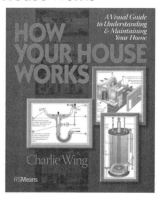

by Charlie Wing

A must-have reference for every homeowner, handyman, and contractor—for repair, remodeling, and new construction. This book uncovers the mysteries behind just about every major appliance and building element in your house—from electrical, heating and AC, to plumbing, framing, foundations and appliances. Clear, "exploded" drawings show exactly how things should be put together and how they function—what to check if they don't work, and what you can do that might save you having to call in a professional.

$21.95 per copy | 160 pages, softcover | Catalog no. 67351

RSMeans Estimating Handbook

3rd Edition

Widely used in the industry for tasks ranging from routine estimates to special cost analysis projects, this handbook has been completely updated and reorganized with new and expanded technical information.

RSMeans Estimating Handbook will help construction professionals:

- Evaluate architectural plans and specifications
- Prepare accurate quantity takeoffs
- Compare design alternatives and costs
- Perform value engineering
- Double-check estimates and quotes
- Estimate change orders

$99.95 per copy | Over 900 pages, hardcover | Catalog No. 67276B

Spanish/English Construction Dictionary

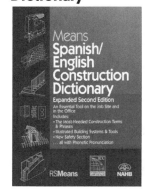

**2nd Edition
by RSMeans and the
International Code Council**

This expanded edition features thousands of the most common words and useful phrases in the construction industry with easy-to-follow pronunciations in both Spanish and English. Over 800 new terms phrases, and illustrations have been added It also features a new stand-alone "Safety Emergencies" section, with colored pages for quick access.

Unique to this dictionary are the systems illustrations showing the relationship of components in the most common building systems for all major trade

$23.95 per copy | Over 400 pages | Catalog no. 67327A

The Gypsum Construction Handbook

by USG

An invaluable reference of construction procedures for gypsum drywall, cement board, veneer plaster, and conventional plaster. This new edition includes the newest product developments, installation methods, fire- and sound-rated construction information, illustrated framing-to-finish application instructions, estimating and planning information, and more. Great for architects and engineers; contractors, builders, and dealers; apprentices and training programs; building inspectors and code officials; and anyone interested in gypsum construction. Features information on tools and safety practices, a glossary of construction terms, and a list of important agencies and associations. Also available in Spanish.

$29.95 | Over 575 pages, illustrated, softcover | Catalog no. 67357A

Means Illustrated Construction Dictionary

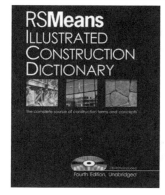

Unabridged 4th Edition, with CD-ROM

Long regarded as the industry's finest, *Means Illustrated Construction Dictionary* is now even better. With nearly 20,000 terms and more than 1,400 illustrations and photos, it is the clear choice for the most comprehensive and current information. The companion CD-ROM that comes with this new edition adds extra features such as: larger graphics and expanded definitions.

$99.95 per copy | Over 790 pages, illust., hardcover | Catalog no. 67292F

Reference Books

For more information visit the RSMeans website at **www.rsmeans.com**

Unit prices according to the latest MasterFormat!

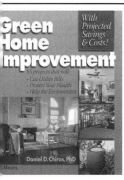

Green
Home Improvement
by Daniel D. Chiras, PhD

With energy costs rising and environmental awareness increasing, people are looking to make their homes greener. This book, with 65 projects and actual costs and projected savings help homeowners prioritize their green improvements.

Projects range from simple water savers that cost only a few dollars, to bigger-ticket items such as HVAC systems. With color photos and cost estimates, each project compares options and describes the work involved, the benefits, and the savings.

$24.95 | 320 pages, illustrated, softcover | Catalog no. 67355

New Titles

Construction
Supervision

This brand new title inspires supervisory excellence with proven tactics and techniques applied by thousands of construction supervisors over the past decade. Recognizing the unique and critical role the supervisor plays in project success, the book's leadership guidelines carve out a practical blueprint for motivating work performance and increasing productivity through effective communication.

Features:

- A unique focus on field supervision and crew management

Coverage of supervision from the foreman to the superintendent level

An overview of technical skills whose mastery will build confidence and success for the supervisor

A detailed view of "soft" management and communication skills

$0.00 per copy | Over 450 pages, softcover | Catalog no. 67358

Risk Management
for Design and Construction

This book introduces risk as a central pillar of project management and shows how a project manager can be prepared for dealing with uncertainty. Written by experts in the field, *Risk Management for Design and Construction* uses clear, straightforward terminology to demystify the concepts of project uncertainty and risk.

Highlights include:

- Integrated cost and schedule risk analysis

- An introduction to a ready-to-use system of analyzing a project's risks and tools to proactively manage risks

- A methodology that was developed and used by the Washington State Department of Transportation

- Case studies and examples on the proper application of principles

- Information about combining value analysis with risk analysis

$125.00 per copy | Over 250 pages, softcover | Catalog no. 67359

Green Building: Project
Planning & Cost Estimating

3rd Edition

Since the widely read first edition of this book, green building has gone from a growing trend to a major force in design and construction.

This new edition has been updated with the latest in green building technologies, design concepts, standards, and costs. Full-color with all new case studies—plus a new chapter on commercial real estate.

$9.95 per copy | Over 450 pages, softcover | Catalog no. 67338B

Qty.	Book no.	COST ESTIMATING BOOKS	Unit Price	Total
	60062	Assemblies Cost Data 2012	$290.95	
	60012	Building Construction Cost Data 2012	177.95	
	60112	Concrete & Masonry Cost Data 2012	162.95	
	50142	Construction Cost Indexes 2012 (subscription)	362.00	
	60142A	Construction Cost Index–January 2012	90.50	
	60142B	Construction Cost Index–April 2012	90.50	
	60142C	Construction Cost Index–July 2012	90.50	
	60142D	Construction Cost Index–October 2012	90.50	
	60342	Contr. Pricing Guide: Resid. R & R Costs 2012	39.95	
	60232	Electrical Change Order Cost Data 2012	174.95	
	60032	Electrical Cost Data 2012	179.95	
	60202	Facilities Construction Cost Data 2012	453.95	
	60302	Facilities Maintenance & Repair Cost Data 2012	399.95	
	60552	Green Building Cost Data 2012	147.95	
	60162	Heavy Construction Cost Data 2012	177.95	
	60092	Interior Cost Data 2012	182.95	
	60122	Labor Rates for the Const. Industry 2012	395.95	
	60182	Light Commercial Cost Data 2012	132.95	
	60022	Mechanical Cost Data 2012	174.95	
	60152	Open Shop Building Const. Cost Data 2012	152.95	
	60212	Plumbing Cost Data 2012	179.95	
	60042	Commercial Renovation Cost Data 2012	144.95	
	60172	Residential Cost Data 2012	127.95	
	60282	Site Work & Landscape Cost Data 2012	172.95	
	60052	Square Foot Costs 2012	187.95	
	62011	Yardsticks for Costing (2011)	174.95	
	62012	Yardsticks for Costing (2012)	176.95	
		REFERENCE BOOKS		
	67329	Bldrs Essentials: Best Bus. Practices for Bldrs	29.95	
	67298A	Bldrs Essentials: Framing/Carpentry 2nd Ed.	24.95	
	67298AS	Bldrs Essentials: Framing/Carpentry Spanish	24.95	
	67307	Bldrs Essentials: Plan Reading & Takeoff	35.95	
	67342	Building & Renovating Schools	99.95	
	67339	Building Security: Strategies & Costs	89.95	
	67353	Complete Book of Framing	29.95	
	67146	Concrete Repair & Maintenance Illustrated	69.95	
	67352	Construction Business Management	49.95	
	67358	Construction Supervision	90.00	
	67314	Cost Planning & Est. for Facil. Maint.	89.95	
	67328A	Designing & Building with the IBC, 2nd Ed.	99.95	
	67230B	Electrical Estimating Methods, 3rd Ed.	64.95	
	67343	Estimating Bldg. Costs for Resi. & Lt. Comm.	29.95	
	67276B	Estimating Handbook, 3rd Ed.	99.95	
	67318	Facilities Operations & Engineering Reference	109.95	
	67301	Facilities Planning & Relocation	89.95	
	67338B	Green Building: Proj. Planning & Cost Est., 3rd Ed.	99.95	
	67355	Green Home Improvement	24.95	
	67357A	The Gypsum Construction Handbook	29.95	
	67357S	The Gypsum Construction Handbook (Spanish)	29.95	
	67148	Heavy Construction Handbook	99.95	
	67323	Historic Preservation: Proj. Planning & Est.	99.95	

Qty.	Book no.	REFERENCE BOOKS (Cont.)	Unit Price	Total
	67308E	Home Improvement Costs–Int. Projects, 9th Ed.	24.95	
	67309E	Home Improvement Costs–Ext. Projects, 9th Ed.	24.95	
	67344	Homeowner's Guide to Mold	21.95	
	67324B	How to Est.w/Means Data & CostWorks, 3rd Ed.	59.95	
	67351	How Your House Works	21.95	
	67282A	Illustrated Const. Dictionary, Condensed, 2nd Ed.	59.95	
	67292B	Illustrated Const. Dictionary, w/CD-ROM, 4th Ed.	99.95	
	67348	Job Order Contracting	89.95	
	67295C	Landscape Estimating Methods, 5th Ed.	64.95	
	67341	Life Cycle Costing for Facilities	99.95	
	67294B	Mechanical Estimating Methods, 4th Ed.	64.95	
	67283B	Plumbing Estimating Methods, 3rd Ed.	59.95	
	67345	Practice of Cost Segregation Analysis	99.95	
	67346	Preventive Maint. for Multi-Family Housing	89.95	
	67326	Preventive Maint. Guidelines for School Facil.	149.95	
	67247B	Project Scheduling & Manag. for Constr. 3rd Ed.	64.95	
	67322B	Resi. & Light Commercial Const. Stds., 3rd Ed.	59.95	
	67359	Risk Management for Design & Construction	125.00	
	67327A	Spanish/English Construction Dictionary, 2nd Ed.	23.95	
	67145B	Sq. Ft. & Assem. Estimating Methods, 3rd Ed.	69.95	
	67321	Total Productive Facilities Management	79.95	
	67350	Understanding and Negotiating Const. Contracts	69.95	
	67303B	Unit Price Estimating Methods, 4th Ed.	59.95	
	67354	Universal Design	21.95	
	67319A	Value Engineering: Practical Applications	79.95	

MA residents add 6.25% state sales tax _____

Shipping & Handling** _____

Total (U.S. Funds)* _____

Prices are subject to change and are for U.S. delivery only. *Canadian customers may call for current prices. **Shipping & handling charges: Add 7% of total order for check and credit card payments. Add 9% of total order for invoiced orders.

Send order to: ADDV-1000

Name (please print) _____

Company _____

☐ Company

☐ Home Address _____

_____

City/State/Zip _____

Phone # _____ P.O. # _____

(Must accompany all orders being billed)